THE WORLD OF BLACK HUMOR

The World of
BLACK HUMOR

AN INTRODUCTORY ANTHOLOGY
OF SELECTIONS AND CRITICISM

Edited, and with an introduction, by

Douglas M. Davis

*A Dutton
Paperback*

New York
E. P. DUTTON & CO., INC.
1967

This paperback edition of
"THE WORLD OF BLACK HUMOR"
First published 1967 by E. P. Dutton & Co., Inc.
All rights reserved. Printed in the U.S.A.
Copyright, ©, 1966, by Douglas M. Davis

FIRST EDITION

No part of this book may be reproduced in any form whatsoever
without permission in writing from the publishers, except by a
reviewer who wishes to quote brief passages in connection with a
review written for inclusion in a magazine or newspaper or
broadcasts.
Published simultaneously in Canada by Clarke, Irwin and Company, Limited, Toronto and Vancouver.

ACKNOWLEDGMENTS

Grateful acknowledgment is made to the following for permission to
quote from copyright material:

FRANZ KAFKA: from *The Castle*. Copyright 1930, 1941, 1954, and renewed
1958 by Alfred A. Knopf, Inc. Reprinted by permission of Alfred A.
Knopf.
NATHANAEL WEST: from *Miss Lonelyhearts*. Copyright 1933 by Nathanael
West. Reprinted by permission of New Directions Publishing Corporation.
VLADIMIR NABOKOV: from *Lolita*. Copyright © 1955 by Vladimir Nabokov.
Reprinted by permission of G. P. Putnam's Sons.
JOHN HAWKES: from *The Cannibal*. Copyright 1949 by New Directions. Re-
printed by permission of New Directions Publishing Corporation.
WILLIAM GADDIS: from *The Recognitions*. Copyright 1952, 1955 by William
Gaddis. Reprinted by permission of Harcourt, Brace & World, Inc.
J. P. DONLEAVY: from *The Ginger Man*. Copyright © 1958 by J. P. Donleavy.
Reprinted by permission of Astor-Honor, Inc.
TERRY SOUTHERN: from *The Magic Christian*. Copyright © 1959, 1960 by
Terry Southern. Reprinted by permission of Random House, Inc.
JOSEPH HELLER: from *Catch-22*. Copyright © 1955, 1961 by Joseph Heller.
Reprinted by permission of Simon and Schuster, Inc.
PETER DE VRIES: from *The Blood of the Lamb*. Copyright © 1961 by Peter
De Vries. Reprinted by permission of Little, Brown and Co.
BRUCE J. FRIEDMAN: from *Stern*. Copyright © 1962 by Bruce J. Friedman.
Reprinted by permission of Simon & Schuster, Inc.
ELLIOTT BAKER: from *A Fine Madness*. Copyright © 1964 by Elliott Baker.
Reprinted by permission of G. P. Putnam's Sons.
WARREN MILLER: from *The Siege of Harlem*. Copyright © 1964 by Warren
Miller. Reprinted by permission of McGraw-Hill Company.
THOMAS PYNCHON: from *The Crying of Lot 49*. Copyright © 1965, 1966 by
Thomas Pynchon. Reprinted by permission of J. B. Lippincott Company.
WALKER PERCY: from *The Last Gentleman*. Copyright © 1966 by Walker
Percy. Reprinted by permission of Farrar, Straus & Giroux, Inc.

CHARLES WRIGHT: from *The Wig.* Copyright © 1966 by Charles Wright. Reprinted by permission of Farrar, Straus & Giroux, Inc.

JAMES PURDY: from *Cabot Wright Begins.* Copyright © 1964 by James Purdy. Reprinted by permission of Farrar, Straus & Giroux, Inc.

WILLIAM BURROUGHS: from *Nova Express.* Copyright © 1964 by William Burroughs. Reprinted by permission of Grove Press, Inc.

JOHN BARTH: from *The Floating Opera.* Copyright © 1956 by John Barth. Reprinted by permission of Lurton Blassingame.

CONRAD KNICKERBOCKER: "Humor with a Mortal Sting." Reprinted from *The New York Times Book Review* by permission of The New York Times Company and Russell & Volkening, Inc. Copyright © 1964 by The New York Times Company.

RICHARD KOSTELANETZ: "The American Absurd Novel." Reprinted from *The New York Times Book Review* by permission of The New York Times Company, Richard Kostelanetz, and The British Broadcasting Corporation's *The Listener.* Copyright © 1965 by The New York Times Company.

GEORGE P. ELLIOTT: "Nihilism." Reprinted from *The New York Times Book Review* by permission of The New York Times Company and George P. Elliott. Copyright © 1964 by The New York Times Company.

MARSHALL McLUHAN: "Notes on Burroughs." From *The Nation.* Copyright © 1964 by *The Nation.* Reprinted by permission of *The Nation.*

RICHARD POIRIER: from "Wescac and the Messiah." Reprinted with permission from *Book Week* of the *World Journal Tribune.* Copyright © 1966 by *Book Week* of the *World Journal Tribune.*

SAUL BELLOW: from "Some Notes on Recent American Fiction." Reprinted from *Encounter* by permission of Saul Bellow.

WYLIE SYPHER: from "Existence and Entropy" in *Loss of the Self in Modern Literature and Art.* Copyright © 1962 by Wylie Sypher. Reprinted by permission of Random House, Inc.

For L. K. and M. B.

CONTENTS

PREFACE

The object of this anthology is to bring *alive* the phenomenon we have decided to call Black Humor. I have not limited myself, therefore, to short stories, one-act plays, and chapters from novels that make little, self-explanatory "stories" in themselves. What I set out to find were passages—almost always within major works (novels, that is to say)—which reveal the author at a particular pitch of performance. In most cases, the selections make quite coherent statements in themselves. Where this is not the case, I have provided in a brief preface all the necessary facts of plot, character, and theme out of which the selection grows. I quite agree, of course, that a fragment is no test of a novel, and my fondest hope is that this anthology will encourage readers to make the complete test themselves. But my purpose is not to condense novels; rather, I am in the position of a gallery dealer, you might say, arranging a group show of his artists, anxious to show what the group can do as a unit, in all its variety and its consistency.

My debts in this matter are several. Mrs. Sharon Krock and Miss Joan Allard provided invaluable research help. Charles Monaghan has conversed often and tellingly, not only about the work of William Gaddis but about innumerable issues raised by it. A number of the writers here included—and some not—have talked ideas with me, too, both in person and in correspondence, and I thank them all.

D.M.D.

INTRODUCTION:
NOTES ON BLACK HUMOR

When it came, it came like it was, like a flood long pent in
the imagination, finally breaking through the barriers of
restraint into the dry, outside, real world. Leevey, the lone
motorcyclist came, and a scoundrel named Recktall Brown.
Limestone John, Izzy the Push, Hamburger Mary, the Sub-
liminal Kid came, too, with a rush. There was a pilot named
Yossarian and a commanding officer named Major Major
Major Major. Guy Grand, "the Magic Christian," came.
So did Benny Profane, Stencil, Papa Cueball, Sebastian Balfe
Dangerfield. There was Doyley Pepscout, "king of the daily
reviewers"; Talcum Downley, "highbrow critic"; Cordell
Bicks, the "great pink critic of the thirties." Ghengis Cogen
came, Mr. H. Halatoid of Fartbrook, Cornelius Christian,
Willy the Take, Sick Dick and the Volkwagens, the Heavy
Metal Boys, a poet named Samson Shillitoe, and another
poet named Muchnik.

They came not only with names but with missions, largely
satirical, in a series of novels that left few corners of that
real world untouched. Guy Grand spends ten million dollars
a year in Terry Southern's *The Magic Christian* "making it
hot" for the masses. Among other projects, he buys a
newspaper with a circulation of 2,000,000 and devotes it
entirely to the printing of readers' opinions. Leevey, the
doomed cyclist in *The Cannibal*, by John Hawkes, occupies
all of West Germany in the name of the American Army.
Recktall Brown subsidizes the production of counterfeit
works of art in *The Recognitions*, by William Gaddis. Cabot
Wright, the hero of *Cabot Wright Begins*, commits more than
300 rapes "out of boredom"; one of the victims sues her
mother because she is the friend of a friend of the rapist.
In *The Siege of Harlem*, a novel by Warren Miller, Harlem
secedes from the United States, petitioning the UN for recog-

nition as an independent country. *Candy,* also by Terry Southern, parodies the pornographic novel. *Flash and Filigree,* another Southern triumph, bludgeons Southern California. *Golk,* by Richard G. Stern, bloodily dissects the television "interviewer." J. P. Donleavy's *The Ginger Man* finishes off marriage; the *Moviegoer,* by Walker Percy, "scientific humanism," among other things; *Catch-22,* by Joseph Heller, war. Psychoanalysts, book publishers, and supermarkets are lacerated in *Cabot Wright Begins;* Greenwich Village in Alan Harrington's *The Secret Swinger. The Crying of Lot 49* demolishes the motel, LSD, the freeway, and folk rock; *A Fine Madness,* by Elliott Baker, literary ladies; *Stern,* by Bruce J. Friedman, the mental hospital. Take your choice—from John Birchery, urban renewal, momism, the Ph.D. thesis, liberalism, militant pacifism—and you will find a Bruce Jay Friedman, a Charles Wright, a John Barth having at it. Or take absolutely everything; take the universe. The novel for that is William Burroughs's magnificent *Nova Express.* It is the super putdown of a putdown age. But its stance differs only in degree, not in kind from its colleagues. *Nova Express,* in common with them, laughs at the absurd tragedy which has trapped us all, man, woman, child, self.

We call this quality in the novel "Black Humor," and in our settling upon that label rather than any of the others available during the early 1960's—like Yankee Existentialism or the American Absurd Novel—we reveal our uneasy stance toward it. We do not particularly care for the color black, but we enjoy, enjoy "humor." We seized upon the term "Black Power" with much the same fascinated horror, much the same ambience of joy and hate. There are further analogies between "Black Power" and "Black Humor." Black Humor in its specifically satirical moments was and is savage, brooking no compromise with its subject. When Conrad Knickerbocker's 1964 article named the "new mood," making it finite and therefore available to a wide audience, we thought it had come out of nowhere, so radically different did the products of this mood seem from the grey-flannel fiction of the 1950's, just as Black Power seemed a sudden bastard hatched by the Civil Rights movement. Following upon Knickerbocker, commentator after commentator volunteered sociological explanations for Black Humor, explanations desperately dependent on the approach of automation, the effect of the space race, the Kennedy assassination, and the population explosion. Others, in time, offered Existentialism as well. We remembered that it alone had given The Absurd a new birth of meaning. We remembered, too, Beckett and Ionesco, and beyond them, Robert Musil, and beyond him, Louis-Ferdinand Céline, Europeans all in the service of Absurdity.

It is past time to say that Black Humor goes far deeper than this. Western letters is a huge house; any man wandering about in it will find room there for his purpose. It is foolish to suppose that what is taught in the seminars makes literature. Scholars and critics profess shock that Black Humor came out of decades dominated by the New Criticism, particularly by all the words attached to it, words like *tension, restraint, discipline*. But legions sit sideways in the seminars, taking what they will out of assigned readings. There is bile, there is absurdity in Aristophanes and Marlowe, Crashaw and Wordsworth. It is not only the modern writer, as Clifford Leech reminds us, who senses the illogicality by which men live. Have we forgotten that Erasmus wrote an entire book in praise of folly? His argument, quite familiar to readers of Black Humor, is that folly prevails in the world, not reason. Have we forgotten how Pope ends *The Dunciad*—with that tragic, moving picture of a society where the light of reason has been totally darkened? Have we forgotten the absurd visions of Christopher Smart, the "black lady" of Shakespeare's sonnets, the shotgun comedy of Johnson, Voltaire, and Swift?

No, the absurd sensibility is not peculiar to our own time. It manifests itself here and there, throughout the history of Western literature. Nor is it unusual for writers to project that sensibility in crude, grotesque, metaphors. Think of James Thompson's *City of Dreadful Night*, of Dostoevski's *House of the Dead*, of Herman Melville's *Billy Budd*, of *Volpone*, of *The White Devil*. It is possible even to consider Shakespeare's *Lear* a drama of absurd ideas, showing us how irrationally the universe can deal with a man. Heathcliffe, Tamburlaine, the Teresa of Avila in Crawshaw's poetry, all are grotesque figures, none of recent origin. The least we can conclude, in fact, is that Western Literature regularly offers us a view of man, his affairs, and his cosmos as nightmarish and unreasonable.

Which is not to say that Black Humor has no flavor peculiar to our time; those who dote on sociology are right in their way. But it is a way that almost defies words and certainly logic. We begin by noting that the Absurd sensibility waxes and wanes, varying in strength from time to time. It seems almost dead during the Victorian era in England; in our time it flourishes more abundantly than ever, hard upon not only Existentialism and Surrealism but Dada also. The Dadaists railed aloud after World War I at the "lie" perpetrated by "reason": in brief, the "nobility" of man. *What is truth? What is beauty? What is art?* asked one of the Dada poets, answering *"don't know! don't know! don't know!"* The Existentialists, following World War II, attacked the metaphysics of modern man at the core. From all of these, the Black Humorists have learned; in each case, too, changes have been made. A wit more ribald than that found in Existentialism, less dour than that which infused Dada, flourishes here in the New World, in the 1960's.

Why? It is a question we cannot hope to answer precisely. To pretend precision in matters beyond logic is the prime flaw of the critical mind. We need most to see that the essence of Black Humor is above all sociology and beneath all criticism, that it comes to us in its particular form from a wide variety of influences, many quite outside the boundaries normally recognized by literary and social historians. There is literary history behind it, of course; there is Aristophanes and Swift and Erasmus. There are also sources outside of literature: sources in philosophy and theology, sources difficult to document or justify but present in the work and in our own subconscious—people and events, if you will, that have reinforced our sense of the absurdity around us, reinforced that sense to the point where we both create and consume Black Humor. There is the Norman O. Brown of *Life Against Death* behind the new mood and the doomed German pastor, Dietrich Bonhoeffer, who wrote during World War II that a day was coming when men would have to get along without God. There is Tristan Tzara, the founder of Dada, Kurt Schwitters, his colleague, who composed one-word "operas," Sartre, and Salvador Dali. There is, as the sociologists say, affluence, the computer, and Jack Ruby, absurdities all, at least to the mind of traditional cast. There is also W. C. Fields and Lenny Bruce, the New Student Left, the Free Speech Movement, and LBJ. There is the instant oven, Telstar, and Sputnik, pornographic comic books (the nickel playground editions), the Guggenheim Foundation, composer John Cage, painter Andy Warhol. There is even the mini-skirt and the eight-lane freeway, both examples of a tendency common to our time and to Black Humor—a disregard for limits imposed by the past. To chart such factors is not to chart at all but to take notes.

I was sick—I can go this far—sick of the young marrieds, the professional brief-case smarties, the sunbathers from the Hamptons comparing their browns, the baseball addicts, race and fight pros, sports-car nuts, TV glaucoma people, jeans-wearing faggots of 40, ginger-beer voices of the off-track betting babboons.—James Purdy, *Cabot Wright Begins*

Listen: their garden of delights is a terminal sewer . . . their immortality cosmic consciousness and love is second-run grade-B shit . . . —William Burroughs, *Nova Express*

I want to be a machine.—Andy Warhol

If there's a sickness in American life, it's lack of materialism. We ought to pay more attention to getting our money's worth.—J. P. Donleavy

Rage that erupts, scarring everyone near it. Rage that holds itself in, behind a deadpan, rage that rarely reveals itself. Rage as well that loves what it hates, mixing with arrogance a strange humility, foreign to Europe. These mixtures can be found even in the quintessential European, Nabokov himself, in the quintessential center of *Lolita*, surely the roof and crown of the new mood, wherein Humbert-Humbert, in attempting to seduce the American nymphet, is himself seduced. Humbert cannot help loving what shocks and offends him—the atrocious motels and ugly towns that stretch across the freeways of middle America. You can see this ambivalence as well in Andy Warhol, the Sage of McKeesport, Pa.: beneath Andy putting on the world there is, unmistakably, the play principle. America is so receptive, after all, so ready to accept, to nourish its critics, to smother them with kisses. The ultimate strategy, this, as the New Left will tell you. General Douglas MacArthur himself said that America, by bending with the wind, never breaks. Such a strategy forces the social critic here to extremes of invective not necessary in Europe. It gives that invective, too, a shrill, inflated sound, for at its core, as everyone knows, there is *ease*, if not a Guggenheim grant.

These qualities, all of them grounded in the affluence of a postwar America—this yoking together of rage, affection, disillusionment, and well-being—distinguish the American Absurd Novel from its European counterpart. They have Americanized the absurd sensibility, at least in our time. The rage implicit in that sensibility, whether expressed in art or in literature, spreads across a spectrum, too—in Pop Art, from the impeccable cool of Warhol to the later canvases of Robert Indiana, which break into declared invective against the state of Alabama ("Just as in the anatomy of man," reads his stencil on one painting, "every nation must have its hind part"). The spectrum in Black Humor ranges from the amiable cool of a John Barth to the small, sharp blade of a Joseph Heller to the bloody hammer in Burroughs and Donleavy. Donleavy's Sebastian Dangerfield is perhaps the best case study of them all: within the confines of one mere novel, he flattens his defenseless wife when she complains that he has spent the last of their money on alcohol, holds a pillow over his baby's mouth, and precipitates a tavern riot. Next day he deserts wife Marion when the toilet spills into the kitchen, covering her with Sebastian's excrement. Later, even while his baby suffers from rickets, he empties the family treasury to fund various freelance sexual liaisons. He jumps leases and deceives grocery clerks with impunity. Down to his last penny, he milks a helpless lady boarder for all she is worth, then deserts her. He lures a second girl to London, where she supports, loves, and nourishes him, only to be deserted as well. Not even pregnancy stays the rage of Dangerfield: in an early outburst, he pushes Marion, full with child, down a steep flight of stairs.

The rage spills over, touching all the agencies with which we traditionally associate the sympathies of literary men. Touching reformers and pacifists and social workers. *I am no do-gooding José Ferrer*, says Binx Bolling, the "Moviegoer" of the novel by Walker Percy, *going around with my little whistle cheering everybody up*. Dangerfield puts it another way: *the common people back down where they belong*. No accident that Nabokov has his arch fiend, Quilty, the enemy of Hum, babble about Schweitzer in the film version of his novel, or that Southern invents a group of crackers in *Candy* who sing:

> We are the crackers, the crackers are we!
> True to each cracker as crackers can be!
> We've got to build, boys and girls,
> for a world of peace!
> A world of peace, a world of peace,
> Without silly police!
> QUACK—QUACK! CRACKER!
> QUACK—QUACK! CRACKER!

The hero figures of the intelligentsia, then, are as much the enemy in Black Humor as are the philistines. Nice-guy white liberals are synonymous with fat bankers now. There is positive venom in Purdy's portrait of Princeton Keith, the brilliant editor in *Cabot Wright Begins*. A good argument can be made—indeed, it already has been made by Alan Trachtenberg—that the continuing subject of all John Barth's novels is a disease frequent among intellectuals: *cosmopsis*. It is the Stevensonian disease, based on the discovery, made by every Ph.D. candidate, that all things are relative, therefore impossible of resolution. The results: Indecision; the Thesis; the Monograph; the Endless Panel Discussions, common to the Arden Houses of our day, at which no conclusion is reached. Binx Bolling puts it sharply: this is, he says, "the very century of merde, the great shithouse of scientific humanism where needs are satisfied, everyone becomes an anyone, a warm and creative person, and prospers like a dung beetle, and 100 per cent of people are humanists. . . ." The proper study has yet to be made, incidentally, that will both properly document the use of excremental metaphors in Black Humor and its relation to the use of the material itself by certain Pop Artists.

Acting as a radical means . . . at this time . . . working with little belief in Utopia. There simply is no active agency of radical change—no race, class, or nation—in which radicals can invest high hopes as they have in previous times. . . .—Tom Hayden, "The Ability to Face Whatever Comes"

If the tower is everywhere and the knight of deliverance no proof against its magic, what else?—Thomas Pynchon, *The Crying of Lot 49*

Liberalism—its rhetoric and its reality—has much more to do with Black Humor then anyone realizes. And that in turn is what lends to the American Absurd Novel its peculiar quality, what in fact produces the pitch of its rage. Europe is conditioned not only to defeat but to the Vanity of Human Wishes. Even in its worst moments of sentimental rapture, Europe knows in its heart the score. The American is different. He believes in his heart that all men are reasonable, that dedication moveth the mountain. These beliefs do not stay the course. They are rigid and break when they fall.

It has been centuries since Europe witnessed such a surge of secular optimism as attended the New Deal, as weighted postwar liberal rhetoric. Where else would a politician prate not only about making a Great Society at home but extending it to whole subcontinents in Asia? Read John F. Kennedy's inaugural address again. In its ardor and optimism lie the very seeds of their opposites— lie the seeds, metaphorically speaking, of Black Humor. The true nihilist, someone once said, has abandoned all standards of right and wrong, of up and down. My point is that no American intellectual can be a nihilist; he is at best an optimist turned inside out, a man whose sense of right is stronger, not weaker than ordinary men, a man whose disillusionment over the inability of liberal politicians to harness greed, apathy, and bigotry is the greater because he believes in the face of every lesson that the harnessing is possible. Joseph Heller's great creation, Yossarian, thus speaks for us all in his dialogue with Colonel Sanderson:

"You're antagonistic to the idea of being robbed, exploited, degraded, humiliated, or deceived [Col. Sanderson says]. Misery depresses you. Ignorance depresses you.
Persecution depresses you. Violence depresses you.
Slums depress you. Greed depresses you. Crime depresses
you. Corruption depresses you. You know, it wouldn't
surprise me if you are manic-depressive!"

"Yes, sir. Perhaps I am."

"Don't try to deny it."

"I'm not denying it, sir," said Yossarian, pleased with the miraculous rapport that finally existed between them. "I agree with all you've said."

"Then you admit you're crazy?"

"Crazy?" Yossarian was shocked. "What are you talking about? Why am I crazy? You're the one who's crazy!"

Yossarian is blood brother as well to Stern, Bruce Jay Friedman's melancholy hero, who breaks down completely when a neighbor calls his wife "kike," and to Pynchon's heroine, Oedipa Maas, who deserts the affluent society of Southern California for an outcast, underground organization that voluntarily shuts itself off from the rest of the world. It is not the awareness that sets Yossarian, Stern, and Oedipa off from Europe. It is the shock, the breakdown, the desertion that follows.

Black Humor brooks no compromise or detente, the late Conrad Knickerbocker wrote. It prefers, he said, *rape*. Is it any wonder, then, that the phenomenon of the New Left dates itself from precisely that period when the new humorists began to flourish—that is, the late 1950's? There is in the rhetoric of young radicals like Tom Hayden and Stokeley Carmichael, as well as in the older rhetoricians knowingly or unknowingly behind them, men like Herbert Marcuse and Norman O. Brown, much the same impatience with the delay and compromise inherent in the "liberal" way, much the same fatalism about reform, much the same lust for cultural aggression found implicit and explicit in Black Humor. In both cases— literary and political—the rhetoricians contradict with their practice what they preach. Hayden tells us reform is impossible, yet works in the slums. Purdy tells us American culture is beyond hope, yet contributes to it. If nothing can be done, why not take pleasure in small victories—like the poverty program or Medicare or the Civil Rights bills? If all men are Colonel Sandersons, why shout into their deafened ears? Leslie Fiedler writes me, furthermore, that the Black Humorists are flowering on the grave of the novel. Yet both political subversion and the creation of novels goes on. In *The Crying of Lot 49*, strange to tell, we see the resemblance of WASTE, that underground organization with its own post office and lines of command to Staughton Lynd's plan for establishing a new nation within the old by calling a second Continental Congress. And in the talk of young ghetto Negroes about sabotaging power lines and blowing up commuter trains, we catch an echo of the rebellion in Warren Miller's *The Siege of Harlem*. In each case, liberalism has turned back on itself. Black Humor aligns itself not only with analogous developments in the visual arts of this decade, therefore, but in radical politics as well, aligns with their vigor and with their illogic.

Traditional forms cannot accommodate a reality which now includes Jack Ruby.—Conrad Knickerbocker

There need be no form in the novel because there is no form in life.—Terry Southern

There is no solution because there is no problem.—Jean Arp

Let us make no mistake about it. The Black Humorists have restored the American novel to relevance. Without Purdy or Donleavy or Burroughs or most of all Barth, we would be whining still about the decline of the novel, as we did throughout the 1950's, when university-bound *professoren* tried to play Jane Austen to the Eisenhower age. But the Black Humorists have restored the novel to relevance in terms of theme and tone only. Knicker-bocker and Southern, for all their brilliance, are quite wrong. Black Humor flirts on the edge of experimentation but never—with the sole exception of Burroughs—goes over. John Barth confesses that he likes to tell tales. He is more honest than his colleagues, who talk constantly of new forms while using old. The American Absurd Novel persists in telling *stories*, stories that begin at one point and end at another, imposing by their very nature a form upon life that does not exist, or at least does not conform to the sense of life everywhere else apparent in Barth, Pynchon, and the rest. The truth is that Black Humor fares very badly at novel length; the truth is that the new mood manifests itself best in random bursts of unhampered freedom, bursts which this book has attempted to capture.

What the literary community has yet to learn is what Marcel Duchamp and Jasper Johns taught Henry Geldzahler. *They have shown us*, he writes, *that art is whatever artists say it is.* The literary world sits solemnly at panels deploring the hold which the visual arts have upon today's young; the next day it returns to the classroom to define "The Novel," as if it were an unchanging jug into which all passions, be they those of Fielding or Thomas Hardy or John Steinbeck or J. P. Donleavy, can be poured. No self-respecting painter in our time would need to be told that Alain Robbe-Grillet must now tell his Anglo-American colleagues about the New Novel:

> There are not, for a writer, two possible ways to write the same book. When he thinks of a future novel, it is always *a way of writing* which first of all occupies his mind, and demands his hand. He has in mind certain rhythms of sentences, certain architectures, a vocabulary, certain grammatical constructions, exactly as a painter has in mind certain lines and colors. What will happen in the book comes afterward, as though secreted by the style itself. And, once the work is concluded, what will strengthen the reader is again this form so many affect to despise, a form whose meaning he often cannot define in any exact way, but which for him will constitute the writer's individual world.

Before that can come, before the writer can join the discovery of form that has vitalized American painting and sculpture since the war and is vitalizing now the new films of Warhol, the new poetry of Michael McClure and Emmett Williams, more basic work must be done. The novel must be taken away from the Arcadians; it must be made again the vehicle of contemporary feeling. And what we feel now, as Richard Schickel said in a landmark essay written for *Critique* in 1963, is a complicated mix of anger and mirth, certainly with respect to ideas. Only in a comic vein, says Schickel, can we treat serious, existential themes without pretension, that greatest of all postwar sins. Black Humor has grasped that feeling, brutally and greedily, perhaps, lacking the form to spare blood, but grasped it nonetheless.

It is only in the work of William Burroughs that we sense a straining toward a form commensurate with our sense of life. It is only Burroughs, as Marshall McLuhan says, who dares explode reality all around us, who dares find a unity above syntax and therefore traditional logic, a novelist, in brief, prepared to compete with our daily newspaper. Burroughs does it clumsily, perhaps, rising only to the right pitch in impassioned flights such as conclude *Nova Express*, composing, as he says, by chance, by folding printed papers in half and copying out the words he sees there. But he comes as close to freeing the word on the printed page in America has yet come. William Burroughs stands alone now for the novel as Happening.

Now in the thirty-first year of my dark pilgrimage on this earth and knowing less than I ever knew before. . . . — on this my thirtieth birthday, I know nothing and there is nothing to do but fall prey to desire.—Walter Percy, *The Moviegoer*

Like a complete unknown. Like a rolling stone.—Bob Dylan

Perhaps nothing makes less sense, in terms either of semantics or literary history, than the wholesale application of the term *antihero* to the novels produced by the Black Humorists. Black Humor, we are told in review after review, dwells on "antiheroes," spurning the ideal qualities of the Aristotelian hero, that it dwells on mindless, inconsequential men, driven by passion rather than ideals, flawed not in one way, but in many, many ways. This is pure bosh, analogous in its destructive harm only to the still current proposition that Abstract Expressionism somehow has to do with deserting reality and Pop Art with returning to it. A historical list of "pro-hero" writers working within the Western tradition would be a small one, indeed, if we were to define our "hero"—in the manner of so many traditional critics—as an exemplar of middle-class virtue. Hamlet, Tom Jones, Frankenstein, Heathcliffe, the Snopes family, and Augie March all rank quite as low on the scales of YMCA virtue as Yossarian or Dangerfield, and lower than Stern, say, or Peter De Vries's Don Wanderhope.

It is the extra-literary connotations of the term "antihero," together with our perennial misreading of Aristotle, that mislead us. What we call the "hero" of a novel, after all, is a formal, even rhetorical necessity dictated by the form, not a moral imperative. The "grandeur" and "virtue" demanded by Aristotle were demands suited to

Greek tragedy, not to the modern novel. The more neutral term, *viewpoint character*, is surely preferable to "hero." Black Humor centers upon viewpoint characters in a quite proper, thoroughly conventional manner. Our memory of Black Humor is a memory hung heavy with characters, even "personalities," you might say—with Dangerfield, Stern, Yossarian, Oedipa Maas, Samson Shillitoe, Binx Bolling, Cabot Wright, Todd Andrews. We are quite wrong, as I have said many times, to impute technical daring of any kind, least of all "antiheroes," to Black Humor. In its use of the nineteenth-century plot of sequential incidents and of the viewpoint character as unifying agent, Black Humor is as conservative, technically speaking, as Pop Art in its use of pictorial realism. In the French *Nouvelle Roman* only—and in certain rare works of Anglo-American fiction animated by it—do we see any legitimate, *formal* rejection of the viewpoint character to the extent that his personal presence is barely noticeable.

What no doubt prompts the indiscriminate use of the term "antihero" has nothing to do with literature but with politics. There is in each of these magnificent, half-mad characters a seeming indifference to the remediable ills of mankind. Stern is as close as you will come in Black Humor to a hero who *cares* in the overt, orthodox manner. Even Stern, however, is not noticeable for his reformist energies. A certain irritating rejection of past accommodations, no matter how favorable, a certain preference for a nirvana free from pamphleteering infects these characters. But Dangerfield and Stern and Cabot Wright are surely as large in imaginal stature, as large in metaphysical rage as any flawed classical hero. It is only their politics that brings on the use of a term which—in the hands of the older critics, at least—has turned pejorative.

"Nothing Is True—Everything Is Permitted—" Last Words Hassan I. Sabban—William Burroughs, *Nova Express*

> In this sad world
> In this dark gloom
> We live like beasts
> —J. P. Donleavy, *The Ginger Man*

Conventional analyses of Black Humor—and other manifestations of new moods in the arts, such as Neo-Dada,
Pop Art, the Happening, electronic poetry, computer music
—always reassure us that the subject under discussion is
but the latest stage in man's long, textbook-approved
search for meaning. I make bold to deny this, in the
name of Black Humor. The reassurance may be true here
and there; there may be in this author or that author,
this passage or that passage, a groping for system like the
groping of a Spinoza or a Dreiser. But if there is, the
search shall fail. We have gone too far in science, in technology, in philosophy, and in political theory for any new
synthesis remotely like the old. It is not absolute meaning
we seek anymore, but how to live at peace with ourselves
and with the universe.

Toward that end the rough cleansing action conducted
by the Black Humorists directs itself. When Wylie Sypher emphasizes that any new humanism derived from
the new art will of necessity desert the arrogance of
individualism, he is right. "The purpose of Dada," said
Jean Arp, "was to destroy the swindle of reason perpetrated on man and restore him to his humble place in
nature." We do not erase the old lies to replace them
with new ones, but to learn how to get along without
either. *God's mercy*, concludes J. P. Donleavy, *on the wild
Ginger Man*. God's mercy, indeed, on everyone; for we
all, whether we know it or not, admit it or not, we are
all, collectively, the Ginger Man at this hour.

DOUGLAS M. DAVIS

Washington, D.C.

Part I

Three Beginnings

Part I

Three Beginnings

As I point out in the Introduction, both the literary and non-literary sources of Black Humor are extensive. To list—not to say present—the determinant *writers* alone, from Aristophanes to Robert Musil, would be impossible. I have thus confined myself only to the most recent influences, certain that the scholars, as is their wont, will give in time more than the necessary credit to older, safer precedents. Then, too, the names of the three writers I include here are often on the lips and pens of the writers included in the main body of this book. Vladimir Nabokov, the last of the three, is still very much alive and developing in his own unique manner. The qualities that made *Lolita* so important to legions of younger writers, however, its boldness of wit and metaphor, its mix of comedy and terror, its elegance of phrase—have reposed in Nabokov's work (Russian, French, and English) for three decades, and even today he occupies the same half-mythical station as Franz Kafka and Nathanael West, a station that puts him above the "scene," which his work does not derive from but shapes.

The selection from *The Castle* depicts the first full confrontation between K, the hero, and the absurd bureaucracy governing "the castle" he has come so many miles to serve. His argument with the Mayor about the value of himself and his mission to the authorities is a brief of the situation Existentialists later were to call Absurd—that is, the inevitable conflict between a rational animal and an irrational universe. Seen from the vantage of that metaphysic, we should find K's position fully as funny as Kafka reputedly did.

The opening scenes of Nathanael West's *Miss Lonelyhearts,* written in 1933, portray a world where the grotesque is the norm, as grotesque as the professional life of Miss Lonelyhearts himself. It is very much the same world that underlies the work of the "Black Humorists" of later vintage; one need only refer to certain passages in Chapter Thirty-nine of *Catch-22*, "The Eternal City," for an almost exact parallel. And the seduction scene in Nabokov's *Lolita* knows no rival for its exquisite manipulation of comedy, tragedy, farce, and horror. Let us remember as we read it how long Humbert-Humbert, the middle-aged European professor with a weakness for young girls, has labored to achieve this moment: how he married the repellant Mrs. Haze, Lolita's mother; how he planned unsuccessfully to murder her, so that he might have ready access to the daughter of the house; how a chance—and fatal—accident suddenly removes Mrs. Haze from his way, sending him out to retrieve little Lo from summer camp; how he has induced the family doctor to feed him stronger and stronger sleeping pills for his strangely incurable "insomnia"—pills intended only for Lolita, rendering his conquest of her sleeping form a certainty. But there are no certainties in Black Humor—or its antecedents.

FRANZ KAFKA
from *The Castle* (1926)*

To his own surprise K. had little difficulty in obtaining an interview with the Mayor. He sought to explain this to himself by the fact that, going by his previous experience, official intercourse with the authorities for him was always very easy. This was caused on the one hand by the fact that the word had obviously gone out once and for all to treat his case with the external marks of indulgence, and on the other by the admirable autonomy of the service, which one divined to be peculiarly effective precisely where it was not visibly present. At the mere thought of those facts K. was often in danger of considering his situation hopeful; nevertheless, after such fits of easy confidence, he would hasten to tell himself that just there lay his danger.

Direct intercourse with the authorities was not particularly difficult then, for well organized as they might be, all they did was to guard the distant and invisible interests of distant and invisible masters while K. fought for something vitally near to him, for himself, and moreover at least at the very beginning, on his own initiative, for he was the attacker; and besides he fought not only for himself, but clearly for other powers as well which he did not know, but in which, without infringing the regulations of the authorities, he was permitted to believe. But now by the fact that they had at once amply met his wishes in all unimportant matters—and hitherto only unimportant matters had come up—they had robbed him of the possibility of light and easy victories, and with that of the satisfaction which must accompany them and the resultant well-grounded confidence for further and

* This is the date of first publication. *The Castle* was first published in English in 1930.

greater struggles. Instead, they let K. go anywhere he liked—of course easily within the village—and thus pampered and enervated him, ruled out all possibility of conflict, and transposed him to an unofficial, totally unrecognized, troubled, and alien existence. In this life it might easily happen, if he was was not always on his guard, that some day or other, in spite of the amiability of the authorities and the scrupulous fulfillment of all his exaggeratedly light duties, he might—deceived by the apparent favor shown him—conduct himself so imprudently as to get a fall; and the authorities, still ever mild and friendly, and as it were against their will, but in the name of some public regulation unknown to him, might have to come and clear him out of the way. And what was it, this other life to which he was consigned? Never yet had K. seen vocation and life so interlaced as here, so interlaced that sometimes one might think that they had exchanged places. What importance, for example, had the power, merely formal up to now, which Klamm exercised over K.'s services, compared with the very real power that Klamm possessed in K.'s bedroom? So it came about that while a light and frivolous bearing, a certain deliberate carelessness, was sufficient when one came in direct contact with the authorities, one needed in everything else the greatest caution and had to look around on every side before one made a single step.

K. soon found his opinion of the authorities of the place confirmed when he went to see the Mayor. The Mayor, a kindly, stout, clean-shaven man, was laid up; he was suffering from a severe attack of gout, and received K. in bed. "So here is our Land-Surveyor," he said, and tried to sit up, failed in the attempt, and flung himself back again on the cushions, pointing apologetically to his leg. In the faint light of the room, where the tiny windows were still further darkened by curtains, a noiseless, almost shadowy woman pushed forward a chair for K. and placed it beside the bed. "Take a seat, Land-Surveyor, take a seat," said the Mayor, "and let me know your wishes." K. read out Klamm's letter and adjoined a few remarks to it. Again he had this sense of extraordinary ease in intercourse with the authorities. They seemed literally to bear every burden, one could lay everything on their shoulders and remain free and untouched oneself. As if he too felt this in his way, the Mayor made a movement of discomfort on the bed. At length he said: "I know about the whole business, as, indeed, you have remarked. The reason why I've done nothing is, first, that I've been unwell, and secondly that you've been so long in coming; I thought finally that you had given up the business. But now that you've been so kind as to look me up, really I must tell you the plain unvarnished truth of the matter. You've been taken on as Land-Surveyor, as you say, but, unfortunately, we have no need of a land-surveyor. There wouldn't be the least use for one here. The frontiers of our little state are marked out and all officially recorded. So what should we do with a land-surveyor?" Though he had not given the matter a moment's thought before, K. was convinced now at the bottom of his heart that he had expected some such response as this. Exactly for that reason he was able to reply immediately: "This is a great surprise for me. It throws all my calculations out. I can only hope that there's some misunderstanding." "No, unfortunately," said the Mayor, "it's as I've said." "But how is that possible?" cried K. "Surely I haven't made this endless journey just to be sent back again!" "That's another question," replied the Mayor, "which isn't for me to decide, but how this misunderstanding became possible, I can certainly explain that. In such a large governmental office as the Count's, it may occasionally happen that one department ordains this, another that; neither knows of the other, and though the supreme control is absolutely efficient, it comes by its nature too late, and so every now and then a trifling miscalculation arises. Of course that applies only to the pettiest little affairs, as for example your case. In great matters I've never known of any error yet, but even little affairs are often painful enough. Now as for your case, I'll be open with you about its history, and make no official mystery of it—I'm not enough of the official for that, I'm a farmer and always will remain one. A long time ago—I had only been Mayor for a few months—there came an order, I can't remember from what department, in which, in the usual categorical way of the gentlemen up there, it was made know that a Land-Surveyor was to be called in, and the municipality were instructed to hold themselves ready for the plans and measurements necessary for his work. This order obviously couldn't have concerned you, for it was many years ago and I shouldn't have remembered it if I wasn't ill just now and with ample time in bed to think of the most absurd things. . . . We replied with thanks to the order that I've

mentioned already, saying that we didn't need a land-surveyor. But this reply doesn't appear to have reached the
original department—I'll call it A—but by mistake went to
another department, B. So Department A remained without
an answer, but unfortunately our full reply didn't reach B
either; whether it was that the order itself was not enclosed by us, or whether it got lost on the way—it was
certainly not lost in my department, that I can vouch for—
in any case all that arrived at Department B was the covering letter, in which was merely noted that the enclosed
order, unfortunately an impractical one, was concerned with
the engagement of a land-surveyor. Meanwhile Department A
was waiting for our answer; they had, of course, made a
memorandum of the case, but as, excusably enough, often
happens and is bound to happen even under the most efficient
handling, our correspondent trusted to the fact that we
would answer him, after which he would either summon the
Land-Surveyor or else, if need be, write us further about
the matter. As a result he never thought of referring to his
memorandum, and the whole thing fell into oblivion. But in
Department B the covering letter came into the hands of a
correspondent famed for his conscientiousness, Sordini by
name, an Italian; it is incomprehensible even to me, though
I am one of the initiated, why a man of his capacities is
left in an almost subordinate position. This Sordini naturally
sent us back the unaccompanied covering letter for comple-
tion. Now months, if not years, had passed by this time since
that first communication from Department A, which is
understandable enough, for when—as is the rule—a document goes the proper route, it reaches the department at
the outside in a day and is settled that day, but when it
once in a while loses its way, then in an organization so
efficient as ours its proper destination must be sought for
literally with desperation, otherwise it mightn't be found;
and then—well, then the search may last really for a long
time. Accordingly, when we got Sordini's note we had only
a vague memory of the affair; there were only two of us
to do the work at that time, Mizzi and myself, the teacher
hadn't yet been assigned to us; we only kept copies in the
most important instances, so we could only reply in the most
vague terms that we knew nothing of this engagement of a
land-surveyor and that as far as we knew there was no
need for one.

"But"—here the Mayor interrupted himself as if, carried on by his tale, he had gone too far, or as if at least it was possible that he had gone too far, "doesn't the story bore you?"

"No," said K., "it amuses me."

Thereupon the Mayor said: "I'm not telling it to amuse you."

"It only amuses me," said K., "because it gives me an insight into the ludicrous bungling that in certain circumstances may decide the life of a human being . . ."

"Good," said K. "Granted that all this is so, I should have lots of good friends in the Castle; looked at rightly the sudden inspiration of that department all these years ago—saying that a land-surveyor should be asked to come—was an act of friendship toward myself; but then in the sequel one act was followed by another, until at last, on an evil day, I was enticed here and then threatened with being thrown out again."

"There's a certain amount of truth in your view of the case," said the Mayor; "you're right in thinking that the announcements of the Castle are not to be taken literally. But caution is always necessary, not only here, and always the more necessary the more important the pronouncement in question happens to be. But when you went on to talk about being enticed, I cease to fathom you. If you had followed my explanation more carefully, then you must have seen that the question of your being summoned here is far too difficult to be settled here and now in the course of a short conversation."

"So the only remaining conclusion," said K., "is that everything is very uncertain and insoluble, including my being thrown out."

"Who would take the risk of throwing you out, Land-Surveyor?" asked the Mayor. "The very uncertainty about your summons guarantees you the most courteous treatment, only you're too sensitive, by all appearances. Nobody keeps you here, but that surely doesn't amount to throwing you out."

"Oh, Mr. Mayor," said K., "now again you're taking far too simple a view of the case. I'll enumerate for your benefit a few of the things that keep me here: the sacrifice I made in leaving my home, the long and difficult journey, the well-grounded hopes I built on my engagement here, my complete lack of means, the impossibility after this of finding some other suitable job at home, and last but not least my fiancée, who lives here."

"Oh, Frieda!" said the Mayor without showing any surprise. "I know. But Frieda would follow you anywhere. As for the rest of what you said, some consideration will be necessary and I'll communicate with the Castle about it. If a decision should be reached, or if it should be necessary first to interrogate you again, I'll send for you. Is that agreeable to you?"

"No, absolutely," said K. "I don't want any act of favor from the Castle, but my rights."

"Mizzi," the Mayor said to his wife, who still sat pressed against him and, lost in a daydream, was playing with Klamm's letter, which she had folded into the shape of a little boat—K. snatched it from her in alarm. "Mizzi, my foot is beginning to throb again, we must renew the compress."

K. got up. "Then I'll take my leave," he said. "Hm," said Mizzi, who was already preparing a poultice, "the last one was drawing too strongly." K. turned away. At his last words the assistants with their usual misplaced zeal to be useful had thrown open both wings of the door. To protect the sickroom from the strong draft of cold air which was rushing in, K. had to be content with making the Mayor a hasty bow. Then, pushing the assistants in front of him, he rushed out of the room and quickly closed the door.

NATHANAEL WEST
from *Miss Lonelyhearts* (1933)

Miss Lonelyhearts,
Help Me, Help Me

The Miss Lonelyhearts of the New York *Post-Dispatch* (Are you in trouble?—Do-you-need-advice?—Write-to-Miss-Lonely-hearts-and-she-will-help-you) sat at his desk and stared at a piece of white cardboard. On it a prayer had been printed by Shrike, the feature editor.

> "Soul of Miss L, glorify me.
> Body of Miss L, nourish me.
> Blood of Miss L, intoxicate me.
> Tears of Miss L, wash me.
> Oh good Miss L, excuse my plea,
> And hide me in your heart,
> And defend me from mine enemies.
> Help me, Miss L, help me, help me.
> In saecula saeculorum. Amen."

Although the deadline was less than a quarter of an hour away, he was still working on his leader. He had gone as far as: Life *is* worth while, for it is full of dreams and peace, gentleness and ecstasy, and faith that burns like a clear white flame on a grim dark altar." But he found it impossible to continue. The letters were no longer funny. He could not go on finding the same joke funny thirty times a day for months on end. And on most days he received more than thirty letters, all of them alike, stamped from the dough of suffering with a heart-shaped cookie knife. On his desk were piled those he had received this morning. He started through them again, searching for some clew to a sincere answer.

Dear Miss Lonelyhearts—

I am in such pain I dont know what to do sometimes I think I will kill myself my kidneys hurt so much. My husband thinks no woman can be a good catholic and not have children irregardless of the pain. I was married honorable from our church but I never knew what married life meant as I never was told about man and wife. My grandmother never told me and she was the only mother I had but made a big mistake by not telling me as it dont pay to be inocent and is only a big disapointment. I have 7 children in 12 yrs and ever since the last 2 I have been so sick. I was operatored on twice and my husband promised no more children on the doctors advice as he said I might die but when I got back from the hospital he broke his promise and now I am going to have a baby and I don't think I can stand it my kidneys hurt so much. I am so sick and scared because I cant have an abortion on account of being a catholic and my husband so religious. I cry all the time it hurts so much and I dont know what to do.

Yours respectfully
Sick-of-it-all

Miss Lonelyhearts threw the letter into an open drawer and lit a cigarette.

Dear Miss Lonelyhearts—

I am sixteen years old now and I dont know what to do and would appreciate it if you could tell me what to do. When I was a little girl it was not so bad because I got used to the kids on the block makeing fun of me, but now I would like to have boy friends like the other girls and go out on Saturday nites, but no boy will take me because I was born without a nose—although I am a good dancer and have a nice shape and my father buys me pretty clothes.

I sit and look at myself all day and cry. I have a big hole in the middle of my face that scares people even myself so I cant blame the boys for not wanting to take me out. My mother loves me, but she crys terrible when she looks at me.

What did I do to deserve such a terrible bad fate? Even if I did do some bad things I didnt do any before I was a year old and I was born this way. I asked Papa

*and he says he doesnt know, but that maybe I did some-
thing in the other world before I was born or that
maybe I was being punished for his sins. I dont believe
that because he is a very nice man. Ought I commit
suicide?*

Sincerely yours,
Desperate

The cigarette was imperfect and refused to draw. Miss
Lonelyhearts took it out of his mouth and stared at it furiously. He fought himself quiet, then lit another one.

Dear Miss Lonelyhearts—
  *I am writing to you for my little sister Gracie because
something awfull hapened to her and I am afraid to
tell mother about it. I am 15 years old and Gracie is
13 and we live in Brooklyn. Gracie is deaf and dumb
and biger than me but not very smart on account of
being deaf and dumb. She plays on the roof of our house
and dont go to school except to deaf and dumb school
twice a week on tuesdays and thursdays. Mother makes
her play on the roof because we dont want her to get
run over as she aint very smart. Last week a man came
on the roof and did something dirty to her. She told me
about it and I dont know what to do as I am afraid to
tell mother on account of her being lible to beat Gracie
up. I am afraid that Gracie is going to have a baby
and I listened to her stomack last night for a long time
to see if I could hear the baby but I couldn't. If I tell
mother she will beat Gracie up awfull because I am the
only one who loves her and last time when she tore her
dress they loked her in the closet for 2 days and if the
boys on the blok hear about it they will say dirty things
like they did on Peewee Conors sister the time she got
caught in the lots. So please what would you do if the
same hapened in your family.*

Yours truly,
Harold S.

He stopped reading. Christ was the answer, but, if he did
not want to get sick, he had to stay away from the Christ
business. Besides, Christ was Shrike's particular joke. "Soul
of Miss L, glorify me. Body of Miss L, save me. Blood of
. . ." He turned to his typewriter.

Although his cheap clothes had too much style, he still looked like the son of a Baptist minister. A beard would become him, would accent his Old-Testament look. But even without a beard no one could fail to recognize the New England puritan. His forehead was high and narrow. His nose was long and fleshless. His bony chin was shaped and cleft like a hoof. On seeing him for the first time, Shrike had smiled and said, "The Susan Chesters, the Beatrice Fairfaxes and the Miss Lonelyhearts are the priests of twentieth-century America."

A copy boy came up to tell him that Shrike wanted to know if the stuff was ready. He bent over the typewriter and began pounding its keys.

But before he had written a dozen words, Shrike leaned over his shoulder. "The same old stuff," Shrike said. "Why don't you give them something new and hopeful? Tell them about art. Here, I'll dictate:

"Art Is a Way Out.

"Do not let life overwhelm you. When the old paths are choked with the débris of failure, look for newer and fresher paths. Art is just such a path. Art is distilled from suffering. As Mr. Polnikoff exclaimed through his fine Russian beard, when, at the age of eighty-six, he gave up his business to learn Chinese, 'We are, as yet, only at the beginning. . . .'

"Art Is One of Life's Richest Offerings.

"For those who have not the talent to create, there is appreciation. For those . . .

"Go on from there."

Miss Lonelyhearts
and the Dead Pan

When Miss Lonelyhearts quit work, he found that the weather had turned warm and that the air smelt as though it had been artificially heated. He decided to walk to Delehanty's speakeasy for a drink. In order to get there, it was necessary to cross a little park.

He entered the park at the North Gate and swallowed mouthfuls of the heavy shade that curtained its arch. He walked into the shadow of a lamp-post that lay on the path like a spear. It pierced him like a spear.

As far as he could discover, there were no signs of spring. The decay that covered the surface of the mottled ground was not the kind in which life generates. Last year, he remembered, May had failed to quicken these soiled fields. It had taken all the brutality of July to torture a few green spikes through the exhausted dirt.

What the little park needed, even more than he did, was a drink. Neither alcohol nor rain would do. Tomorrow, in his column, he would ask Broken-hearted, Sick-of-it-all, Desperate, Disillusioned-with-tubercular-husband and the rest of his correspondents to come here and water the soil with their tears. Flowers would then spring up, flowers that smelled of feet.

"Ah, humanity . . ." But he was heavy with shadow and the joke went into a dying fall. He tried to break its fall by laughing at himself.

Why laugh at himself, however, when Shrike was waiting at the speakeasy to do a much better job? "Miss Lonelyhearts, my friend, I advise you to give your readers stones. When they ask for bread don't give them crackers as does the Church, and don't, like the State, tell them to eat cake. Explain that man cannot live by bread alone and give them stones. Teach them to pray each morning: 'Give us this day our daily stone.' "

He had given his readers many stones; so many, in fact, that he had only one left—the stone that had formed in his gut.

Suddenly tired, he sat down on a bench. If he could only throw the stone. He searched the sky for a target. But the gray sky looked as if it had been rubbed with a soiled eraser. It held no angels, flaming crosses, olive-bearing doves, wheels within wheels. Only a newspaper struggled in the air like a kite with a broken spine. He got up and started again for the speakeasy.

Delehanty's was in the cellar of a brownstone house that differed from its more respectable neighbors by having an armored door. He pressed a concealed button and a little round window opened in its center. A blood-shot eye appeared, glowing like a ruby in an antique iron ring.

The bar was only half full. Miss Lonelyhearts looked around apprehensively for Shrike and was relieved at not finding him. However, after a third drink, just as he was set-tling into the warm mud of alcoholic gloom, Shrike caught his arm.

"Ah, my young friend!" he shouted. "How do I find you? Brooding again, I take it."

"For Christ's sake, shut up."

Shrike ignored the interruption. "You're morbid, my friend, morbid. Forget the crucifixion, remember the renais-sance. There were no brooders then." He raised his glass, and the whole Borgia family was in his gesture. "I give you the renaissance. What a period! What pageantry! Drunken popes . . . Beautiful courtesans . . . Illegitimate children. . . ."

Although his gestures were elaborate, his face was blank. He practiced a trick used much by moving-picture come-dians—the dead pan. No matter how fantastic or excited his speech, he never changed his expression. Under the shin-ing white globe of his brow, his features huddled together in a dead, gray triangle.

"To the renaissance!" he kept shouting. "To the renais-sance! To the brown Greek manuscripts and mistresses with the great smooth marbly limbs. . . . But that reminds me, I'm expecting one of my admirers—a cow-eyed girl of great intelligence." He illustrated the word *intelligence* by carv-ing two enormous breasts in the air with his hands. "She works in a book store, but wait until you see her behind."

Miss Lonelyhearts made the mistake of showing his an-noyance.

"Oh, so you don't care for women, eh? J. C. is your only sweetheart, eh? Jesus Christ, the King of Kings, the Miss Lonelyhearts of Miss Lonelyhearts. . . ."

At this moment, fortunately for Miss Lonelyhearts, the young woman expected by Shrike came up to the bar. She had long legs, thick ankles, big hands, a powerful body, a slender neck and a childish face made tiny by a man's haircut.

"Miss Farkis," Shrike said, making her bow as a ventrilo-quist does his doll, "Miss Farkis, I want you to meet Miss Lonelyhearts. Show him the same respect you show me. He, too, is a comforter of the poor in spirit and a lover of God."

She acknowledged the introduction with a masculine hand-shake.

"Miss Farkis," Shrike said, "Miss Farkis works in a book store and writes on the side." He patted her rump.

"What were you talking about so excitedly?" she asked.

"Religion."

"Get me a drink and please continue. I'm very much interested in the new thomistic synthesis."

This was just the kind of remark for which Shrike was waiting. "St. Thomas!" he shouted. "What do you take us for—stinking intellectuals? We're not fake Europeans. We were discussing Christ, the Miss Lonelyhearts of Miss Lonelyhearts. America has her own religions. If you need a synthesis, here is the kind of material to use." He took a clipping from his wallet and slapped it on the bar.

"ADDING MACHINE USED IN RITUAL OF WESTERN SECT . . . *Figures Will Be Used for Prayers for Condemned Slayer of Aged Recluse.* . . . DENVER, COLO., Feb. 2 (A.P.) Frank H. Rice, Supreme Pontiff of the Liberal Church of America has announced he will carry out his plan for a 'goat and adding machine' ritual for William Moya, condemned slayer, despite objection to his program by a Cardinal of the sect. Rice declared the goat would be used as part of a 'sack cloth and ashes' service shortly before and after Moya's execution, set for the week of June 20. Prayers for the condemned man's soul will be offered on an adding machine. Numbers, he explained, constitute the only universal language. Moya killed Joseph Zemp, an aged recluse, in an argument over a small amount of money."

Miss Farkis laughed and Shrike raised his fist as though to strike her. His actions shocked the bartender, who hurriedly asked them to go into the back room. Miss Lonelyhearts did not want to go along, but Shrike insisted and he was too tired to argue.

They seated themselves at a table inside one of the booths. Shrike again raised his fist, but when Miss Farkis drew back, he changed the gesture to a caress. The trick worked. She gave in to his hand until he became too daring, then pushed him away.

Shrike again began to shout and this time Miss Lonelyhearts understood that he was making a seduction speech.

"I am a great saint," Shrike cried, "I can walk on my own water. Haven't you ever heard of Shrike's Passion in the Luncheonette, or the Agony in the Soda Fountain? Then I compared the wounds in Christ's body to the mouths of a miraculous purse in which we deposit the small change of our sins. It is indeed an excellent conceit. But now let us consider the holes in our own bodies and into what these congenital wounds open. Under the skin of man is a wondrous jungle where veins like lush tropical growths hang along over-ripe organs and weed-like entrails writhe in squirming tangles of red and yellow. In this jungle, flitting from rock-gray lungs to golden intestines, from liver to lights and back to liver again, lives a bird called the soul. The Catholic hunts this bird with bread and wine, the Hebrew with a golden ruler, the Protestant on leaden feet with leaden words, the Buddhist with gestures, the Negro with blood. I spit on them all. Phooh! And I call upon you to spit. Phooh! Do you stuff birds? No, my dears, taxidermy is not religion. No! A thousand times no. Better, I say unto you, better a live bird in the jungle of the body than two stuffed birds on the library table."

His caresses kept pace with the sermon. When he had reached the end, he buried his triangular face like the blade of a hatchet in her neck.

Miss Lonelyhearts and the Lamb

Miss Lonelyhearts went home in a taxi. He lived by himself in a room that was as full of shadows as an old steel engraving. It held a bed, a table and two chairs. The walls were bare except for an ivory Christ that hung opposite the foot of the bed. He had removed the figure from the cross to which it had been fastened and had nailed it to the wall with large spikes. But the desired effect had not been obtained. Instead of writhing, the Christ remained calmly decorative.

He got undressed immediately and took a cigarette and a copy of *The Brothers Karamazov* to bed. The marker was in a chapter devoted to Father Zossima.

"Love a man even in his sin, for that is the semblance of Divine Love and is the highest love on earth. Love all God's creation, the whole and every grain of sand in it. Love the animals, love the plants, love everything. If you love everything, you will perceive the divine mystery in things. Once you perceive it, you will begin to comprehend it better every day. And you will come at last to love the whole world with an all-embracing love."

It was excellent advice. If he followed it, he would be a big success. His column would be syndicated and the whole world would learn to love. The Kingdom of Heaven would arrive. He would sit on the right hand of the Lamb.

But seriously, he realized, even if Shrike had not made a sane view of this Christ business impossible, there would be little use in his fooling himself. His vocation was of a different sort. As a boy in his father's church, he had discovered that something stirred in him when he shouted the name of Christ, something secret and enormously powerful. He had played with this thing, but had never allowed it to come alive.

He knew now what this thing was—hysteria, a snake whose scales are tiny mirrors in which the dead world takes on a semblance of life. And how dead the world is . . . a world of doorknobs. He wondered if hysteria were really too steep a price to pay for bringing it to life.

For him, Christ was the most natural of excitements. Fixing his eyes on the image that hung on the wall, he began to chant: "Christ, Christ, Jesus Christ. Christ, Christ, Jesus Christ." But the moment the snake started to uncoil in his brain, he became frightened and closed his eyes.

With sleep, a dream came in which he found himself on the stage of a crowded theater. He was a magician who did tricks with doorknobs. At his command, they bled, flowered, spoke. After his act was finished, he tried to lead his audience in prayer. But no matter how hard he struggled, his prayer was one Shrike had taught him and his voice was that of a conductor calling stations.

"Oh, Lord, we are not of those who wash in wine, water, urine, vinegar, fire, oil, bay rum, milk, brandy, or boric acid. Oh, Lord, we are of those who wash solely in the Blood of the Lamb."

The scene of the dream changed. He found himself in his college dormitory. With him were Steve Garvey and Jud Hume. They had been arguing the existence of God from midnight until dawn, and now, having run out of whisky, they decided to go to the market for some applejack.

Their way led through the streets of the sleeping town

into the open fields beyond. It was spring. The sun and the smell of vegetable birth renewed their drunkenness and they reeled between the loaded carts. The farmers took their horse-play good-naturedly. Boys from the college on a spree.

They found the bootlegger and bought a gallon jug of applejack, then wandered to the section where livestock was sold. They stopped to fool with some lambs. Jud suggested buying one to roast over a fire in the woods. Miss Lonelyhearts agreed, but on the condition that they sacrifice it to God before barbecuing it.

Steve was sent to the cutlery stand for a butcher knife, while the other two remained to bargain for a lamb. After a long, Armenian-like argument, during which Jud exhibited his farm training, the youngest was selected, a little, stiff-legged thing, all head.

They paraded the lamb through the market. Miss Lonelyhearts went first, carrying the knife, the others followed, Steve with the jug and Jud with the animal. As they marched, they sang an obscene version of "Mary Had a Little Lamb."

Between the market and the hill on which they intended to perform the sacrifice was a meadow. While going through it, they picked daisies and buttercups. Half way up the hill, they found a rock and covered it with the flowers. They laid the lamb among the flowers. Miss Lonelyhearts was elected priest, with Steve and Jud as his attendants. While they held the lamb, Miss Lonelyhearts crouched over it and began to chant.

"Christ, Christ, Jesus Christ. Christ, Christ, Jesus Christ."

When they had worked themselves into a frenzy, he brought the knife down hard. The blow was inaccurate and made a flesh wound. He raised the knife again and this time the lamb's violent struggles made him miss altogether. The knife broke on the altar. Steve and Jud pulled the animal's head back for him to saw at its throat, but only a small piece of blade remained in the handle and he was unable to cut through the matted wool.

Their hands were covered with slimy blood and the lamb slipped free. It crawled off into the underbrush.

As the bright sun outlined the altar rock with narrow shadows, the scene appeared to gather itself for some new violence. They bolted. Down the hill they fled until they reached the meadow, where they fell exhausted in the tall grass.

After some time had passed, Miss Lonelyhearts begged them to go back and put the lamb out of its misery. They refused to go. He went back alone and found it under a bush. He crushed its head with a stone and left the carcass to the flies that swarmed around the bloody altar flowers.

Miss Lonelyhearts and the Fat Thumb

Miss Lonelyhearts found himself developing an almost insane sensitiveness to order. Everything had to form a pattern: the shoes under the bed, the ties in the holder, the pencils on the table. When he looked out of a window, he composed the skyline by balancing one building against another. If a bird flew across this arrangement, he closed his eyes angrily until it was gone.

For a little while, he seemed to hold his own but one day he found himself with his back to the wall. On that day all the inanimate things over which he had tried to obtain control took the field against him. When he touched something, it spilled or rolled to the floor. The collar buttons disappeared under the bed, the point of the pencil broke, the handle of the razor fell off, the window shade refused to stay down. He fought back, but with too much violence, and was decisively defeated by the spring of the alarm clock.

He fled to the street, but there chaos was multiple. Broken groups of people hurried past, forming neither stars nor squares. The lamp-posts were badly spaced and the flagging was of different sizes. Nor could he do anything with the harsh clanging sound of street cars and the raw shouts of hucksters. No repeated group of words would fit their rhythm and no scale could give them meaning.

He stood quietly against a wall, trying not to see or hear. Then he remembered Betty. She had often made him feel that when she straightened his tie, she straightened much more. And he had once thought that if her world were larger, were *the* world, she might order it as finally as the objects on her dressing table.

He gave Betty's address to a cab driver and told him to

hurry. But she lived on the other side of the city and by the time he got there, his panic had turned to irritation.

She came to the door of her apartment in a crisp, white linen dressing-robe that yellowed into brown at the edges. She held out both her hands to him and her arms showed round and smooth like wood that has been turned by the sea.

With the return of self-consciousness, he knew that only violence could make him supple. It was Betty, however, that he criticized. Her world was not the world and could never include the readers of his column. Her sureness was based on the power to limit experience arbitrarily. Moreover, his confusion was significant, while her order was not.

He tried to reply to her greeting and discovered that his tongue had become a fat thumb. To avoid talking, he awkwardly forced a kiss, then found it necessary to apologize. "Too much lover's return business, I know, and I . . ." He stumbled purposely, so that she would take his confusion for honest feeling. But the trick failed and she waited for him to continue:

"Please eat dinner with me."

"I'm afraid I can't."

Her smile opened into a laugh.

She was laughing at him. On the defense, he examined her laugh for "bitterness," "sour-grapes," "a-broken-heart," "the devil-may-care." But to his confusion, he found nothing at which to laugh back. Her smile had opened naturally, not like an umbrella, and while he watched her laugh folded and became a smile again, a smile that was neither "wry," "ironical" nor "mysterious."

As they moved into the living-room, his irritation increased. She sat down on a studio couch with her bare legs under and her back straight. Behind her a silver tree flowered in the lemon wall-paper. He remained standing.

"Betty the Buddha," he said. "Betty the Buddha. You have the smug smile; all you need is the pot belly."

His voice was so full of hatred that he himself was surprised. He fidgeted for a while in silence and finally sat down beside her on the couch to take her hand.

More than two months had passed since he had sat with her on this same couch and had asked her to marry him. Then she had accepted him and they had planned their life after marriage, his job and her gingham apron, his slippers beside the fireplace and her ability to cook. He had avoided her since. He did not feel guilty; he was merely annoyed at having been fooled into thinking that such a solution was possible.

He soon grew tired of holding hands and began to fidget again. He remembered that toward the end of his last visit he had put his hand inside her clothes. Unable to think of anything else to do, he now repeated the gesture. She was naked under her robe and he found her breast.

She made no sign to show that she was aware of his hand. He would have welcomed a slap, but even when he caught at her nipple, she remained silent.

"Let me pluck this rose," he said, giving a sharp tug. "I want to wear it in my buttonhole."

Betty reached for his brow. "What's the matter?" she asked. "Are you sick?"

He began to shout at her, accompanying his shouts with gestures that were too appropriate, like those of an old-fashioned actor.

"What a kind bitch you are. As soon as any one acts viciously, you say he's sick. Wife-torturers, rapers of small children, according to you they're all sick. No morality, only medicine. Well, I'm not sick. I don't need any of your damned aspirin. I've got a Christ complex. Humanity . . . I'm a humanity lover. All the broken bastards . . ." He finished with a short laugh that was like a bark.

She had left the couch for a red chair that was swollen with padding and tense with live springs. In the lap of this leather monster, all trace of the serene Buddha disappeared.

But his anger was not appeased. "What's the matter, sweetheart?" he asked, patting her shoulder threateningly. "Didn't you like the performance?"

Instead of answering, she raised her arm as though to ward off a blow. She was like a kitten whose soft helplessness makes one ache to hurt it.

"What's the matter?" he demanded over and over again. "What's the matter? What's the matter?"

Her face took on the expression of an inexperienced gambler about to venture all on a last throw. He was turning for his hat, when she spoke.

"I love you."

"You what?"

The need for repeating flustered her, yet she managed to keep her manner undramatic.

"I love you."

"And I love you," he said. "You and your damned smiling through tears."

"Why don't you let me alone?" She had begun to cry. "I felt swell before you came, and now I feel lousy. Go away. Please go away. . . ."

VLADIMIR NABOKOV
from *Lolita* (1955)

Gentlewomen of the jury! Bear with me! Allow me to take just a tiny bit of your precious time! So this was *le grand moment*. I had left my Lolita still sitting on the edge of the abysmal bed, drowsily raising her foot, fumbling at the shoelaces and showing as she did so the nether side of her thigh up to the crotch of her panties—she had always been singularly absent-minded, or shameless, or both, in matters of legshow. This, then, was the hermetic vision of her which I had locked in—after satisfying myself that the door carried no inside bolt. The key, with its numbered dangler of carved wood, became forthwith the weighty sesame to a rapturous and formidable future. It was mine, it was part of my hot hairy fist. In a few minutes—say, twenty, say half-an-hour, *sicher ist sicher* as my uncle Gustave used to say—I would let myself into that "342" and find my nymphet, my beauty and bride, emprisoned in her crystal sleep. Jurors! If my happiness could have talked, it would have filled that genteel hotel with a deafening roar. And my only regret today is that I did not quietly deposit key "342" at the office, and leave the town, the country, the continent, the hemisphere,—indeed, the globe—that very same night.

Let me explain. I was not unduly disturbed by her self-accusatory innuendoes. I was still firmly resolved to pursue my policy of sparing her purity by operating only in the stealth of night, only upon a completely anesthetized little nude. Restraint and reverence were still my motto—even if that "purity" (incidentally, thoroughly debunked by modern science) had been slightly damaged through some juvenile erotic experience, no doubt homosexual, at that accursed camp of hers. Of course, in my old-fashioned, old-world way, I, Jean-Jacques Humbert, had taken for granted, when I first met her, that she was as unravished as the stereotypical notion of "normal child" had been since the lamented end of the Ancient World B.C. and its fascinating practices. We are not surrounded in our enlightened era by little slave flowers that can be casually plucked between business and bath as they used to be in the days of the Romans; and we do not, as dignified Orientals did in still more luxurious times, use tiny entertainers fore and aft between the mutton and the rose sherbet. The whole point is that the old link between the adult world and the child world has been completely severed nowadays by new customs and new laws. Despite my having dabbled in psychiatry and social work, I really knew very little about children. After all, Lolita was only twelve, and no matter what concessions I made to time and place—even bearing in mind the crude behavior of American schoolchildren—I still was under the impression that whatever went on among those brash brats, went on at a later age, and in a different environment. Therefore (to retrieve the thread of this explanation) the moralist in me by-passed the issue by clinging to conventional notions of what twelve-year-old girls should be. The child therapist in me (a fake, as most of them are—but no matter) regurgitated neo-Freudian hash and conjured up a dreaming and exaggerating Dolly in the "latency" period of girlhood. Finally, the sensualist in me (a great and insane monster) had no objection to some depravity in his prey. But somewhere behind the raging bliss, bewildered shadows conferred—and not to have heeded them, this is what I regret! Human beings, attend! I should have understood that Lolita had *already* proved to be something quite different from innocent Annabel, and that the nymphean evil breathing through every pore of the fey child that I had prepared for my secret delectation, would make the secrecy impossible, and the delectation lethal. I should have known (by the signs made to me by something in Lolita—the real child Lolita or some haggard angel behind her back) that nothing but pain and horror would result from the expected rapture. Oh, winged gentlemen of the jury!

And she was mine, she was mine, the key was in my fist, my fist was in my pocket, she was mine. In the course of the evocations and schemes to which I had dedicated so many insomnias, I had gradually eliminated all the superfluous blur, and by stacking level upon level of translucent vision, had evolved a final picture. Naked, except for one sock and her charm bracelet, spread-eagled on the bed where my philter had felled her—so I foreglimpsed her; a velvet hair ribbon was still clutched in her hand; her honey-brown body, with the white negative image of a rudimentary swimsuit patterned against her tan, presented to me its pale breastbuds; in the rosy lamplight, a little pubic floss glistened on its plump hillock. The cold key with its warm wooden addendum was in my pocket.

I wandered through various public rooms, glory below, gloom above: for the look of lust always is gloomy; lust is never quite sure—even when the velvety victim is locked up in one's dungeon—that some rival devil or influential god may still not abolish one's prepared triumph. In common parlance, I needed a drink; but there was no barroom in that venerable place full of perspiring philistines and period objects.

I drifted to the Men's Room. There, a person in clerical black—a "hearty party" *comme on dit*—checking with the assistance of Vienna, if it was still there, inquired of me how I had liked Dr. Boyd's talk, and looked puzzled when I (King Sigmund the Second) said Boyd was quite a boy. Upon which, I neatly chucked the tissue paper I had been wiping my sensitive finger tips with into the receptacle provided for it, and sallied lobbyward. Comfortably resting my elbows on the counter, I asked Mr. Potts was he quite sure my wife had not telephoned, and what about that cot? He answered she had not (she was dead, of course) and the cot would be installed tomorrow if we decided to stay on. From a big crowded place called The Hunters' Hall came a sound of many voices discussing horticulture or eternity. Another room, called The Raspberry Room, all bathed in light, with bright little tables and a large one with "refreshments," was still empty except for a hostess (that type of worn woman with a glassy smile and Charlotte's manner of speaking); she floated up to me to ask if I was Mr. Braddock, because if so, Miss Beard had been looking for me. "What a name for a woman," I said and strolled away.

In and out of my heart flowed my rainbow blood. I would give her till half-past-nine. Going back to the lobby,

I found there a change: a number of people in floral dresses or black cloth had formed little groups here and there, and some elfish chance offered me the sight of a delightful child of Lolita's age, in Lolita's type of frock, but pure white, and there was a white ribbon in her black hair. She was not pretty, but she was a nymphet, and her ivory pale legs and lily neck formed for one memorable moment a most pleasurable antiphony (in terms of spinal music) to my desire for Lolita, brown and pink, flushed and fouled. The pale child noticed my gaze (which was really quite casual and debonair), and being ridiculously self-conscious, lost countenance completely, rolling her eyes and putting the back of her hand to her cheek, and pulling at the hem of her skirt, and finally turning her thin mobile shoulder blades to me in specious chat with her cow-like mother.

I left the loud lobby and stood outside, on the white steps, looking at the hundreds of powdered bugs wheeling around the lamps in the soggy black night, full of ripple and stir. All I would do—all I would dare to do— would amount to such a trifle . . .

Suddenly I was aware that in the darkness next to me there was somebody sitting in a chair on the pillared porch. I could not really see him but what gave him away was the rasp of a screwing off, then a discreet gurgle, then the final note of a placid screwing on. I was about to move away when his voice addressed me:

"Where the devil did you get her?"

"I beg your pardon?"

"I said: the weather is getting better."

"Seems so."

"Who's the lassie?"

"My daughter."

"You lie—she's not."

"I beg your pardon?"

"I said: July was hot. Where's her mother?"

"Dead."

"I see. Sorry. By the way, why don't you two lunch with me tomorrow. That dreadful crowd will be gone by then."

"We'll be gone too. Good night."

"Sorry. I'm pretty drunk. Good night. That child of

yours needs a lot of sleep. Sleep is a rose, as the Persians say. Smoke?"

"Not now."

He struck a light, but because he was drunk, or because the wind was, the flame illumined not him but another person, a very old man, one of those permanent guests of old hotels—and his white rocker. Nobody said anything and the darkness returned to its initial place. Then I heard the old-timer cough and deliver himself of some sepulchral mucus.

I left the porch. At least half an hour in all had elapsed. I ought to have asked for a sip. The strain was beginning to tell. If a violin string can ache, then I was that string. But it would have been unseemly to display any hurry. As I made my way through a constellation of fixed people in one corner of the lobby, there came a blinding flash— and beaming Dr. Braddock, two orchid-ornamentalized matrons, the small girl in white, and presumably the bared teeth of Humbert Humbert sidling between the bridelike lassie and the enchanted cleric, were immortalized—insofar as the texture and print of small-town newspapers can be deemed immortal. A twittering group had gathered near the elevator. I again chose the stairs. 342 was near the fire escape. One could still—but the key was already in the lock, and then I was in the room.

The door of the lighted bathroom stood ajar; in addition to that, a skeleton glow came through the Venetian blind from the outside arclights; these intercrossed rays penetrated the darkness of the bedroom and revealed the following situation.

Clothed in one of her old nightgowns, my Lolita lay on her side with her back to me, in the middle of the bed. Her lightly veiled body and bare limbs formed a Z. She had put both pillows under her dark tousled head; a band of pale light crossed her top vertebrae.

I seemed to have shed my clothes and slipped into pajamas with the kind of fantastic instantaneousness which is implied when in a cinematographic scene the process of changing is cut; and I had already placed my knee on the edge of the bed when Lolita turned her head and stared at me through the striped shadows.

Now this was something the intruder had not expected. The whole pill-spiel (a rather sordid affair, *entre nous soit dit*) had had for object a fastness of sleep that a whole regiment would not have disturbed, and here she was staring at me, and thickly called me "Barbara." Barbara, wearing my pajamas which were much too tight for her, remained poised motionless over the little sleep-talker. Softly with a hopeless sigh, Dolly turned away, resuming her initial position. For at least two minutes I waited and strained on the brink, like that tailor with his homemade parachute forty years ago when about to jump from the Eiffel Tower. Her faint breathing had the rhythm of sleep. Finally I heaved myself onto my narrow margin of bed, stealthily pulled at the odds and ends of sheets piled up to the south of my stone-cold heels—and Lolita lifted her head and gaped at me.

As I learned later from a helpful pharmaceutist, the purple pill did not even belong to the big and noble family of barbiturates, and though it might have induced sleep in a neurotic who believed it to be a potent drug, it was too mild a sedative to affect for any length of time a wary, albeit weary, nymphet. Whether the Ramsdale doctor was a charlatan or a shrewd old rogue, does not, and did not, really matter. What mattered was that I had been deceived. When Lolita opened her eyes again, I realized that whether or not the drug might work later in the night, the security I had relied upon was a sham one. Slowly her head turned away and dropped onto her unfair amount of pillow. I lay quite still on my brink, peering at her rumpled hair, at the glimmer of nymphet flesh, where half a haunch and half a shoulder dimly showed, and trying to gauge the depth of her sleep by the rate of her respiration. Some time passed, nothing changed, and I decided I might risk getting a little closer to that lovely and maddening glimmer; but hardly had I moved into its warm purlieus than her breathing was suspended, and I had the odious feeling that little Dolores was wide awake and would explode in screams if I touched her with any part of my wretchedness. Please, reader: no matter your exasperation with the tenderhearted, morbidly sensitive, infinitely circumspect hero of my book, do not skip these essential pages! Imagine me; I shall not exist if you do not imagine me; try to discern the doe in me, trembling in the forest of my own iniquity; let's even smile a little. After all, there is no harm in smiling. For instance (I almost wrote "frinstance"), I had no place to rest my head, and a fit of heartburn (they call those fries "French," *grand Dieu!*) was added to my discomfort.

She was again fast asleep, my nymphet, but still I did not dare to launch upon my enchanted voyage. *La Petite Dormeuse ou l'Amant Ridicule.* Tomorrow I would stuff her with those earlier pills that had so thoroughly numbed her mummy. In the glove compartment—or in the Gladstone bag? Should I wait a solid hour and then creep up again? The science of nympholepsy is a precise science. Actual contact would do it in one second flat. An interspace of a millimeter would do it in ten. Let us wait.

There is nothing louder than an American hotel; and, mind you, this was supposed to be a quiet, cozy, old-fashioned, homey place—"gracious living" and all that stuff. The clatter of the elevator's gate—some twenty yards northeast of my head but as clearly perceived as if it were inside my left temple—alternated with the banging and booming of the machine's various evolutions and lasted well beyond midnight. Every now and then, immediately east of my left ear (always assuming I lay on my back, not daring to direct my viler side toward the nebulous haunch of my bed-mate), the corridor would brim with cheerful, resonant and inept exclamations ending in a volley of good-nights. When *that* stopped, a toilet immediately north of my cerebellum took over. It was a manly, energetic, deep-throated toilet, and it was used many times. Its gurgle and gush and long afterflow shook the wall behind me. Then someone in a southern direction was extravagantly sick, almost coughing out his life with his liquor, and his toilet descended like a veritable Niagara, immediately beyond our bathroom. And when finally all the waterfalls had stopped, and the enchanted hunters were sound asleep, the avenue under the window of my insomnia, to the west of my wake—a staid, eminently residential, dignified alley of huge trees—degenerated into the despicable haunt of gigantic trucks roaring through the wet and windy night.

And less than six inches from me and my burning life, was nebulous Lolita! After a long stirless vigil, my tentacles moved towards her again, and this time the creak of the mattress did not awake her. I managed to bring my ravenous bulk so close to her that I felt the aura of her bare shoulder like a warm breath upon my cheek. And then, she sat up, gasped, muttered with insane rapidity something about boats, tugged at the sheets and lapsed back into her rich, dark, young unconsciousness. As she tossed, within that abundant flow of sleep, recently auburn, at present lunar, her arm struck me across the face. For a second I held her. She freed herself from the shadow of my embrace—doing this not consciously, not violently, not with any personal distaste, but with the neutral plaintive murmur of a child demanding its natural rest. And again the situation remained the same: Lolita with her curved spine to Humbert, Humbert resting his head on his hand and burning with desire and dyspepsia.

The latter necessitated a trip to the bathroom for a draft of water which is the best medicine I know in my case, except perhaps milk with radishes; and when I re-entered the strange pale-striped fastness where Lolita's old and new clothes reclined in various attitudes of enchantment on pieces of furniture that seemed vaguely afloat, my impossible daughter sat up and in clear tones demanded a drink, too. She took the resilient and cold paper cup in her shadowy hand and gulped down its contents gratefully, her long eyelashes pointing cupward, and then, with an infantile gesture that carried more charm than any carnal caress, little Lolita wiped her lips against my shoulder. She fell back on her pillow (I had subtracted mine while she drank) and was instantly asleep again.

I had not dared offer her a second helping of the drug, and had not abandoned hope that the first might still consolidate her sleep. I started to move toward her, ready for any disappointment, knowing I had better wait but incapable of waiting. My pillow smelled of her hair. I moved toward my glimmering darling, stopping or retreating every

time I thought she stirred or was about to stir. A breeze
from wonderland had begun to affect my thoughts, and now
they seemed couched in italics, as if the surface reflecting
them were wrinkled by the phantasm of that breeze. Time
and again my consciousness folded the wrong way, my shuf-
fling body entered the sphere of sleep, shuffled out again,
and once or twice I caught myself drifting into a melancholy snore. Mists of tenderness enfolded mountains of longing. Now and then it seemed to me that the enchanted prey
was about to meet halfway the enchanted hunter, that her
haunch was working its way toward me under the soft sand
of a remote and fabulous beach; and then her dimpled dim-
ness would stir, and I would know she was farther away
from me than ever.

If I dwell at some length on the tremors and gropings of
that distant night, it is because I insist upon proving that
I am not, and never was, and never could have been, a brutal
scoundrel. The gentle and dreamy regions through which I
crept were the patrimonies of poets—not crime's prowling
ground. Had I reached my goal, my ecstasy would have
been all softness, a case of internal combustion of which she
would hardly have felt the heat, even if she were wide awake.
But I still hoped she might gradually be engulfed in a com-
pleteness of stupor that would allow me to taste more than a
glimmer of her. And so, in between tentative approximations,
with a confusion of perception, metamorphosing her into
eyespots of moonlight or a fluffy flowering bush, I would
dream I regained consciousness, dream I lay in wait.

In the first antemeridian hours there was a lull in the
restless hotel night. Then around four the corridor toilet cascaded and its door banged. A little after five a reverberating
monologue began to arrive, in several installments, from
some courtyard or parking place. It was not really a monologue, since the speaker stopped every few seconds to listen
(presumably) to another fellow, but that other voice did
not reach me, and so no real meaning could be derived from
the part heard. Its matter-of-fact intonations, however,
helped to bring in the dawn, and the room was already
suffused with lilac gray, when several industrious toilets went
to work, one after the other, and the clattering and whining
elevator began to rise and take down early risers and down-
ers, and for some minutes I miserably dozed, and Charlotte
was a mermaid in a greenish tank, and somewhere in the

passage Dr. Boyd said "Good morning to you" in a fruity voice, and birds were busy in the trees, and then Lolita yawned.

Frigid gentlewomen of the jury! I had thought that months, perhaps years, would elapse before I dared to reveal myself to Dolores Haze; but by six she was wide awake, and by six fifteen we were technically lovers. I am going to tell you something very strange: it was she who seduced me.

Upon hearing her first morning yawn, I feigned handsome profiled sleep. I just did not know what to do. Would she be shocked at finding me by her side, and not in some spare bed? Would she collect her clothes and lock herself up in the bathroom? Would she demand to be taken at once to Ramsdale—to her mother's bedside—back to camp? But my Lo was a sportive lassie. I felt her eyes on me, and when she uttered at last that beloved chortling note of hers, I knew her eyes had been laughing. She rolled over to my side, and her warm brown hair came against my collarbone. I gave a mediocre imitation of waking up. We lay quietly. I gently caressed her hair, and we gently kissed. Her kiss, to my delirious embarrassment, had some rather comical refinements of flutter and probe which made me conclude she had been coached at an early age by a little Lesbian. No Charlie boy could have taught her *that*. As if to see whether I had my fill and learned the lesson, she drew away and surveyed me. Her cheekbones were flushed, her full underlip glistened, my dissolution was near. All at once, with a burst of rough glee (the sign of the nymphet!), she put her mouth to my ear—but for quite a while my mind could not separate into words the hot thunder of her whisper, and she laughed, and brushed the hair off her face, and tried again, and gradually the odd sense of living in a brand new, mad new dream world, where everything was permissible, came over me as I realized what she was suggesting. I answered I did not know what game she and Charlie had played. "You mean you have never—?"—her features twisted into a stare of disgusted incredulity. "You have never—" she started again. I took time out by nuzzling her a little. "Lay off, will you," she said with a twangy whine, hastily removing her brown shoulder from my lips. (It was very curious the way she considered—and kept doing so for a long time—all caresses except kisses on the mouth or the stark act of love either "romantic slosh" or "abnormal.")

"You mean," she persisted, now kneeling above me, "you never did it when you were a kid?"

"Never," I answered quite truthfully.

"Okay," said Lolita, "here is where we start."

However, I shall not bore my learned readers with a detailed account of Lolita's presumption. Suffice it to say that not a trace of modesty did I perceive in this beautiful hardly formed young girl whom modern co-education, juvenile mores, the campfire racket and so forth had utterly and hopelessly depraved. She saw the stark act merely as part of a youngster's furtive world, unknown to adults. What adults did for purposes of procreation was no business of hers. My life was handled by little Lo in an energetic, matter-of-fact manner as if it were an insensate gadget unconnected with me. While eager to impress me with the world of tough kids, she was not quite prepared for certain discrepancies between a kid's life and mine. Pride alone prevented her from giving up; for, in my strange predicament, I feigned supreme stupidity and had her have her way—at least while I could still bear it. But really these are irrelevant matters; I am not concerned with so-called "sex" at all. Anybody can imagine those elements of animality. A greater endeavor lures me on: to fix once for all the perilous magic of nymphets.

I have to tread carefully. I have to speak in a whisper. Oh you, veteran crime reporter, you grave old usher, you once popular policeman, now in solitary confinement after gracing that school crossing for years, you wretched emeritus read to by a boy! It would never do, would it, to have you fellows fall madly in love with my Lolita! Had I been a painter, had the management of The Enchanted Hunters lost its mind one summer day and commissioned me to redecorate their dining room with murals of my own making, this is what I might have thought up, let me list some fragments:

There would have been a lake. There would have been an arbor in flame-flower. There would have been nature studies—a tiger pursuing a bird of paradise, a choking snake sheathing whole the flayed trunk of a shoat. There would have been a sultan, his face expressing great agony (belied, as it were, by his molding caress), helping a callypygean slave child to climb a column of onyx. There would have been those luminous globules of gonadal glow that travel up the opalescent sides of juke boxes. There would have been all kinds of camp activities on the part of the intermediate group, Canoeing, Coranting, Combing Curls in the lakeside sun. There would have been poplars, apples, a suburban Sunday. There would have been a fire opal dissolving within a ripple-ringed pool, a last throb, a last dab of color, stinging red, smarting pink, a sigh, a wincing child.

I am trying to describe these things not to relive them in my present boundless misery, but to sort out the portion of hell and the portion of heaven in that strange, awful, maddening world—nymphet love. The beastly and beautiful merged at one point, and it is that borderline I would like to fix, and I feel I fail to do so utterly. Why?

The stipulation of the Roman law, according to which a girl may marry at twelve, was adopted by the Church, and is still preserved, rather tacitly, in some of the United States. And fifteen is lawful everywhere. There is nothing wrong, say both hemispheres, when a brute of forty, blessed by the local priest and bloated with drink, sheds his sweat-drenched finery and thrusts himself up to the hilt into his youthful bride. "In such stimulating temperate climates [says an old magazine in this prison library] as St. Louis, Chicago and Cincinnati, girls mature about the end of their twelfth year." Dolores Haze was born less than three hundred miles from stimulating Cincinnati. I have but followed nature. I am nature's faithful hound. Why then this horror that I cannot shake off? Did I deprive her of her flower? Sensitive gentlewomen of the jury, I was not even her first lover.

Part II

Eleven in Opposition

Here we have, I believe, as broad a panorama of protest as will be found in any "school," "group," or "trend" in modern letters. Within the context of these selections alone, admittedly limited by both prejudice and space, no definable segment of society remains untouched (or should I say unbludgeoned), including critics (see the second chapter of William Gaddis's *The Recognitions*). Rather than belabor this point, I would like to turn now to another, raised briefly in the Introduction. If we turn these eleven complaints around, in a search for the standard behind them, we will find, I believe, a quite consistent attachment to the democratic norms of rationality, decorum, and brotherly love, norms violated with impeccable consistency by the characters who people this section. It would be easy to conclude for the basic naïvete of Black Humor—its refusal to face the fact of human limitation—were there not a metaphysical ground beneath that refusal. It is not ultimately the perfectibility of man that goads these writers on, but the hostility of the universe. I believe this response, this impatience with that hostility, to be just; as just, in any case, as its alternatives, both of which men have tried—outright denial and outright repression of the fact.

JOHN HAWKES
from *The Cannibal* (1949)

The Cannibal both derives from the sources already mentioned (particularly Surrealism) and antedates the major body of Black Humor. Its plot proceeds on several levels of time and its setting is essentially surreal. The basic fact of the novel is the post-World War II occupation of Germany by Allied armies. In the world of John Hawkes, however, the army of occupation dissolves into one lone, tragicomic figure—the American named Leevey, astride his motorcycle, riding down the *Autobahn* to meet his ridiculous fate at the hands of the German townspeople and of the universe.

Several viewpoint characters take their turns in this selection—as do many throughout the novel itself. The first-person here largely belongs to Zizendorf, the leader of the three villagers who wait beside the road to kill Leevey. While they wait, we are presented with a broad panorama of the village, both its people and its recent history. The brilliant riot at the "mad house," for example, belongs to the last days of the war itself. The Kaiser's face, peeping through Madame Snow's window, belongs to World War I, of course.

All during the day the villagers had been burning out the pits of excrement, burning the fresh trenches of latrines where wads of wet newspapers were scattered, burning the dark round holes in the back stone huts where moisture traveled upwards and stained the privy seats, where pools of water became foul with waste that was as ugly as the aged squatter. These earthen pots were still breathing off their odor of burned flesh and hair and biddy, and this strange odor of gas and black cheese was wafted across the roads, over the fields, and collected on the damp leaves and in the bare night fog along the embankment of the *Autobahn*. This smell not only rested over the mud, but moved, and with every small breath of air, the gas of mustard, soft goat pellets and human liquid became more intimate, more strong and visible in reddening piles. One's own odor could always be sifted out and recognized, a disturbingly fresh stream in the turning ash, a personal mark that could be sniffed and known after midnight, sometimes as if the tongue were poking in the incinerator and the warm air curling about the hewn seat.

The three of us waited by the side of the road, stockingless feet burning and itching in our unlaced shoes, plucking at nostrils, listening to a wasted mongrel paw the leaves, hearing an occasional tile slide from a roof and fall to the mud with the swishing of a tail. The flats turned away before us, unpeopled, dark, an occasional shell-case filling with seepage, the fingers of a lost glove curling with dew. Behind us the ghosts left the stalled tank and filed downward toward the canal.

"He's late," said Fegelein.

"Yes."

"No sleep for us then."

"Wait, have patience," I answered.

We crowded invisibly together with the road high overhead that extended far beyond this edge of town, and there were no precision transits or plumb lines to point the kilometers of travel or show the curve on the map where the blank spot of this town would be. We never ventured away, though we still wore the grey shirts and had signed our way to the outside world.

"It's a good machine he's riding," said Fegelein.

"Don't worry. I won't shoot at it."

"Good."

"Remember, no talking. Stintz would be sure to say something when the next rider comes through in a month looking for this one." I constantly had to give commands.

"In a month we'll be ready."

"Yes."

"And the motorbike will be useful."

"Yes." I had to humor them.

In every town there are a few who, though they don't remember how it came about, or how they returned, or when they went away, or what the enemy expects, gather together in the night to rise again, despite the obstacle of their own people or the swarming invader. Behind us the town grew smaller; the sleepers were cold and numberless.

"No one will see?"

"No," I answered.

"I don't want to go forward tonight; you mustn't make me . . ."

"Stop that. You know there isn't any forward."

"I'm sorry."

The cold night air quickened my hunger, and I put the thought out of mind, concentrated on the hunched man in goggles and helmet. Once the old horse clattered by above our ears and then moved off as if he smelled nothing, neither fresh grass nor humans nearby. . . .

A hundred miles from *Spitzen-on-the-Dein* in the early morning of the day when the killing occurred, the intended victim, Leevey, lay wearied and injured beside a laughing slut who was covered with invisible red clap. All through the darkness they had struggled, baring each other with the point of a knee, angry and calling each other *schmuck*, and she had struck his face so that the eyes bled. She raised her white legs above the sheets, then grimaced and threw him off, jabbing with her fists as he fell against the wall. Over and over she said, "My house, you come to *my* house," but Leevey was afraid that if he left the safety of his room she would shellac him, cut with the scissors, and finally leave him dead with a pin through his neck. For he had heard the stories, stories of murder in the empty lot, the special deaths, the vaginae packed with deadly poison. He clung to her, "You stay here," and her sharp wooden sandals sliced at his shins and her unwashed hair fell over his aching shoulder. His white helmet, goggles, and gauntlets lay beside the bunk, his tunic and trousers the girl used as a pillow. "Candy," she said, pinching and poking with her strong fingers. "Go to hell," he whined and the forearm crushed down on his nose and mouth, bruising and dull. Finally, unsuccessful, Leevey tried to sleep, but she scratched and pushed, whistled in his ear, squeezed, cried, jammed with her feet, and just as he dozed would slap with all her strength.

The sun gradually brightened the grey walls, the girl's white laughing eyes never left his face, a quick pinch. The heavy tiredness and pain swept over him and he wished he was back in the delicatessen, his long nose pushed among the cheeses.

When she reached the door she turned, leaned her shoulder against the jamb, thrust out her hip and smiled at the feeble one, also filmed now with red invisible clap, tousled and unprotesting, sick in the bunk:

"Auf Wiedersehen, Amerikaner," she said, *"Amerikaner!"*

Leevey doused his face in the basin, slicked down his black hair. "That's life," he said, "that's life," and as the sun rose clear and cold he slung the Sten-gun on his back, polished his boots, fastened the gauntlets, climbed on his rusty motorcycle, and began the tour of his district.

He traveled ninety miles with his palms shivering on the steerhorn handlebars, the white cold air glazed endlessly ahead, his insides smacking against the broad cowhide saddle. He stopped a few times beside an abandoned farm or mis-turned sign or unburied Allied corpse to take a few notes, laying the machine on its side in the mud, and he sweated over the smeared pad and stubby pencil. He was overseer for a sector of land that was one-third of the nation and he frowned with the responsibility, sped along thinking of the letters he would write home, traveled like a gnome behind a searchlight when the sun finally set and the foreign shadows settled. He saw the bare spire rising less than a mile beyond, and crouching down, spattered with grease, he speeded up, to go past *Spitzen-on-the-Dein* with a roar. The late night and crowded broken road twisted around him, flames shot up from exhaust.

"Wait a minute, I'll be right up, *Kinder*," called Herr Stintz to the upper window. He caught one last glimpse of the slim light with its tail of angry short tongues of fire like a comet, and flinging on a thin coat he bolted for the stairs. He made noise, hurried, was neither meek nor ineffectual, for he felt at last he had the right, the obligation, and his tattling could be open, commanding; for he had seen the light, the unexpected journeyman, the foreign arrival, a fire in the night that no one knew about but he, and now he moved without caution, tripping and whispering, to take possession. Again he opened the door to the top floor apartment, hurried through the first room past the unwaking Jutta where her high breast gleamed from under the sheet, past the full basin and into the smaller, cold lair. "Quickly," he said, "we must hurry. It's up to you and me." She made no protest but watched him with sharp appraising eyes, holding her breath. Stintz picked the little girl from the bundle of clothes, wrapped her in a shortened quilt, tied it with string around her waist, fastened the thick stockings on her feet. He knew exactly what he was about as he dressed the child, considered no question, gave no thought to the sleeping mother. Never before had he been so close; he tied the quilt high about her throat, smoothed the hair once quickly with his hand.

"The moon will see," she murmured, as his good eye swept over her.

"No, no, there isn't any moon at all. Come along." They walked past the woman, hand in hand, into the bitter hallway and he carried her down the stairs, slipped, caught himself, in the hurry. They left the front door ajar and began their walk over the streets smelling of smoke.

The ghosts raised their heads in unison by the canal and sniffed the night air.

I, Zizendorf, my gun drawn, crouching on my knees with my comrades who were tensed like sprinters or swimmers, heard above gusts of wind the approaching light machine. The uprising must be successful, inspired, ruthless.

The Duke carefully reached out his hand and the boy fairy did not move, while the marquee banged to and fro, the projector steamed, and the invisible lost audience stamped booted feet and rummaged in box lunches.

Unconscious, drowned cold in acid, the Census-Taker lay on the third floor, dressed, uncovered, where Jutta had dropped him.

The Mayor, at this hour, groaned, awoke, and found himself pained by a small black-pebble cluster of hemorrhoids, felt it blister upwards over his spine.

The ghosts returned to their cupped hands and sipped the green water, while soft faecal corbans rolled below their faces through the cluttered waves in tribute to Leevey.

Madame Snow thought for a moment that she heard Herr Stintz's voice yelling somewhere up above through the darkest part of the night and drew the robe closer about the kneeling man. Balamir trembled with being awake, frowned and grinned at the old woman, shook as if he was starving on these sleepless hours, tried to speak of the mob of risers, the strength, fear, out in the night, but could not. Stella wondered what they were doing, this anonymous nation, and felt, such an old woman, that she would never sleep again. The candle swayed, her powdered hands fluttered and moved, and then she heard Stint's sharp footfall and the padding of the girl, and when they left, a breath of air from the front door ajar swept across the floor and stirred the draped figure of her kneeling charge.

Neither could sleep, and somehow the hard yellow eyes of their brethren had told them men were moving, the night was not still. Madame Snow did not find the rooms changed by this darkness or added cold, simply the cups eluded her fingers, slipped more easily, the tea was like black powder and too much escaped, the pot assumed enormous proportions. But waking, she found the same day and night except that in the darkness it was more clear, the air smelled more heavily of the sewer in the canal, the carpets smelled more of dust.

On the fifth floor Jutta awoke and feeling less tired, began to wash a blouse in the hand-basin.

The tea was so near the chipped brim that it spilled over his robe when he peered closely at the cup and twisted it about. Stella drew the curtains but could see nothing, from the front windows neither street nor light, from the rear windows neither the line of the canal nor the shed. At first when the main pipes were destroyed she boiled the water that had to be taken from the canal, but for months the fire did not last long enough, the effort to prod the dull coals was too great, and tonight the tea tasted more sour than usual. In unlocking the basement door she had noticed that the smell of the canal was becoming stronger, the water seeping from its imperfect bed, and she decided that she must find a new place to keep the harmless unmoving man. The old woman, hair thin about her scalp but falling thickly to her waist, ankles frail without stockings in the high unbuttoned shoes, sipping tea through her thin once bowed lips, hated nothing, did not actually despise the gross invader or the struggling mistaken English, but would have been pleased to see them whipped. She knew the strength of women, and sometimes vaguely hoped that a time would come again when they could attack flesh with their husband's sickles, and the few husbands themselves could take the belts from their trousers to flay the enemy. It was the women who really fought. The uprising must be sure, and the place to strike with the tip of the whip's tail was between the legs. The candle went out and the brilliant old woman and crazed man sat in the darkness for a long while.

They had waited weeks for the riot to come at the institution and when it finally did descend like a mule to its haunches it lasted barely an hour. During those weeks disorder accumulated, both inside and outside the high walls. The German army was suffering unreasonable blows, the town was bereft of all men, the food trucks were overtaken by hordes of frenzied children, the staff itself worked in the gardens and nurses spent part of their duty in the bakery. Switchboard connections were crossed; Supply sent barrels of molasses but no meat; the cold came in dreadful waves. All reading material went to the furnaces; several cases of insulin went bad; and the board of directors learned of the deaths of their next of kin. Bedpans were left unemptied in the hallways; and for days on end the high bright gates of iron were never opened. Finally they burned linen for fuel and a thick smudge poured from the smokestack, the snow rose higher against the walls, and they served only one meal a day. One of the oldest night nurses died and her body was smuggled from the institution under cover of darkness. Reports crept out on the tongues of frightened help, of unshaven men, quarreling women, of patients who slept night after night fully dressed, of men who had hair so long that it hung on their shoulders. And those inside the walls heard that greater numbers of the more fit women were being taken to war, that there wasn't a single man left in the town, that Allied parachute rapists were to be sent on the village, that pregnant women went out of doors at night to freeze themselves to death.

The patients would no longer go to their rooms but crowded together in the long once immaculate corridors and baited each other or lay in sullen heaps, white with the cold. They had to be prodded into going out to the garden, white, filled with frozen thistle, and threatened, pushed, forced to retreat back to the buildings. Fearing more than ever erratic outbursts or startled, snarling attacks, the nurses quickly used up the last row of bottled sedatives, and old ferocious men lay only half-subdued, angrily awake through the long nights. One of these nurses, short, man-like, tense, lost the only set of keys that locked the windows shut, so for the last few days and nights, the horrible cold swept in and out of the long guarded wings. Underneath the ordered town-like group of brick buildings, there were magnificent tile and steel tunnels connecting them to underground laboratories, laundries, kitchens, and ventilated rooms that housed monkeys and rats for experimentation. Through these tunnels ran thin lines of gleaming rails where hand-carts of refuse, linen, chemicals, and food were pushed and the carts were guided by a meticulous system of red and yellow lights. During these bad days the carts were pushed too fast, knocked each other from the tracks, the system of lights smashed, the upturned carts blocked the corridors, and broken bottles and soiled linen filled the passages. The lighting system short-circuited and orderlies, now trying to carry the supplies in their arms, stumbled through the narrow darkness, through the odor of ferment, and shouted warning signals.

At last the rats and monkeys died. Their bodies were strewn over the main grounds, and since they froze, they looked life-like, tangled together on the snow.

All attempts at cure ceased. The bearded, heartening groups of doctors on rounds no longer appeared, nothing was written on charts. The tubs were left cold and dry, and patients no longer came back to the wards red, unconscious, shocked. Not only was treatment stopped, but all activity impossible. They no longer wove the useless rugs, no longer ran uncertainly about the gymnasium, no longer argued over cards or shot the billiard balls back and forth across the table. There were no showers, no baths, no interviews, no belts to make and take apart and make; and the news from the outside was dangerous. They could only be driven out to the garden and driven in.

Some insisted that the monkeys on the blanket of snow moved about during the night, and in the day it was difficult to keep the curious patients from the heaps of small black corpses.

The village, as the days grew worse, became a dump for abandoned supplies, long lines of petrol tins along the streets, heaps of soiled torn stretchers and cases of defective prophylactics piled about doorways, thrown into cellars. Piles of worthless cow-pod Teller mines blocked the roads in places and a few looted armored cars still smelled of burned cloth and hair. Women nursed children as large as six years old, and infrequently some hurrying official, fat, drunk with fear, would come into the village of women and bring unreliable news of the dead. Wives did not know whether their husbands were dead, or simply taken prisoner, did not know whether they had been whipped on capture or stood against a wall and shot. Hatless children ran through the deepening snow and chased the few small birds still clinging to the stricken trees. On the day before the riot an American deserter was discovered in a barn and, untried, was burned to death. Several pockets of sewer gas exploded in the afternoon.

It snowed for nights on end, but every morning the monkeys appeared uncovered, exactly the same as the day they were tossed into the yard, wiry, misshapen, clutching in their hands and feet the dead rats. When vigilance became more and more impractical, all poisons, orange crystals of cyanide and colorless acids, were thrown into the incinerator, and with despondent precaution all sharp instruments were destroyed. They were disturbed; several unrecognized, unwashed doctors wandered without memory in the pack of patients and one young dietician thought she was the common-law wife of a fifty-nine-year-old hebephrenic. On the night before the uprising, thieves tore down the wooden sign inscribed with the haven word "asylum," burned it during the coldest dawn recorded, and the institution was no longer a retreat.

Before dawn on the morning of the riot, Madame Snow stood alone by candlelight in a back room where cordwood had been piled, holding a stolen chicken struggling lightly beneath her fingers. She did not see the four stone walls or the narrow open window, and standing in a faded gown with the uneven hem that was once for balls, the untied soiled kimono flapping against her legs, she looked into the frightful eyes of the chicken and did not feel the cold. Her bare feet were white, the toes covered with grains of sawdust. The door behind her was locked, tallow dripped from the gilt holder and the bird fluttered, tried to shake its wings from the firm grasp. The old woman's pulse beat slowly, more slowly, but steadily, and the narrow unseen window began to turn grey. The feathers, bitten with mange, trembled and breathed fearfully. The soft broken claws kicked at her wrist. For a moment the Kaiser's face, thin, depressed, stared in at the cell window, and then was gone, feeling his way over a land that was now strange to his touch. The old woman watched the fowl twisting its head, blinking the pink-lidded eyes, and carefully she straddled the convulsing neck with two fingers, tightened them across the mud-caked chest, and with the other hand seized the head that felt as if it were all bone and moving bits of scale. The pale yellow feet paddled silently backwards and forwards, slits breathed against her palm. Madame Snow clenched her fists and quickly flung them apart so that the fowl's head spurted across the room, hit the wall and fell into a heap of shavings, its beak clicking open and shut, eyes staring upwards at the growing light. She dropped the body with its torn neck and squeezed with fingermarks into a bucket of water, and stooping in the grey light, squinted, and plucked the feathers from the front of her kimono.

A few moments later the messenger, angry, half-asleep, pounded on the window of the front room and shouted, "Riot, riot up at the madhouse," and clattered off, banging on more doors, calling to startled women, distracted, wheezing.

By the time Stella reached the Mayor's, still in the

kimono, hair flying, she found a great quarreling crowd of women already gathered. The Mayor, before taking control of the villagers asked to send aid, had girdled the red sash around his nightgowned stomach, and distrait but strong, he stood on the ice-covered steps passing out equipment and words of encouragement to the already violent hags.

"Ah, Madame Snow, Madame Snow," he called, "you will take command on the march and in the attack. I leave it all up to you." Outstretched hands clamored in his face.

"Did you hear?" he shouted.

"Yes, I heard."

When all of the women had shouldered the barrel-staves which he had distributed, and fastened the black puttees about their bare legs, they started off, Stella in the lead and running as fast as she could. Jutta was tickling the Census-Taker at the time and only heard of the trouble afterwards. Madame Snow's hands were still covered with the blood of the chicken, and back in the small room its beak was clamped open. When they reached the iron fence and the gates were thrown open, the women stopped short, silent, moved closer together, brandished the staves, and looked at the band of inmates huddled together on the other side of the heap of monkeys. One of the monkeys seemed to have grown, and frozen, was sitting upright on the bodies of the smaller beasts, tail coiled about his neck, dead eyes staring out through the gates, through the light of early morning as dim and calm as the moon. "Dark is life, dark, dark is death," he suddenly screamed as the women charged across the snow.

All was hushed that morning, and in a dark wing of building 41, Balamir lay waiting among his unsleeping brothers and wished that someone would let in the cat. The male nurse who had been on duty three days and nights sat dozing in the stiff-backed chair and Balamir could see the white lifeless watch with its hanging arms. Along the length of the corridor were the rows of small empty rooms, and the signal lights over the swinging doors were burned out. An old cleaning woman, stooped and bent with the hem of her grey skirt hiding her feet, shuffled from the upper end to the lower of the monastic hall, dragging a mop over the outstretched legs, mumbling to herself, "Now it's quite all right, you'll all be well soon, yes, you'd be surprised at all I've seen come and go." The feathers of the mop were dry and frozen.

From the windows of building 41 one could see the irregular white fields stretching off to patched acres of sparse forest land, the game field with its bars and benches heaped with snow. Sometimes dimly through the grillwork of adjacent buildings, an unrecognizable single figure passed back into the shadows. The cleaning woman fumbled with the key ring fastened by a thin brass chain around her waist and went through the smooth metal door and down the deserted stairs. Suddenly a little wiry man with small fragile hands and feet and a clay pipe clutched in his teeth, ran to the door and facing it, trembled with anger.

"Don't you ever say such a thing to me again, don't you dare say that, if I hear it again, if you dare speak to me I'll break your back, I'll break it and cripple you, so help me," he screamed.

The nurse awoke with a start, reached for his smoldering cigarette. "Here, Dotz," he called, "Stop that yelling . . ." but quickly, before he could move, the whole hallway of men, stamping and crying, followed Dotz through the door and out into the fresh air. Once out, no one knew the way in, and already a few white coats were excited and gave chase.

From a fourth floor window the Director, wrapped in a camel's hair coat, watched the struggle until he saw the women, led by Stella, rush the ridiculous inmates; he drew the blinds and returned to his enormous files.

During that hour the monkeys were so underfoot that the patients were saved from worse injury by the clumsiness of the women who shouted and tore and pelted everything in sight. As these women in the midst of changing years ran to and fro beating, slashing, the stiff tails and hard outstretched arms and furry brittle paws smacked against black puttees and were trampled and broken in the onslaught. Several wooden shoes were left jammed in rows of teeth smashed open in distortion by the stamping feet. The barrel-staves broke on unfeeling shoulders, the rats' bodies were driven deeper into the snow.

"Here, you," suddenly cried the cleaning woman from

the main doorway, "come back in here," and the troop of men disappeared, kicking the stained snow in violent flurries. Suddenly the deputized women found themselves alone and standing on the mutilated carcasses of little men, and with a pained outcry, they fled from the grounds. "You won't say it again?" said Dotz, but no one answered and they settled back to rest in silence. The sun came out high and bright at nine o'clock and lasted the whole day, striking from the tiles and bricks, melting the snow, and the Director finally issued an order for the burial of the animals.

Leevey was killed outright when his motorcycle crashed into the log. He was pitched forward and down into an empty stretch of concrete. The Sten-gun, helmet, and boots clattered a moment, canvas and cloth and leather tore and rubbed; then he lay quiet, goggles still over his eyes, pencil, pad, whistle and knife strewn ahead. The three of us quickly leaped upward over the embankment, crouched in the darkness a moment, and then eagerly went to work. I was the first to reach the motorcycle and I cut the ignition, guided it over the bank. We picked up Leevey and carried him down to his machine, lost none of his trinkets, then together rolled the log until it slid down the muddy slope and settled in silence in a shallow stream of silt.

"It's not smashed badly," said Fegelein and ran his fingers over the bent front rim, felt broken spokes brushing against his sleeve, felt that the tank was slightly caved-in and petrol covered his hand. "You'll be riding it in a month."

I put my ear to the thin chest but could hear nothing, for Leevey had gone on to his native sons who sat by the thousands amid fields of gold, nodding their black curly heads, and there, under a sunshine just for them, he would never have to bear arms again. The night had reached its darkest and most silent hour, just before dawn comes. Still there were no stars, the mist grew more dense overhead and even the dogs no longer howled. My fingers brushed the stiffening wrist.

"Are you ready?" asked my comrade by the machine.

I felt closer, more quickly, pulled away the cuff of the

jacket, tore as quietly as possible at the cloth over the wrist.

"What's the matter with you? What are you doing anyway?" The voice was close; Stumpfegle also drew closer to my side.

"Eh, what's up?" The hoarse whispers were sharp.

I pulled at the strap, carefully, faster, and finally spoke, "He's got a watch." I leaned closer to the corpse.

"Well, give it here, you can't keep it just like that . . ."

I brought the pistol dimly into sight again, shoved the watch into my pocket, "I'm the leader and don't forget it. It's only right that I have the watch. Take the sacks off the machine and leave them here. We'll share what we can find, but not the watch."

Fegelein was already back tinkering with the engine. I listened to the watch and heard its methodical beat and could see the intricate clean dials rotating in precise fractions. The tongue was now sucked firmly and definitely into the back of Leevey's throat and his knees had cracked upwards and grown rigid. "We had better get him out of here." We picked him up and with the motorman between us stepped into the shallow ooze of the stream and headed out beyond the wall of fog towards the center of the lowlands.

On the opposite side of the highway, hidden in the shadows of unoccupied low buildings and the high bare spire wet with dew, stood Herr Stintz fixing everything closely in his mind, holding the little girl tightly by the hand. The child crossed and uncrossed the cold white legs, watched the black shadows leaping about in the middle of the road. Then they were gone.

Jutta yawned, carried the damp blouse into the next room, and opening the rear window, hung it from a short piece of wire dangling from a rusty hook. For a moment she smelled the sour night air, heard the lapping of water, and then returned to the still warm bed to wait the morning.

The limping English ghosts made their way back to the tank and stood silently waiting for the light when they would have to climb again through the hatch and sit out the day in the inferno of the blackened Churchill.

The Duke, breathing heavily, slowly extended his arm,

and as the boy moved, clamped the diamond ringed fingers over the light shoulder and breathed easier. Footsteps sounded in the upper part of the clay-smelling theater and the projector began to grind and hum, then stilled again.

Very cold, the Mayor crawled out of bed, went to his closet and taking an armful of coats and formal trousers, heaped them on the bed. But it was still cold.

Madame Snow lit the candle again and saw that the quilted man was sleeping, and hearing no sound, no one returning to the second floor apartment, she decided to get dressed and simply await the day. She began to tie up the long strands of white and gold hair, and reaching into a bulky wardrobe found herself a formless white chemise.

"My God, the fog is thick."

"We're almost there," I replied.

"Which way?"

"A little to the right, I think."

The formless white puddles of fog moved, shifted among the stunted trees, rose, fell, trailed away in the areas of sunken swampwood where once tense and cowed scouting parties had dared to walk into the bayonet on guard, or to walk on a trigger of a grenade that had blown up waist high. An axle of a gun carriage stuck up from the mud like a log, a British helmet, rusted, old, hung by a threadbare strap from a broken branch.

"He's heavy."

"They feed the Americans well, you know," I answered.

"Well, he's going where they all belong."

Several times we stopped to rest, sitting the body upright in the silt that rose over his waist. A shred of cloth was caught about a dead trunk, the fog dampened our skin. Each time we stopped, the white air moved more than ever in and out of the low trees, bearing with it an overpowering odor, the odor of the ones who had eaten well. More of the trees were shattered and we, the pallbearers, stumbled with each step over half-buried pieces of steel.

"Let's leave him here."

"You know we cannot. Follow the plan."

Past the next tree, past the next stone of a gun breech blasted open like a mushroom, we saw a boot, half a wall, and just beyond, the swamp was filled with bodies that slowly appeared one by one from the black foliage, from the mud, from behind a broken wheel. A slight skirmish had developed here and when the flare had risen over this precise spot, glowed red and died in the sky, some twenty or thirty dead men were left, and they never disappeared. The fog passed over them most thickly here, in relentless circles, and since it was easier to breathe closer to the mud, we stooped and dragged the body forward.

"You see, no one could ever find him among these. No one would ever look for him here." My idea for disposing of the body was excellent.

After searching the body once more, we left it and found our way again to the roadside. We took the machine and its valuable saddlebags silently through the town to the newspaper office.

"It's time we had our meeting," I said, "I'll be back." Fegelein began to work on the engine; Stumpfegle broke the head from a bottle.

The slut slept alone in her own house.

WILLIAM GADDIS
from *The Recognitions* (1955)

Gaddis's novel both prefigures in some measure its colleagues and subjugates itself to motives quite outside those normally associated with Black Humor—the extension of and play with the techniques inherent in Joyce's *Ulysses,* for one example. But there is much that is pure black in Gaddis: his penchant for puns, burlesque humor, slapstick names, and a mystical variant of nihilism. The theme of his novel is the counterfeit in society, his major character one Recktall Brown, who employs a gifted artist to forge masterpieces for him. Though Brown makes no entrance here, in this widescreen analysis of a city and a people totally devoted to illusion, his spirit is everywhere present. It is the spirit of the counterfeit, which is behind the art critic Crémer, the grand cathedral of Sacré Coeur, and Paris itself. Gaddis's study of Paris is a sweeping, unrestrained assault that brooks, to borrow from the late Conrad Knickerbocker, no detente with society.

Tres curieux, vos maîtres anciens. Seulement les plus beaux, ce sont les faux.—Paul Eudel, *Trucs et truqueurs*

On the terrace of the Dôme sat a person who looked like the young George Washington without his wig (at about the time he dared the Ohio Territory). She read, with silently moving lips, from a book before her. She was drinking a bilious-colored liquid from a globular goblet; and every twenty or so pages would call to the waiter, in perfect French, —Un Ricard . . . , and add one to the pile of one-franc saucers before her. —Voilà ma propre Sainte Chapelle, she would have said of that rising tower (the sentence prepared in her mind) if anyone had encouraged conversation by sitting down at her table. No one did. She read on. Anyone could have seen it was *transition* she was reading, if any had looked. None did. Finally an unshaven youth bowed slightly, as with pain, murmured something in American, and paused with a dirty hand on the back of a chair at her table. —J'vous en prie, she said, lucid, lowering *transition,* waiting for him to sit down before she went on. —Mursi, he muttered, and dragged the chair to another table.

Paris lay by like a promise accomplished: age had not withered her, nor custom staled her infinite vulgarity.

Nearby, a man exhibited two fingers, one dressed as a man, one as a woman, performing on a table top. Three drunken young Englishmen were singing *The Teddy Bears' Picnic.* Three dirty children from Morocco were selling peanuts from the top of the basket and hashish from the bottom. Someone said that there was going to be a balloon ascension that very afternoon, in the Bois. Someone else said that Karl Marx's bones were buried at Highgate. Someone said, —I'm actually going to be analyzed. *Psycho-*analyzed. A boy with a beard, in a state of black corduroy (*corde du roi*) unkemptness which had taken as long as the beard to evolve, said, —I've got to show these pictures, I've got to sell some of them, but how can I have people coming up there with him there? He's dying. I can't put him out on the street, dying like that . . . even in Paris. A girl said that she had just taken a villa right outside Paris, a place called Saint Forget. —Of course it's a hideous place, and Ah had to pay a feaful sum to get the tiasome French family that was there out of it, but it's such a sweet little old address to get mail at. Another girl said, —My conçerage has been returning all my mail marked ankonoo just because I oney gave her ten francs poorbwar. People who would soon be seen in New York reading French books were seen here reading Italian. Someone said, in slurred (blasé) French, —Un café au lait.

Over this grandstand disposal of promise the waiters

stared with a distance of glazed indulgence which all collected under it admired, as they admired the rudeness,
which they called self-respect; the contempt, which they
called innate dignity; the avarice, which they called self-
reliance; the tasteless ill-made clothes on the men, lauded
as indifference, and the far-spaced posturings of haute couture
across the Seine, called inimitable or shik according. to
one's stay. Marvelous to wide eyes, pricked ears, and minds
of that erectile quality betraying naive qualms of transatlantic origin (alert here under hair imitative long-grown,
uncombed, on the male, curtly shorn on the girls) was this
spectacle of culture fully realized. They regarded as the
height of excellence that nothing remained to be done, no
tree to be planted nor building torn down (they had not
visited Le Bourget; found the wreckage up behind the
Hôtel de Ville picturesque), no tree too low nor building
too high (those telescoping lampposts on the Pont du
Carrousel), no bud of possibility which had not opened in
the permanent bloom of artificial flowers, no room for
that growth which is the abiding flower of humility.

"A mon très aimé frère Lazarus, ce que vous me mandez
de Petrus l'apostre de notre doux Jesus . . . ," wrote Mary
Magdalen. "Notre fils Césarion va bien . . . ," wrote Cleo-
patra to Julius Caesar. There was a letter from Alexander the
Great to Aristotle ("Mon ami . . ."); from Lazarus to
Saint Peter (concerning Druids); from Pontius Pilate to
Tiberius; Judas's confession (to Mary Magdalen); a pass-
port signed by Vercingetorix; notes from Alcibiades, Pericles,
and a letter to Pascal (on gravitation) from Newton, who
was nineteen when Pascal died. But M. Chasles, eminent
mathematician of the late nineteenth century, paid 140,000
francs for this collection of autographs, for he believed
them genuine: they were, after all, written in French. So
the Virgin appeared to Maximin and Mélanie at La Salette,
identified Herself by speaking to them in French which they
did not understand, broke into their local patois for long
enough to put across Her confidences, and then returned to
Her native language for farewell: any wonder that transatlantic visitors approached it with qualms? murmured in
tones spawned in forests, on the plains in unrestricted liberty, from the immensity of mountains, the cramped measure
of their respect, approached in reverence the bier where

every shade of the corpse was protected from living prof-
anation by the pallbearers of the Académie Française.

Before their displacement from nature, baffled by the
grandeur of their own culture which they could not define,
and so believed did not exist, these transatlantic visitors had
learned to admire in this neatly parceled definition of
civilization the tyrannous pretension of many founded upon
the rebellious efforts of a few, the ostentation of thousands
presumed upon the strength of a dozen who had from time
to time risen against this vain complacence with the past
to which they were soon to contribute, giving, with their
harried deaths, grounds for vanity of language, which they
had perfected; supercilious posturing of intellect, which they
had suffered to understand and deliver, in defiance; insolent
arbitration of taste, grown from the efforts of those condemned as having none; contempt for others flourishing
from seedlings which they had planted in the rain of contempt for themselves; dogmata of excellence founded upon
insulting challenges wrought in impossible hope, and then
grasped, for granted, from their hands fallen clenching it
as dogma.

From the intractable perfection of the crepusculous Île de
la Cité (seen from the Pont des Arts) to the static depravity
of the Grands Boulevards, it was unimpeachable: in super-
ficiating this perfection, it absorbed the beholder and shut
out the creator: no more could it have imitation than a
mermaid (though echoes were heard of the Siren of Dji-
bouti).

—Voici votre Perrier m'sieur. —Mais j'ai dit café au lait,
pas d'eau Perrier . . . A small man in a sharkskin suit said,
—Son putas, y nada mas. Putas, putas, putas . . . Someone
said, —Picasso . . . Someone else said, —Kafka . . . A
girl said, —You deliberately try to misunderstand me. Of
course I like art. Ask anybody. Nearby, a young man with
a beard received compliments on his recent show. It was a
group of landscapes in magenta and madder lake. Très
amusant, gai, très très original (he was French). It was
quite a rage. He said he had walked four kilometers out of
Saint Germain en Laye, found he'd forgotten all of his
colors but magenta and madder lake, so he went ahead
and painted anyhow. He said, —Quelquefois je passe la
nuit entière à finir un tableau . . . Someone said that there

was a town in Switzerland called Gland. Someone told the joke about Carruthers and his horse.

On the right bank, a lady said,—You'll like Venice. It's so like Fort Lauderdale. At the same table, a man said, —I'm going to look her up. She's lived here for years, right outside Paris, a place called Banlieu. At another table someone said, —By God, you know, they're almost as rude to us as they are to each other.

On Montmartre, someone looked up at the Sacré Coeur and said, —What the hell do you think they call *that*? The woman with him said, —Why bother to go all the way to the top, I haven't got my camera. A girl said, —Voulez vous voir le ciné cochon? Deux femmes . . .

Above, the thing itself towered exotic and uninvited, affording the consolation of the grotesque: that dead white Byzantine-Romanesque surprise which was heaped in bulbiferous pyramids atop the Hill of the Martyrs in the late nineteenth century, soon after the city had finished installing a comprehensive new sewage system. It was a monument (the church) not, as many had it, to the French victory over Prussia, but to the Jesuit victory over France. The birth of Ignatius of Loyola was early understood to have erred only in its location: Spain was origin, but none has ever excelled France in vocational guidance for the ideas of others, and it was obvious (in France) that his Society of Jesus could be best advanced through the medium of the French mind. In the mid-seventeenth century, the Society was having difficulty with the Jansenists, and the contributions of Pascal upset them almost as much as did the Miracle of the Holy Thorn, a relic which cured little Marguerite Périer of fistula lachrymalis: it was a Jansenist miracle. The Society recouped: found its own Marguerite and, with the kindly instruction and encouragement of Père La Colombière, her confessor, she revealed to the world a parade of the marvelous which shocked even those who were compelled to believe, an account which made a cure of fistula lachrymalis, never a pretty thought, pale into organic commonplace. The searing narrative of Marguerite Marie Alacoque passed from hand to hand for some two centuries until at last, in 1864, Pope Pius IX was assailed with a petition asking highest recognition for the Sacred Heart (the afflicted organ). In fact the petition itself participated in the miraculous, bearing as it did twelve million signatures forth from a country whose district records showed three-fourths of its brides and grooms unable to write their names. A bare decade after the beatification, papal decree consecrated the Universal Catholic Church to the Sacred Heart, and the Society has since defended its successful exploit against all comers with the same dexterous swashbuckling that was shown in its achievement: against the Virgin of La Salette, against promoters of the Devotion of the Perpetual Rosary, even against the prodigal (85 liters per minute) Virgin of Lourdes, whose bottled testimonials were soon flowing broadcast when proved not liable to the excise levies and export taxes of the Republic. Amid a crowd equaling the population of Afghanistan, the Sacré Coeur launched its church on the crown of that hill Saint Denis had once approached carrying his head under his arm. The new "public utility," so it was called, was dedicated by Cardinal Archbishop Guibert, disdaining insular mutterings which insinuated that the Society had plagiarized the Sacred Heart from England's leading philosophe, William Godwin, who thought of it first. And eventually, the Devotions within the favored land made truce: after all, as Monseigneur Ségur said, the Virgin shows very good taste in choosing France as the theater for her apparitions.

Near the Bourse, a lady said, —Des touristes, oui, mais des sales anglais, . . . là, regardez ce type là . . . She indicated a figure across the street, not a dirty Englishman, as she noted, but Wyatt, who lived nearby. With no idea of Paris when he arrived, he had been fortunate enough to find quarters in this neighborhood which maintained anonymity in the world of arts. Few people lived here. Activity centered around the stock exchange. On Sunday it was empty.

He knew few people, and them he saw infrequently. In three years, he had not written his father; and after a year in Paris he had finished seven pictures, working with a girl named Christiane, a blond model with small figure and features. As she exposed the side of her face, or a fall of cloth from her shoulder, he found there suggestion of the lines he needed, forms which he knew but could not discover in the work without this allusion to completed reality before him. He had by now little money, and so in addition to his own work he did some restoring of old paintings for an antique dealer who paid him regularly and badly. He did not spend time at café tables talking about form, or line, color, composition, trends, materials: he worked on this painting, or did not think about it. He knew no more of surréalisme than he did of the plethora of daubs turned out on Montmartre for tourists, those arbiters of illustration to whom painting was a personalized representation of scenes and creatures they held dear; might not know art but they knew what they liked, hand-painted pictures (originals) for which they paid in the only currency they understood, to painters whose visions had shrunk to the same proportions. He might walk up there occasionally and see them, the alleys infested with them painting the same picture from different angles, the same painting varying from easel to easel as different versions of a misunderstood truth, but the progeny of each single easel identical reproduction, following a precept of Henner who called this the only way of being original. Passing, he showed all the interest for them he might have for men whitewashing walls. . . .

After a glass of coffee he climbed the stairs to his room. Someone was waiting in the dim light of the hall. As Wyatt approached the figure turned, put out a hand and murmured a greeting. —My name is Crémer, he said. —I met you last week, in the Muette Gallery. May I come in for a moment? He spoke precise English. Wyatt opened the door to his room, ordered and large, blank walls, a spacious north window. —You will be showing some of your pictures next week, I believe?

—Seven pictures, Wyatt said, making no effort to expose them.

—I am interested in your work.

—Oh, you've . . . seen it?

—No, no, hardly. But I see here (motioning toward the straight easel, where a canvas stood barely figured)—that it is interesting. I am writing the art column in *La Macule*. Crémer's cigarette, which he had not taken from his lips since he appeared, had gone out at about the length of a thumbnail. He looked rested, assured, hardly a likely visitor at dawn. —I shall probably review your pictures next week, he added after a pause which had left Wyatt smoothing the hair on the back of his head, his face confused.

—Oh, then, . . . of course, you want to look at them now?

—Don't trouble yourself. Crémer said, walking off toward the window. —You are studying in Paris?

—No. I did in Munich.

—In Germany. That is too bad. Your style is German, then? German impressionism?

—No, no, not . . . quite different. Not so . . .

—Modern? German impressionism, modern?

—No, I mean, the style of the early Flemish . . .

—Van Eyck . . .

—But less . . .

—Less stern? Yes. Roger de la Pasture, perhaps?

—What?

—Van der Weyden, if you prefer. Crémer shrugged. He was standing with his back to the window. —In Germany . . .

—I did one picture in the manner of Memling, very much the manner of Memling. The teacher, the man I studied with, Herr Koppel, Herr Koppel compared it to David, Gheerardt David's painting *The Flaying of the Unjust Judge*.

Memlinc, alors . . .

—But I lost it there, but . . . do you want to look at the work I've done here?

—Don't trouble. But I should like to write a good review for you.

—I hope you do. It could help me a great deal.

—Yes. Exactly.

They stood in silence for almost a minute. —Will you sit down? Wyatt asked finally.

Crémer showed no sign of hearing him but a slight shrug. He half turned to the window and looked out. —You live in a very . . . clandestine neighborhood, for a painter? he murmured agreeably. In the darkening room the cigarette gone out looked like a sore on his lip.

—The anonymous atmosphere . . . Wyatt commenced.

—But of course, Crémer interrupted. There was a book on the floor at his feet, and he moved it with the broad toe of one shoe. —We recall Degas, eh? he went on in the same detached tone of pleasantry, —his remark, that the artist must approach his work in the same frame of mind in which the criminal commits his deed. Eh? Yes . . . He approached Wyatt slightly hunched, his hands down in his pockets. —The reviews can make a great difference. He smiled. —All the difference.

—Difference?

—To selling your pictures.

—Well then, Wyatt said looking away from the blemished smile, down to the floor, bringing his arms together behind him twisted until he'd got hold of both elbows, and his face, thin and exhausted, seemed to drain of life. —Yes, that . . . that's up to the pictures.

—It's not, of course, Crémer said evenly.

—What do you mean? Wyatt looked up, startled, dropping his arms.

—I am in a position to help you greatly.

—Yes, yes but . . .

—Art criticism pays very badly, you know.

—But . . . well? Well? His face creased.

—If you should guarantee me, say, one-tenth of the sale price of whatever we sell . . .

—We? You? You?

—I could guarantee you excellent reviews. Nothing changed in Crémer's face. Wyatt's eyes burned as he looked, turning green. —Are you surprised? Crémer asked, and his face changed now, expressing studied surprise, scorning to accept; while before him Wyatt looked about to fall from exhaustion.

—You? For my work . . . you want me to pay you, for . . . for . . .

—Yes, think about it, said Crémer, turning to the door.

—No, I don't need to. It's insane, this . . . proposition. I don't want it. What do you want of me? he went on, his voice rising as Crémer opened the door.

There was hardly light, not enough to cast a shadow, left in the room. As they had talked, each became more indistinct, until Crémer opened the door, the light of the minuterie threw his flat shadow across the sill. —I regret that I disturbed you, he said. —I think you need rest, perhaps? But think about it. Eh?

Wyatt followed him to the door, crying out, —Why did you come here? Now? Why do you come at dawn with these things?

Crémer had already started down the stairs. —At dawn? he called back, pausing. —Why my dear fellow, it's evening. It's dinner time. Then the sounds of his feet on the stairs, and the light of the minuterie failed abruptly, leaving Wyatt in his doorway clutching at its frame, while the steps disappeared below unfaltering in the darkness.

Il faut toujours en avoir sur soi, de l'argent, vous savez . . .

Like lions, out of the gates, into the circus arena, cars roared into the open behind the Opéra from the mouth of the Rue Mogador. Around it this faked Imperial Rome lay in pastiche on the banks of its Tiber: though Tiber's career, from the Apennine ravines of Tuscany, skirting the Sabine mountains to course through Rome and reach with two arms into the sea, finds unambitious counterpart in the Seine diked and dammed across the decorous French countryside, proper as wallpaper. Nevertheless, they had done their best with what they had. The Napoleons tried very hard. The first one combed his hair, and that of his wife and brothers, like Julius Caesar and his family combed theirs. J. L. David (having painted pictures of Brutus, Andromache, and the Horatii) painted his picture looking, as best he could manage, like Julius Caesar; and Josephine doing her very best (the *Coronation*) to look above suspicion herself. Everyone rallied round, erecting arches, domes, pediments, and copied what the Romans had copied from the Greeks. Empire furniture, candlesticks, coiffures . . . somewhere beyond them hung the vision of Constantine's Rome, its eleven forums, ten basilicas, eighteen aqueducts, thirty-seven city gates, two arenas, two circuses, thirty-seven triumphal arches, five obelisks, four hundred and twenty-three temples with their statues of the gods in ivory and gold. But all that was gone. There was no competition now. Not since Pope Urban VIII had declared the Coliseum a public quarry.

As the spirit of collecting art began in Rome, eventually it began in Paris, reached the proportions of the astounding collection of that wily Sicilian blood the Cardinal Mazarin, murmuring to his art as he left in decline and exile, —Que j'ai tant aimé, French enough to add, —et qui m'ont tant coûté. If the Roman connoisseur could distinguish among five kinds of patina on bronze by the smell, French sensitivities soon became as cultivated. If, to please the Roman connoisseur, sapphires were faked from Obsidian, sardonyx from cheap colored jasper, French talents were as versatile: "Un client désire des Corots? L'article manque sur le marché? Fabriquons-en . . ." (And one day, of Corot's twenty-five hundred paintings, seventy-eight hundred were to be found in America.) Even then they knew the value of art. Or of knowing the value of art. As Coulanges said to Madame de Sévigné, —Pictures are bullion.

Paris, fortunate city! by now a swollen third of the way into the twentieth century, still to be importuned by those who continued to take her at her own evaluation. Perhaps a kindred homage which rang across the sea was well earned (from a land whose length was still ringing with the greeting —Hello sucker!): perhaps fifty million Frenchmen couldn't be wrong. Four million of them, at any rate, were nursing venereal diseases; and among the ladies syphilis brought about some forty thousand miscarriages that year. "Paris": a sobriquet to conjure with (her real name Lutetia), it bore magic in the realm of Art, as synonymous with the word itself as that of Mnesarete, "Phryne," had once been with Love. Long since, of course, in the spirit of that noblesse oblige which she personified, Paris had withdrawn from any legitimate connection with works of art, and directly increased her entourage of those living for Art's sake. One of these, finding himself on trial just two or three years ago, had made the reasonable point that a typical study of a Barbizon peasant signed with his own name brought but a few hundred francs, but signed *Millet,* ten thousand dollars; and the excellent defense that this subterfuge had not been practiced on Frenchmen, but on English and Americans "to whom you can sell anything" . . . here, in France, where everything was for sale.

Under the eyes of Napoleon I (atop a column in the Place Vendôme, "en César") the Third Republic bickered on. Having established their own squalid bohemias, there was no objection to handing the original over to their hungry neighbor across the Maginot Line, who was busy scrapping the Versailles treaty, fragment by fragment, until the day when a German envoy would be shot in Paris, and, weeks later, a peace pact signed to prepare for a re-enactment of the bloodshed which had provoked this expression of faith from one killed in it, "Il y a tant de saints, ils forment un tel rempart autour de Paris, que les zeppelins ne passeront jamais." And Paris waited, as ever ready as Phryne beset by slanders and threats, to rend her robe and bare her breasts to the mercy of her judges.

In an alley, a dog hunting in a garbage can displayed infinite grace in the unconscious hang of his right foreleg. Little else happened that Saturday night in August. Saint Bartholomew's Day was warm. It was the dead heat of Paris summer, when Paris cats go to sleep on Paris windowsills, and ledges high up, and fall off, and plunge through the glass roof of the lavabo. The center of the city was empty. A sight-seeing bus set off from the Place de l'Opéra. A truck and a Citroën smashed before the Galeries Lafayette. At the Pont d'Auteuil, a man's body was dragged out of the Seine with a bicycle tied to it. Among the fixtures, tiled and marbled shapes remindful of a large outdoor bathroom, in the cemetery at Montrouge a widower argued with his dead wife's lover over who had the right to place flowers on her grave. In front of the Bourse, a deaf-mute soccer team carried on conversation in obstreperous silence. On the Quai du Pont Neuf, a Frenchman sat picking his nose. Then he put his arm around his girl and kissed her. Then he picked his nose. It was Sunday in Paris, and very quiet.

On the terrace of Larue, under the soiled stature of the Madeleine's peripteral imposture, Wyatt considered a German newspaper. Taxis limped past, bellicose as wounded animals, collapsing further on at Maxim's, late lunch. Unrepresentatively handsome people passed on foot. Some of them stopped and sat at tables. —In Istanbul in the summer, a lady said, —it was Istanbul, wasn't it? We used to take long rides in the cistern, in the summer . . .

Wyatt read slowly and with difficulty in *Die Fleischflaute,* an art publication. His show was over. No pictures had been sold. He had thrown away *La Macule* quickly, after reading there Crémer's comments: —Archaïque, dur comme la pierre, dérivé, sans coeur, sans sympathie, sans vie, enfin, un esprit de la mort sans l'espoir de la Résurrection. But at this moment the details of that failure were forgotten, and the thing itself intensified, as he made out in *Die Fleischflaute* that there had just been discovered in Germany an original painting by Hans Memling. Crude overpainting had transformed the whole scene into an interior, with the same purpose that Holofernes' head had once been transformed into a tray of fruit on

Judith's tray (making it less offensive as a 'picture'): this one proved to be a figure being flayed alive on a rack, since over-painted with a bed, and those engaged in skinning him were made to minister to the now bedridden figure. A fragment of landscape seen through an open window, said *Die Fleischflaute*, had excited the attention of an expert, and once it was taken to the Old Pinakothek in Munich and cleaned, the figure stretched in taut agony was identified as Valerian, third-century persecutor of Christians, made captive by the Persian Sapor whose red cloak was thrown down in the foreground before the racked body thin in unelastic strength, anguish and indifference in the broken tyrant's face, its small eyes empty with blindness. Possibly, the experts allowed, it might be the work of Gheerardt David, but more likely that of Memling, from which David had probably drawn his *Flaying of the Unjust Judge*. There followed a eulogy on German painters, and Memling in particular, who had brought the weak beginnings of Flemish art to the peak of their perfection, and crystallized the minor talents of the Van Eycks, Bouts, Van der Weyden, in the masterpieces of his own German genius.

Saint Bartholomew's Day in Notre Dame, reflecting commemoration of the medal which Gregory XIII had struck honoring Catherine de' Medici's massacre of fifty thousand heretics: the music surged and ebbed in the cathedral, and in the Parisian tradition of preconcerted effects the light suddenly poured down in fullness, then faded, together they swelled and died. At the end of the service, as the organ filled that place with its sound, the body of the congregation turned its many-faced surface to look back and up at the organ loft, and from the organ loft they formed a great cross so. Then the cross disintegrated, its fragments scattered over their city, safe again in the stye of contentment.

Paris simmered stickily under the shadowed erection of the Eiffel Tower. Like the bed of an emperor's mistress, the basin she lay in hadn't a blade or stitch out of place; and like the Empress Theodora, "fair of face and charming as well, but short and inclined to pallor, not indeed completely without color but slightly sallow . . . ." Paris articulated her charm within the lower registers of the spectrum. So Theodora, her father a feeder of bears, went on the stage with no accomplishment but a gift for mockery, no genius but for whoring and intrigue. An empress, she triumphed: no senator, no priest, no soldier protested, and the vulgar clamored to be called her slaves; bed to bath, breakfast to rest, she preened her royalty. —May I never put off this purple or outlive the day when men cease to call me queen . . . She died of cancer.

Toward evening the shadow of the Eiffel Tower inclined to the Latin Quarter across her body. She prepared, made herself up from a thousand pots and tubes, was young, desperately young she knew herself and the mirror forgotten, the voice brittle, she lolled uncontested in the mawkish memories of men married elsewhere to sodden reality, stupefied with the maturity they had traded against this mistress bargained in youth. Revisiting, they could summon youth to her now, mark it in the neon blush uncowed by the unquerulous façades maintained by middle age, and the excruciating ironwork and chrome, the cancerous interiors.

At a bar in Rue Caumartin a girl said to an American, —Vous m'emmenez? Moi, je suis cochonne, la plus cochonne de Paris . . . Vous voulez le toucher? ici? Donnez moi un billet . . . oui un billet, pour le toucher . . . ici . . . discrètement . . .

A girl lying in a bed said, —We only know about one per cent of what's happening to us. We don't *know* how little heaven is paying for how much hell.

Someone said, —But you've been over here so *long*, to an American in a hotel room who was showing his continental savoir faire by urinating in the sink. He said, —I wanted to marry her, but you know, she's tied to her envirement. Someone said, —I never knew him very well, he's of the Negro persuasion. On the left bank, someone had just left his wife and taken up the guitar. It was at home in bed. —I dress it in her bathrobe every night, he said. Someone else suggested using a duck, putting its head in a drawer and jamming the drawer shut at the critical moment. A young gentleman was treating his friends to shoeshines for the seventh time that hour. He was drunk. The dirty Arab children sold peanuts from the top of the basket and hashish from the bottom. They spoke a masterful unintimidated French in guttural gasps, coming from a land where it was regarded neither as the most beautiful language, as in America, nor the only one, as in France. At that table someone said, —This stuff doesn't affect me at all. But don't you notice that the sky is getting closer? —Of course I love art, that's why I'm in Paris, a girl said. The boy with her said, —Je mon foo, that's French for . . . —Putas, putas, putas, muttered the man in the sharkskin suit. Someone said, —My hands are full, would you mind getting some matches out of my pocket? . . . here, my trouser pocket. Someone said, —Do you like it here? Someone else said, —In the morning she didn't want to, so I put it under her arm while she was grinding the coffee. A man in an opaque brown monocle said, —Gzhzhzhzhzt . . . hu . . . and fell off his chair. Someone told the joke about Carruthers and his horse.

On the quai, the man kissed his girl and returned to his more delicate preoccupation. Along the Rue de Montmartre stubby hands lifted glasses of red wine. These were the people, slipping, sliding, perishing: they had triumphed once in revolution, and celebrated the Mass in public parody; installing the Goddess of Reason with great celebration, she proved, when unveiled, to be a dancing girl with whom many had extensive acquaintance. The People, of whom one of their officers, Captain de Mun, said —"Galilean, thou has conquered!" Ah, for them no mercy: they are not the people, they are hell itself! . . . But they knew what they wanted: Liberté, égalité, fraternité . . . evaded the decorous façades decreed by their elders, or betters, and gathered in public interiors of carnivorous art nouveau.

In Père Lachaise an American woman bought a plot so that she might be buried near . . . who was it? Byron? Baudelaire? In the Place Vendôme another transatlantic visitor overturned a stolen taxicab at Napoleon's feet, was jailed, fined, and made much of by his friends. In Notre Dame du Flottement a millionairess from Maine married her colored chauffeur and was made much of by his friends. On the terrace of the Dôme, beset behind the clattering bastion of her own Sainte Chapelle, the young George Washington read with silently moving lips, broke wind pensively and looked around to see if she had attracted notice. On the Boulevard de la Madeleine a girl walking alone, swinging her purse, paused to glance in at the feet showing below the shield of the pissoir, and waited to accost their owner. Someone, looking above, cried out, —What's that? What is it? —The balloons. The balloons have gone up. In the washroom of the Café de la Régence, someone scrawled *Vive le roi* over the sink.

To one side, a man read the *Tribune*. To the other, *Al Misri*. —Votre journal, m'sieur, the waiter called, waving *Die Fleischflaute*, —votre journal . . .

And the shadow he cast behind him as he turned away fell back seven centuries, to embrace the dissolute youth of Raymond Lully, and infatuation with the beautiful Ambrosia de Castello, which she discouraged; and if she seemed to succumb at last, offering to bare her breasts in return for a poem he had written to their glory, it was to show him, as he approached in that rapture of which only flesh is capable, a bosom eaten away by cancer: he turned away to his conversion, to his death years later stoned in North Africa, and to his celebration as a scholar, a poet, a missionary, a mystic, and one of the foremost figures in the history of alchemy.

J. P. DONLEAVY
from *The Ginger Man* (1958)

Once in Berkeley, California, I was told that Sebastian
Balfe Dangerfield, the "Ginger Man" of the title, was to
the literature of protest what John Thomson was to
the Free Speech Movement there in the spring of 1964.
It was Thomson, you will recall, who sat upon the
steps of Sproul Hall with a four-letter sign. This, I was
told, is the tactic of the "social radical," not the "political radical." The social radical hates society in its present form every bit as much as the Mario Savios. He
differs, however, in regard to reform, which he in fact
holds to be impossible. Not for him, then, the way of
politics and organized protest; his way, the way of Thomson and presumably Dangerfield, is the thumb of the nose,
the extension, in public, of the middle finger—that is,
when there is nothing better to do. Perhaps in this brief
account we can find an explanation of Dangerfield's appeal
for the young and for the critics. There is something
here between the lines that each reader must or must not
find for himself. If he doesn't, the series of wifebeatings
perpetrated here by Dangerfield becomes at worst modern
Byronism, at best nouveau Falstaffery—the latest in the
long Western literary tradition of loveable rogues. If the
reader does find that something, however, he will see in
the Ginger Man himself and his sorry predicament.

There was a tugging at his leg. Slowly opening eyes to see the irate face of Marion looming over him on this Monday morn of chaos.

"Good God, what's happened to the house? Why weren't you at the station to meet me? Look at you. Gin. This is horrid. I had to take a taxi out here, do you hear me? A taxi, fifteen shillings."

"Now, now, for Christ's sake have some patience and let me explain everything."

"I say, explain? Explain what? There's nothing to explain, it's all quite evident."

Marion holding aloft the gin.

"All right, I'm not blind, I see it."

"O dear, this is frightful. Why you honestly are a cad. If Mommy and Daddy could only see what I've got to come back to. What are you doing on the table?"

"Shut up."

"I won't shut up and don't look at me like that. What are these feathers doing all over the place? Dishes broken on the floor. What were you doing?"

"Goat dance."

"How frightfully sordid it all is. Disgusting. Feathers in everything. You damn, damn drinker. Where did you get the money? Didn't meet me at the train. Why? Answer me."

"Shut up. Be quiet for the love of Jesus. The alarm didn't work."

"You're a liar. You were drinking, drinking, drinking. Look at the grease, the mess, the filth. And what's this?"

"A sea bird."

"Who paid for all this? You had smelly O'Keefe out here. I know you did, I can smell him."

"Just leave me alone."

"Did you pay the milk?"

"Yes, now sweet Jesus shut up, my head."

"So you paid it, did you? Here it is. Here it is. Ex-

actly where I left it and the money gone. Lies. You blighter.
You nasty blighter."

"Call me a bugger, I can't stand the gentility on top of
the yelling."

"O stop it, stop it. I don't intend to go on living like
this, do you hear me? Your brazen lies, one after the
other and I was trying to get Father to do something for
us and I come back to this."

"Your father. Your father is a sack of excrement, genteel excrement, as tight as they come. What has he been
doing, playing battleship in the tub?"

Marion lunged, her slap landing across his jaw. The
child began to scream in the nursery. Sebastian up off the
table. He drove his fist into Marion's face. She fell backward against the cupboard. Dishes crashing to the floor.
In tattered underwear he stood at the nursery door. He
kicked his foot through and tore off the lock to open it.
Took the child's pillow from under its head and pressed
it hard on the screaming mouth.

"I'll kill it, God damn it, I'll kill it, if it doesn't shut
up."

Marion behind him, digging her nails into his back.

"You madman, leave the child alone, I'll get the police.
I'll divorce you, you blackguard, coward, coward, coward."

Marion clasping the child to her breast. Sobbing, she
lay her long English body and child across the bed. The
room echoing the hesitations of her wailing voice. Sebastian walked white faced from the room, slamming the
broken door, cutting off the sound of suffering from a
guilty heart.

Dangerfield took a late morning bus to Dublin. Sat up
the top side in front, clicking the teeth. Out there the
mud flats and that windy golf course. North Bull Island
shimmering in the sun. Cost money to leave Marion. Vulgar blood in her somewhere, may be from the mother.
Mother's father kept a shop. Bad blood leaks out. I know
it leaks out. And I ought to get out. One way on the
boat. She doesn't have the nerve for divorce. I know her
too well for that. Never gave me a lousy chance to explain the account. Let her rot out there. I don't care. Got
to face the facts of this life. The facts, the facts. Could
square things with her. She's good with the cheese dishes.
Few days without food will weaken her. Maybe I'll come

back with a tin of peaches and cream. She's always airing the house. Opening up the windows at every little fart. Tells me she never farts. At least mine come out with a bang.

Fairview Park looks like a wet moldy blanket. Feel a little better. O'Keefe broke a toilet bowl in that house. Fell into it when he was trying to sneak a look behind a woman's medicine chest. Long suffering O'Keefe, bent over tomes in the National Library studying Irish and dreaming of seduction.

Amiens Street Station, Dangerfield stepping down from the bus, crossing and using the ostrich step up the Talbot Street. My God, I think I see prostitutes with squinting eyes and toothless mouths. Don't relish a trip up an alley with one without wearing impenetrable armour and there is no armour at all in Dublin. I asked one how much it was and she said I had an evil mind. Invited her for a drink and she said the American sailors were rough and beat her up in the backs of taxicabs and told her to take a bath. She said she liked chewing gum. And when she had a few drinks she got frightfully crude. I was shocked. Asked me how big it was. I almost slapped her face. With it. Provocation I calls it. And told her to confess. Dublin has more than a hundred churches. I bought a map and counted them. Must be a nice thing to have faith. But I think a pot of Gold Label run from the barrel in the house of the aspidistras. Settle the nerves. No time to be nervous now. With youth on my side. I'm still a young man in the late twenties, although the Lord knows I've been through some trying times. A lot of people tell you, caution you. Now young man, don't get married without money, without a good job, without a degree. E. E. E. They are right.

Into the pub with stuffed foxes behind the potted plants. And the snug stained brown. Reach over and press this buzzer for action.

A young man's raw face flicked around the door.

"Good morning, Mr. Dangerfield."

"A fine spring morning, a double and some Woodbines."

"Certainly, sir. Early today?"

"Little business to attend to."

"It's always business isn't it."

"O aye."

Some fine clichés there. Should be encouraged. Too many damn people trying to be different. Coining phrases when a good platitude would do and save anxiety. If Marion wants to make the barbarous accusation that I took the milk money, it's just as well I took it.

A tray comes in the discreet door.

"On your bill, Mr. Dangerfield?"

"If you will, please."

"Grand to be having some decent weather and I think you're looking very well."

"Thank you. Yes, feel fine."

I think moments like sitting here should be preserved. I'd like friends to visit me at my house and maybe have a cocktail cabinet, but nothing vulgar. And Marion could make nice little bits. Olives. And kids playing on the lawn. Wouldn't mind a room a bit on the lines of this. Fox on the mantelpiece and funereal fittings. Outside, the world, I think is driven. And I'm right out in front. To keep friends, photographs and letters. Me too. And women stealing alimony for young lovers. Wrinkled buttocks astride rose wood chairs, weeping signing each check. Become a lover of women over fifty. They're the ones that's looking for it. Good for O'Keefe. But he might balk. A knowledgeable man but a botcher. And now get that check. I want to see dollars. Thousands of them. Want them all over me to pave the streets of me choosey little soul.

"Bye, bye."

"Bye now, Mr. Dangerfield. Good luck."

Across the Butt Bridge. Covered with torn newspapers and hulking toothless old men watching out the last years. They're bored. I know you've been in apprenticeships and that there was a moment when you were briefly respected for an opinion. Be in the sight of God soon. He'll be shocked. But there's happiness up there, gentlemen. All white and gold. Acetylene lighted sky. And when you go, go third class. You damn bastards.

And walking along Merrion Square. Rich up this way. Wriggle the fingers a bit. American flag hanging out there. That's my flag. Means money, cars and cigars. And I won't hear a word said against it.

Spinning up the steps. Big black door. With aplomb, approaching the receptionist's desk. Unfallow Irishwomen

of middle age and misery. Belaboring poor micks headed
for that land across the seas. Giving them the first taste
of being pushed around. And ingratiating to the middle
western college boy who bounces by.

"Could you tell me if the checks have arrived?"

"You're Mr. Dangerfield, aren't you?

"I am."

"Yes the checks have arrived. I think yours is here
somewhere. However, isn't there some arrangement with
your wife? I don't think I can give it to you without
her consent."

Dangerfield warming to irritated erection.

"I say, if you don't mind I will take that check immediately."

"I'm sorry, Mr. Dangerfield but I have had instructions
not to give it to you without the permission of your wife."

"I say, I will take that check immediately."

Dangerfield's mouth a guillotine. This woman a little
upset. Insolent bitch.

"I'm very sorry but I will have to ask Mr. Morgue."

"You will ask no one."

"I'm terribly sorry, but I will have to ask Mr. Morgue."

"What?"

"You must remember that I am in charge of handling
these checks."

Dangerfield's fist swished through the air, landing with
a bang on the desk. Receptionist jumped. And her jaw
came down with a touch of obedience.

"You'll ask no one and unless that check is given me
this instant I'll have you charged with theft. Do you
understand me? Am I clear? I will not have an Irish
serf interfering in my affairs. This irregularity will be
reported to the proper authorities. I will take that check
and no more nonsense."

Receptionist with mouth open. Trickle of spittle twisted
on her jaw. An instant's hesitation and fear forced a
nervous hand to deliver the white envelope. Dangerfield
burning her with red eyes. A door opening in the hall.
Several bog men, watching from the staircase, slipped
hurriedly back to seats, caps over folded hands. A final
announcement from Dangerfield.

"Now, God damn it, when I come in here again I want
that check handed to me instantly."

From the door, a middle western accent.

"Say buddy, what's going on here?"

"Twiddle twat."

"What?"

Dangerfield suddenly convulsed with laughter. Spinning on his heel, he pushed open this Georgian door and hopped down the steps. The rich green of the park across the street. And through the tops of the trees, red brick buildings on the other side. Look at these great slabs of granite to walk on. How very nice and solid. Celtic lout. I'm all for Christianity but insolence must be put down. With violence if necessary. People in their place, neater that way. Eke. Visit my broker later and buy a French Horn and play it up the Balscaddoon road. About four a.m. And I think I'll step into this fine house here with ye oldish windows.

This public house is dark and comforting with a feeling of scholarship. With the back gate of Trinity College just outside. Makes me feel I'm close to learning and to you students who don't take the odd malt. Maybe I put too much faith in atmosphere.

Put the money away safely. A bright world ahead. Of old streets and houses, screams of the newly born and grinning happy faces escorting the lately dead. American cars speeding down Nassau Street and tweedy bodies of ex-Indian Army officers stuttering into the well-mannered gloom of the Kildare Street Club for a morning whiskey. The whole world's here. Women from Foxrock with less thick ankles and trim buttocks shod closely and cleanly with the badge of prosperity, strutting because they owned the world and on their way to coffee and an exhibition of paintings. I can't get enough. More. See Marion like that. Going to make money. Me. A sun out. With Jesus for birth control. This great iron fence around Trinity serves a good purpose. World in resurrection. Yellow banners in the sky, all for me, Sebastian Bullion Dangerfield.

> And dear God
> Give me strength
> To put my shoulder
> To the wheel
> And push
> Like the rest. . . .

O summer and soft wind. Relieves the heart and makes living cheaper. Get that fire out in the grate. Get it out. That's better.

There's the butcher a few houses up the street. A tram line goes by the window. And across the road is the most fantastic laundry with forty girls and great steaming vats. O I think they are a bunch for using just the little touch of acid.

Mr. and Mrs. Sebastian Dangerfield and their daughter, Felicity Wilton, late of Howth, are now residing at 1 Mohammed Road, The Rock, Co. Dublin.

It was decided to get out of the haunted house of Howth. But there were hesitations till the morning after the storm when Marion opened the kitchen door to get the milk and she screamed and Sebastian came running and they looked down into a mud stained sea into which had fallen the back garden and turf shed. They moved.

The new house was not new. And you didn't want to walk too fast in the front door or you'd find yourself going out the back. Mr. Egbert Skully took Mr. Dangerfield aside and said he was glad he could rent to an American because he and his wife had worked for twenty years in Macy's Department Store and loved New York and was pleased he could find tenants like themselves. And I hope you, your wife and little one will be happy here. I know it's a little small but I think you'll like the cozy quality, ha, you look like a gentleman, Mr. Dangerfield as likes his cozy comforts, and do you play golf? O aye. But my clubs are indisposed. Having them looked over by a professional for flaws, particular about alignment, you know. A very good idea, Mr. Dangerfield and perhaps my wife can give yours some recipes. Great.

Walls newly papered with brown flowers even feel soggy to the touch. And a nice brown, fourth-hand Axminster rug on the sitting room floor and a scabrous, blue settee. The kitchen was fine but the tap and sink were out the door. Up steep narrow stairs, a closet with plate sized skylight, the conservatory. And a toilet bowl wedged between two walls, the lavatory. Tory was a great suffix in this house. And the sitting room window two feet off the sidewalk was perfect for the neighbors passing by, so don't want to get caught with the pants down. But the tram rumbling by keeps one on one's guard.

A visit to the fuel merchant for coal to keep piled under the stairs. Marion got crates and covered them with table cloths for color and respectability. And my special maps one or two of which are rare and old. The one I have of a cemetery I keep under thick glass. And got the card table for a desk under the window. The laundry girls will take me mind off the awful grind of studying. They come out twice a day, hair in curlers and breasts like needles in these American uplift bras. Think the Bishop had something to say about that and rightly too. Then watch them line up for the tram, a row of steamed white faces. And some of them giving a giggle in this direction at the madman behind the curtain.

Facing the summer ahead. Living in this little house was calm. No drinking and minding the baba when Marion was off to shop. Had a cup of beef tea in the morning. Also see a rather pleasant creature up there in the window. Catch her looking in here with rather large brown eyes, no smiles or giggles. A little disdain, her dark hair straight and thick. And I think I see intelligence, a little embarrassing that look. Retreat into the kitchen. Most exciting.

Made a little case and filled it with books of law, a short life of Blessed Oliver Plunket and others on birds. Bottom shelf for business magazines for the big days ahead. And then a section for my extensive collection, which, God forgive me, I stole from Catholic Churches. But I did it because I needed strength in paupery. My favorites are, "This Thing Called Love," "Drink Is A Curse," and "Happiness In Death."

The first morning tram almost shakes one to the floor and Felicity gives the twisted cry from the conservatory. Growl back to sleep. Pull the legs up in the foetal crouch. Marion wearing my underwear. Sometimes the sun would sneak in. Then Marion beating barefoot on the linoleum. Entreaties. O do get up. Don't leave me to do everything every morning. In my heart where no one else can hear me I was saying, now for God's sake, Marion, be a good Britisher and get down there in that little nest of a kitchen and buzz on the coffee like a good girl and would you, while you're at it, kind of brown up a few pieces of bread and I wouldn't mind if maybe there was just the suggestion of bacon on it, only

a suggestion, and have it all ready on the table and then I'll
come down and act the good husband with, ah darling good
morning, how are you, you're looking lovely this morning
darling and younger every morning. A great one that last.
But I come down martyred and mussed, feeble and fussed,
heart and soul covered in cement.

But later in the morning great things were to be seen.
Sound of horses on the cobble stones. Then up to the bedroom to look down in the street. These sleek black animals
glistening in soft rain. Heads high, driving slits of steam in
the morning air. Sometimes I see through the little glass
windows, a lily on a pine box. Take me with you too. And
I can't help murmuring from memory poems I read in the
Evening Mail:

> Sleep thy last sleep,
> Free from care and sorrow.
> Rest where none weep,
> And we too, shall follow.

And I see the grinning faces popping out the windows of
the cab, radiant with the importance of the dead. Hats being
tipped along the road and hands moving in a quick sign of
the cross. Whiskey passed from hand to hand. Green, greedy
mouth is dead. A fiddle across the fields. Mushrooms fatten
in the warm September rain. Gone away.

Then time to go for the paper. And back with it to the
lavatory. Between the green peeling walls. Always feel I'm
going to get stuck. One morning there was sunshine and I
was feeling great. Sitting in there grunting and groaning,
looking over the news, and then reach up and pull the chain.
Downstairs in the kitchen, Marion screamed.

"I say, Marion, what is it?"

"For God's sake, stop it, stop it, Sebastian, you fool. What
have you done?"

Moving with swift irritability down the narrow stairs,
stumbling into the kitchen at the bottom. Perhaps things have
gotten too much for Marion and she's gone mad.

"You idiot, Sebastian, look at me, look at the baby's
things."

Marion trembling in the middle of the kitchen floor covered with strands of wet toilet paper and fecal matter. From

a gaping patch in the ceiling poured water, plaster and excrement.

"God's miserable teeth."

"Oh damnable, damnable. Do something, you fool."

"For the love of Jesus."

Sebastian stalking away.

"How dare you walk away, you damnable rotter. This is horrible and I can't bear any more."

Marion broke into sobs, slammed into silence with the front door.

Walking past the parking lot, down the little hill to the station. Stand by this wall here and watch the trains go by. Just take a crap and look what happens. This damn Skully probably put in rubber pipes. Three pounds a week for a rat hole, with brown swamp grass on the walls and cardboard furniture. And Marion has to be standing right under it. Couldn't she hear it coming? And the sun's gone in and it looks like rain. Better get back to the house or it'll weaken my position. Get her a little present, a fashion magazine filled with richery.

Marion sitting in the easy chair sewing. Pausing at the door, testing the silence.

"I'm sorry, Marion."

Marion head bent. Sebastian tendering his gift.

"I really am sorry. Look at me, I've got a present for you. It's hot tamale with ink dressing, see."

"O."

"Nice?"

"Yes."

"Like the gold teeth of God?"

"Don't spoil it now."

"My little Marion. I'm such a bastard. I tell you the whole thing up there is just a bunch of roots."

"I'll have something to read in bed."

"I'm an incredible pig, Marion."

"Aren't these suits nice."

"Don't you hear me, Marion? I'm a pig."

"Yes, but I wish we were rich and had money. I want to travel. If we could only travel."

"Let me kiss you, Marion, at least."

Marion arose, embracing him with blond arms, driving her long groin against his and her tongue deep into his mouth.

Marion you're good underneath it all and not a bad feel. Just irritable at times. Now go in there and cook the dinner. And I'll relax here in the chair and read my *Evening Mail*. I see listed conscience money. Great thing, the conscience. And letters about emigration and women who marry for quids. And here's a letter about Blessed Oliver Plunket. Went up to see him there in the St. Peter's Church, Drogheda. A decapitated, two hundred and sixty year old head. Made me feel hushed. Gray, pink and battered and a glint of dead, bared teeth in the candle light. Charwomen told me to touch it, touch it now, sir, for it's great for luck. I put my finger, afeared, in the mouldy nose hole, for you can't have too much luck these days.

Now I see them across the street coming out of the laundry. Pouring into the road, faces lining up for the tram. There's the girl with the brown eyes and dark hair, her face colorless but for handsome lips. Her legs in lisle stockings and feet in army surplus boots. Hatless and hair in a bun. Goes to the newsboy, calves knotting softly on the backs of her legs. Tucks the paper under her arm and waits in the queue.

In my heart I know she isn't a virgin, but perhaps childless with pink buds for nipples or even if they're sucked and dark I don't mind. Wears a green scarf around her nice neck. Necks should be white and long with a blue nervous vein twitching with the nervousness of life in general. My good gracious savior, she's looking over here. Hide? What am I? A scoundrel, a sneak? Not a bit. Face her. You're lovely. Absolutely lovely. Put my face on your spring breasts. Take you to Paris and tie your hair in knots with summer leaves.

"Sebastian, it's ready, do bring in the chair."

In the kitchen cutting a thick slice off the loaf, scraping butter out of a cup.

"Sebastian, what about the toilet?"

"What about it?"

"Who's going to fix it?"

"Marion, I beg of you, this is dinner time. Do you want to give me ulcers?"

"Why won't you take some responsibility?"

"After dinner. Don't drive me up the wall over Irish plumbing, it's new to the country and the pipes got mixed."

"But who'll pay?"

"Skully out of his little gold egg."

"And the smell, Sebastian. What can we do about the smell?"

"It's just healthy shit."

"How dare you use that ugly word."

"Shit's shit, Marion, even on judgement day."

"It's foul and I won't have it said in the same house as Felicity."

"She'll hear it and also in the matter of foulness I'll see to it she's laid before she's fifteen."

Marion silently seized. Putting egg shell in the coffee to make it settle. Notice her fingers bitten. She moves through the mess.

"All right, Marion, take it easy. It's just adjustment. Got to get used to it here."

"Why must you be so raw?"

"The mean meat in me."

"Be sincere. You weren't like this before we came to Ireland. This vulgar filthy country."

"Easy now."

"Children running barefoot in the streets in the middle of winter and men wagging their things at you from doorways. Disgusting."

"Untruths. Lies."

"They're a foul lot. I understand now why they're only fit to be servants."

"I say, Marion, a little bitterness?"

"You know it's true. Look at that frightful O'Keefe and his dirty ideas. America doesn't seem to help. Brings the worst out in them. He's not even fit to be a servant."

"I think Kenneth's a gentleman in every respect. Have you ever heard him fart? Now, have you?"

"Absolute frightful rot. One has only to watch him leering over the cat when it's in heat to see he's dreadfully base. When he comes into the room I feel he's criminally assaulting me in his mind."

"It's legal."

"It's the revolting lechery of an Irish peasant. And he tries to give the impression of good breeding. Watch him eating. It's infuriating. Grabs everything. That first time we had him to dinner he just came in as if we were servants and proceeded to eat before I even had time to sit down.

And pulling hunks out of the bread, how can you be blind to these things."

"Now, now, a little patience with the people who have given your country a Garden of Eden to play in, make your fires and serve your tea."

"I wished we had stayed in England. You could have waited for Oxford or Cambridge. And we could have at least maintained a measure of dignity."

"I'll admit there's not much of that."

Long limbed Marion settled in the chair. What makes you so tall and slender. You raise your eyelids and cross your legs with something I like and wear sexless shoes with sexiness. And Marion I'll say this for you, you're not blatant. And when we get our house in the West with Kerry cattle out on the hills sucking up the grass and I'm Dangerfield K.C., things will be fine again.

A tram pounding by the window, grinding, swaying and rattling on its tracks to Dalkey. A comforting sound. Maps shaking on the wall. Ireland a country of toys. And maybe I ought to go over to Marion on the couch. We're experimenting with marriage. Got to find the contraceptives or else another screaming mouth for milk. The brown-eyed girl in the laundry is about twenty-five. Marion sucking on her false teeth again, I think it must be a sign of wanting it.

In the bedroom, Dangerfield rubbing stockinged feet on the cold linoleum. And the sound of Marion using the piss pot behind Skully's genuine Ming dynasty screen. And a little tug at these tattered shades for the privacy. Even in this great Catholic country you've got to keep covered, you know, or they watch you undress, but mind you, the Protestants use a field glass.

And Marion clutching the hem of her dress and drawing it over her shifting shoulders. She said there was only thirty shillings left.

"Our good accents and manners will see us right. Didn't you know, Marion, they can't put Protestants in jail?"

"You've no responsibility and to have my child raised among a lot of savage Irish and be branded with a brogue for the rest of her life. Pass me my cream, please."

Sebastian passing the cream, smiling and waving his feet from the edge of the bed. Letting his body fall with a squeal of springs and looking at the patches of pink in the ceiling.

Marion a bit upset and confused. Difficult for her. She was breaking. Isn't as strong as me, led a sheltered life. Maybe shouldn't have married me. Matter, all of it, of time. Pumping it around and around and around, air in, air out and then it all goes like the shutters of a collapsing house. Starts and ends in antiseptic smell. Like to feel the end would be like closing leaves of honeysuckle, pressing out a last fragrance in the night but that only happens to holy men. Find them in the morning with a smile across the lips and bury them in plain boxes. But I want a rich tomb of Vermont marble in Woodlawn Cemetery, with automatic sprinkler and evergreens. If they get you in the medical school they hang you up by the ears. Never leave me unclaimed, I beg of you. Don't hang me all swollen, knees pressing the red nates of others where they come in to see if I'm fat or lean and all of us stabbed to death on the Bowery. Kill you in the tenement streets and cover you in flowers and put in the juice. By God, you hulking idiots, keep the juice away from me. Because I'm a mortician and too busy to die.

"Marion, do you ever think of death?"

"No."

"Marion, do you ever think you're going to die?"

"I say, Sebastian, would you mind awfully stopping that sort of talk. You're in that nasty mood."

"Not at all."

"You are. Coming up here every morning to watch the funerals of these wretched people. Dreadful and sordid. I think you get a perverse pleasure out of it."

"Beyond this vale of tears, there is a life above, unmeasured by the flight of years and all that life is love."

"You think you're frightening me with these sinister airs of yours. I find them only boring and they tend to make you repulsive."

"What?"

"Yes, they do."

"For the love of Jesus, look at me. Look at my eyes. Go ahead, come on."

"I don't want to look in your eyes."

"Honest globes they are."

"You can't talk seriously about anything."

"I just asked you about death. Want to know how you feel, really get to know you. Or maybe you think this is forever."

"Rubbish. You think it's forever, I know you do. You're not as flippant as this in the mornings, I notice."

"Takes me a few hours to adapt. Snap out of the dream."

"And you scream."

"What?"

"You were yelling a few nights ago, how do I get out of this. And another time you were screaming, what's that white thing in the corner, take it away."

Dangerfield holding his belly, laughing on the squeaking springs.

"You can laugh, but I think there's something serious at the root of it."

"What's at the root? Can't you see I'm mad. Can't you see? Look. See. Madness. E. I'm mad."

Sebastian ogled and wagged his tongue.

"Stop it. Always willing to clown but never to do anything useful."

Dangerfield watched from the bed as she flexed her long arms behind her back and her breasts fell from the cups of her brassiere, tan nipples hardening in the cold air. Red line on her shoulder left by the strap. Stepping wearily out of her underpants, facing the mirror and rubbing white cream into her hands and face. Little brown strands growing round the nipples. You've often said, Marion, about giving it the wax treatment but I like them that way after all.

Sebastian quietly stepping from the bed approaching the naked body. Pressing his fists against her buttocks and she pushes his hands away.

"I don't like you touching me there."

And kissing her on the back of the neck. Wet the skin with the tongue and the long blond hair gets in the mouth. Marion taking the blue nightdress from the nail. Sebastian stripping and sitting naked on the edge of the bed, taking white fluff out of the navel, and doubling himself, plucking the congealed dirt from between his toes.

"Sebastian, I wish you'd take a bath."

"Kills the personality."

"You were so clean when I first knew you."

"Given up the cleanliness for a life of the spirit. Preparation for another and better world. Hardly take offence at a little scruffiness. Clean soul's my motto. Take off your nightie."

"Where are they?"

"Under my shirts."

"And the vaseline?"

"Behind the books on the box."

Marion ripping the silver paper. Americans great for packages. Wrap anything up. And she draws the opening of her nightdress back from her shoulders, letting it fall to her feet and folding it carefully across the books. She kneels on the bed. What are other men like, do they grunt and groan, are they all curved and circumcised, with or without. She climbs into bed, a soft voice.

"Let's do it the way we used to in Yorkshire."

"Umn."

"Do you still like my breasts the way they are?"

"Umn."

"Tell me things, Sebastian, talk to me. I want to know."

Sebastian rolled near, pressing the long, blond body to his, thinking of a world outside beating drums below the window in the rain. All slipping on the cobble stones. And standing aside as a tram full of Bishops rumbles past, who hold up sacred hands in blessing. Marion's hand tightening and touching in my groin. Ginny Cupper took me in her car out to the spread fields of Indiana. Parking near the edge of woods and walking out into the sunny rows of corn, waving seeds to a yellow horizon. She wore a white blouse and a gray patch of sweat under her arms and the shadow of her nipples was gray. We were rich. So rich we could never die. Ginny laughed and laughed, white saliva on her teeth lighting up the deep red of her mouth, fed the finest food in the world. Ginny was afraid of nothing. She was young and old. Her brown arms and legs swinging in wild optimism, beautiful in all their parts. She danced on the long hood of her crimson Cadillac, and watching her, I thought that God must be female. She leaped into my arms and knocked me to the ground and screamed into my mouth. Heads pressed in the hot Indiana soil and pinned me in a cross. A crow cawed into the white sun and my sperm spurted into the world. Ginny had driven her long Cadillac through the guard rails of a St. Louis bridge and her car shone like a clot of blood in the mud and murk of the Mississippi. We were all there in the summer silence of Suffolk, Virginia, when the copper casket was gently placed in the cool marble vault. I smoked a cigarette and crushed it out on the black and white squares of the tomb. In the stagnant emptiness of the train station after the cars were gone, I walked into the women's toilet and saw the phallic obscenities on the wooden doors and gray walls. I wonder if people will think I'm a lecher. Ginny had gardenias in her lovely brown hair. I hear the train, Marion's breath in my ear. My stomach's shaking, my last strength. The world's silent. Crops have stopped growing. Now they grow again.

TERRY SOUTHERN
from *The Magic Christian* (1959)

Southern clearly represents the ultimate cool in Black
Humor. You will search long here before you will catch
any hint that Southern either approves or disapproves the
behavior of his hero, Guy Grand, the imaginative billionaire. Indeed, such evidence as there is points to the former.
The Magic Christian, by the way, is a series of vignettes
in the manner of *Catch-22* and *Candy* itself, vignettes that
alternate with fragments of a banal conversation between
Grand and his elderly sisters, vignettes that pile one Grand
monstrosity upon another. This selection introduces Grand,
describes one of his earliest and nastiest experiments and
ends with his last and grandest.

␣

Out of the gray granite morass of Wall Street rises one building like a heron of fire, soaring up in blue-white astonishment—*Number 18 Wall*—a rocket of glass and blinding copper. It is the *Grand Investment Building*, perhaps the most
contemporary business structure in our country, known in
circles of high finance simply as *Grand's*.

Offices of *Grand's* are occupied by companies which deal
in *mutual funds*—giant and fantastic corporations whose
policies define the shape of nations.

August Guy Grand himself was a billionaire. He had 180
millions cash deposit in New York banks, and this ready capital was of course but a part of his gross holdings.

In the beginning, Grand's associates, wealthy men them-

selves, saw nothing extraordinary about him; a reticent man
of simple tastes, they thought, a man who had inherited
most of his money and had preserved it through large safe
investments in steel, rubber, and oil. What his associates managed to see in Grand was usually a reflection of their own
dullness: a club member, a dinner guest, a possibility, a
threat—a man whose holdings represented a prospect and a
danger. But this was to do injustice to Grand's private life,
because his private life was atypical. For one thing, he was
the last of the big spenders; and for another, he had a very
unusual attitude towards *people*—he spent about ten million a year in, as he expressed it himself, *"making it hot
for them."*

. . . .

At fifty-three, Grand had a thick trunk and a large balding
bullet-head; his face was quite pink, so that in certain half-
lights he looked like a fat radish-man—though not displeas-
ingly so, for he always sported well-cut clothes and, near
the throat, a diamond the size of a nickel . . . a diamond
now that caught the late afternoon sun in a soft spangle
of burning color when Guy stepped through the soundless
doors of *Grand's* and into the blue haze of the almost empty
street, past the huge doorman appearing larger than life in
gigantic livery, he who touched his cap with quick but easy
reverence.

"Cab, Mr. Grand?"

"Thank you no, Jason," said Guy, "I have the car today."
And with a pleasant smile for the man, he turned adroitly
on his heel, north towards Worth Street.

Guy Grand's gait was brisk indeed—small sharp steps,
rising on the toes. It was the gait of a man who appears
to be snapping his fingers as he walks.

Half a block on he reached the car, though he seemed to
have a momentary difficulty in recognizing it; beneath the
windshield wiper lay a big parking ticket, which Grand
slowly withdrew, regarding it curiously.

"Looks like you've got a *ticket*, bub!" said a voice somewhere behind him.

Out of the corner of his eye Grand perceived the man, in a
dark summer suit, leaning idly against the side of the build-

ing nearest the car. There was something terse and smug in the tone of his remark, a sort of nasal piousness.

"Yes, so it seems," mused Grand, without looking up, continuing to study the ticket in his hand. "How much will you eat it for?" he asked then, raising a piercing smile at the man.

"How's that, mister?" demanded the latter with a nasty frown, pushing himself forward a bit from the building.

Grand cleared his throat and slowly took out his wallet— a long slender wallet of such fine leather it would have been limp as silk, had it not been so chock-full of thousands.

"I asked what would you take to *eat* it? You know . . ." Wide-eyed, he made a great chewing motion with his mouth holding the ticket up near it.

The man, glaring, took a tentative step forward.

"Say, I don't *get* you, mister!"

"Well," drawled Grand, chuckling down at his fat wallet, browsing about in it, "simple enough really . . ." And he took out a few thousand. "*I* have this ticket, as you know, and I was just wondering if you would care to *eat* it, for, say"—a quick glance to ascertain—"six thousand dollars?"

"What do you mean, *'eat it'?*" demanded the dark-suited man in a kind of a snarl. "Say, what're you anyway, bub, a *wise*-guy?"

" '*Wise*-guy' or '*grand* guy'—call me anything you like . . . as long as you don't call me '*late-for-chow!*' Eh? Ho-ho." Grand rounded it off with a jolly chortle, but was quick to add, unsmiling, "How 'bout it, pal—got a taste for the easy green?"

The man, who now appeared to be openly angry, took another step forward.

"*Listen*, mister . . ." he began in a threatening tone, half-clenching his fists.

"I think I should warn you," said Grand quietly, raising one hand to his breast, "that I am armed."

"*Huh?*" The man seemed momentarily dumfounded, staring down in dull rage at the six bills in Grand's hand; then he partially recovered, and cocking his head to one side, regarded Grand narrowly, in an attempt at shrewd skepticism, still heavily flavored with indignation.

"Just who do you think you *are*, Mister! Just what is your *game?*"

"Grand's the name, easy-green's the game," said Guy with

a twinkle. "Play along?" He brusquely flicked the corners of the six crisp bills, and they crackled with a brittle, compelling sound.

"*Listen* . . ." muttered the man, tight-lipped, flexing his fingers and exhaling several times in angry exasperation, ". . . are *you* trying . . . are you trying to tell ME that you'll give *six thousand dollars* . . . to . . . to EAT that?"— he pointed stiffly at the ticket in Guy's hand—"to *eat* that TICKET?!?"

"That's about the size of it," said Grand; he glanced at his watch. "It's what you might call a 'limited offer'—expiring in, let's say, *one minute*."

"Listen, mister," said the man between clenched teeth, "if this is a gag, *so help me* . . ." He shook his head to show how serious he was.

"No threats," Guy cautioned, "or I'll shoot you in the temple—well, what say? Forty-eight seconds remaining."

"Let's *see* that goddamn money!" exclaimed the man, quite beside himself now, grabbing at the bills.

Grand allowed him to examine them as he continued to regard his watch. "Thirty-nine seconds remaining," he announced solemnly. "Shall I start the *big count down*?"

Without waiting for the latter's reply, he stepped back and, cupping his hands like a megaphone, began dramatically intoning, "*Twenty-eight* . . . *twenty-seven* . . . *twenty-six* . . ." while the man made several wildly gesticulated and incoherent remarks before seizing the ticket, ripping off a quarter of it with his teeth and beginning to chew, eyes blazing.

"*Stout fellow!*" cried Grand warmly, breaking off the count down to step forward and give the chap a hearty clap on the shoulder and hand him the six thousand.

"You needn't actually eat the ticket," he explained. "I was just curious to see if you had your price." He gave a wink and a tolerant chuckle. "Most of us have, I suppose. Eh? Ho-ho."

And with a grand wave of his hand, he stepped inside his car and sped away, leaving the man in the dark summer suit standing on the sidewalk staring after him, fairly agog.

Guy Grand had owned a newspaper for a while—one of Boston's popular dailies, with a circulation of 900,000. When Grand assumed control, there was, at first, no change in the paper's format, nor in its apparently high journalistic standards, as Grand stayed on in New York on the periphery of the paper's operations, where he would remain, he said until he "could get the feel of things."

During the second month, however, French words began to crop up unaccountably in news of local interest:

Boston, Mar. 27 (AP)—Howard Jones, vingt-huit ans, convicted on three counts of larceny here, was sentenced this morning to 20-26 months in Folsom State Prison, Judge Grath of 17th Circuit Court of Appeals announced aujourd'hui.

Working then through a succession of editors, proofreaders, and linotype operators, Grand gradually put forward the policy of misspelling the names of cities, islands, and proper nouns in general—or else having them appear in a foreign languge:

YANKS HIT PARIGI
MOP-UP AT TERWEEWEE

During the war, when geographic names were given daily prominence in the headlines, these distortions served to antagonize the reader and to obscure the facts.

The circulation of the paper fell off sharply, and after three months it was down to something less than one-twentieth of what it had been when Grand took over. At this point a major policy change was announced. Henceforth the newspaper would not carry comics, editorials, feature stories, reviews, or advertising and would present only the factual news in a straightforward manner. It was called *The Facts,* and Grand spent the ransom of a dozen queens in getting at the facts of the news, or at least a great many of them, which he had printed then in simple sentences. The issues of the first two days or so enjoyed a fair sale, but the contents on the whole appeared to be so incredible or so irrelevant that by the end of the week demand was lower than at any previous phase of the paper's existence. During the third week, the paper had no sale at all to speak of, and was simply given away; or, refused by the distributors, it was left in stacks on the street corners each morning, about two million copies a day. In the beginning people were amused by the sight of so many newspapers lying around unread; but when it continued, they became annoyed. Something funny was going on—*Communist? Atheist? Homosexual? Catholic? Monopoly? Corruption? Protestant? Insane? Negro? Jewish? Puerto Rican? POETRY?* The city was filthy. It was easy for people to talk about *The Facts* in terms of litter and debris. Speeches were made, letters written, yet the issue was vague. The editor of *The Facts* received insulting letters by the bagful. Grand sat tight for a week. then he gave the paper over exclusively to printing these letters; and its name was changed again—*Opinions*.

These printed letters reflected such angry divergence of thought and belief that what resulted was sharp dissension throughout the city. Group antagonism ran high. The paper was widely read and there were incidents of violence. Movements began.

At about two P.M. on June 7th, crowds started to gather in Lexington Square near the center of the city. The *Jewish, Atheist, Negro, Labor, Homosexual,* and *Intellectual* groups were on one side—the *Protestant* and *American Legion* on the other. The balance of power, or so it seemed, lay with the doughty *Catholic* group.

It was fair and windless that day in Boston and while the groups and the groups-within-groups bickered and jockeyed in the center of Lexington Square, Guy Grand brought off a *tour de force*. Hovering just overhead, in a radio-equipped helicopter, he directed the maneuver of a six-plane squadron of skywriters, much higher, in spelling out the mile-long smoke-letter words: F**K YOU . . . and this was immediately followed by a veritable host of outlandish epithets, formulated as insults on the level of group Gestalt: Protestants are assholes . . . Jews are full of crap . . . Catholics are shitty . . . and so on *ad nauseam* actually.

It set the crowd below hopping mad. Grand Guy Grand dropped to about a hundred feet, where he canted the plane towards them and opened the door to peer out and observe. The crowd, associating the low-flying helicopter with the outrageous skywriting going on above, started shouting obscenities and shaking their fists.

"You rotten Mick!"

"You dirty Yid!"

"You black bastard!"

That was how the fighting began.

During the Lexington Square Riots, Grand set his plane down to twenty-five feet, where he cruised around, leaning out the door, expressionless, shouting in loud, slow intonation:

"WHAT'S . . . UP? WHAT'S . . . UP?"

. . .

By four o'clock the square was in shambles and all Boston on the brink of eruption. The National Guard had to be brought into the city and martial law obtained. It was thirty-six hours before order was fully restored.

The press made capital of the affair. Investigations were demanded. Guy Grand had paid off some big men in order to carry forward the project, but this was more than they had bargained for. Back in New York it cost him two million to keep clear.

It was along towards the end though that Grand achieved, in terms of public outrage, his *succés d'estime*, as some chose to call it, when he put out to sea in his big ship, the S.S. *Magic Christian* . . . the ship sometimes later referred to as "The Terrible Trick Ship of Captain Klaus." Actually it was the old *Griffin*, a passenger liner which Grand bought and had reconditioned for about fifty million.

A vessel of 30,000 tons, the *Christian* had formerly carried some eleven-hundred-odd passengers. Grand converted it into a one-class ship, outfitted to accommodate four hundred passengers, in a style and comfort perhaps unknown theretofore outside princely domains of the East. Each cabin on the *Christian* was a palace in miniature; the appointments were so lavish and so exquisitely detailed that they might better be imagined than described. All the cabins were of course above deck and outside, each with a twenty-foot picture window and French doors to a private patio commanding a magnificent expanse of sea and sky. There were fine deep rugs throughout each suite and period-furnishings of first account, private bars, chaise longues, log-burning fireplaces, king-sized beds (canopy optional), an adjoining library-den (with a set of the *Britannica* and the best in smart fiction), tape recorders, powder rooms, small Roman bath and steam cabinet. Walls were generally in a quiet tone of suede with certain paneling of teak and rosewood.

Ship's dining room was styled after Maxim's in Paris whose staff had been engaged to prepare the meals and to serve them with inconspicuous grace against a background of soft music provided by the Juilliard String Quartette. The balance of ship's appointments were in harmonious key— there was, for example, a veritable jewel box of a theatre, seating just four hundred, fashioned in replica of the one in the Monte Carlo Casino; and the versatile repertory group, Old Vic Players, were on stand-by for two shows a day.

Ship's doctor, aside from being an able physician, was also a top-flight mental specialist, so that Problem-Counseling was available to the passengers at all hours.

But perhaps the most carefully thought-out nicety of the *Christian* was its principal lounge, the Marine Room—a large room, deep below decks, its wall (that which was part of ship's hull) glassed so that the passengers sat looking out into the very heart of the sea. An ocean-floor effect was maintained by the regular release of deep-sea creatures from a waterline station near the bow, and through the use of powerful daylight kliegs there was afforded a breathtaking panorama—with giant octopi, huge rainbow-colored ray, serpents, great snowy angelfish, and fantastic schools of luminous tetra constantly gliding by or writhing in silent majestic combat a few feet from the relaxed passengers.

Though the *Magic Christian* received its share of prevoyage hullabaloo (*Life* magazine devoted an issue to photographs, enthusiastically captioned), its only form of paid advertisement was a simple announcement of its sailing date, which appeared in *The Times* and in the *National Geographic*. The fare was not mentioned (though *Life* had said it was "about five thousand") and the announcement was set in small heavy type, boxed with a very black border. "For the Gracious Few . . ." it opened, and went on to state in a brief, restrained apology, that *not everyone* could be accepted, that applications for passage on the *Christian* were necessarily carefully screened, and that those who were refused should not take offense. "Our criteria," it closed, "may *not* be yours."

Ship's quarters were not shown until the applicant had been accepted, and then were shown by appointment.

The ship was christened by the Queen of England.

All of this had a certain appeal and the applications poured in. More than a few people, in fact, were *demanding* passage on the *Christian's* first voyage. Those just back from holiday were suddenly planning to go abroad again; scores rushed home simply to qualify and make the trip. For many, the maiden voyage of the *Magic Christian* became a must.

Meanwhile Guy Grand, well in the background, was personally screening the applications according to some obscure criteria of his own, and apparently he had himself a few laughs in this connection. In the case of one application, for example, from a venerable scioness of Roman society, he simply scrawled moronically across it in blunt pencil: "Are *you* kidding?!? *No* wops!" The woman was said to have had a nervous breakdown and did later file for a million on defamation. It cost Grand a pretty to clear it.

On the other hand, he accepted—or rather, engaged—as passengers, a group from a fairly sordid freak show, most of whom could not be left untended, along with a few gypsies, Broadway types, and the like, of offensive appearance and doubtful character. These, however, were to be kept below decks for the first few days out, and, even so, numbered only about forty in all, so that a good nine-tenths of the passenger list, those on deck when the *Christian* set sail in such tasteful fanfare that Easter morn, were top-drawer gentry and no mistake.

Unique among features of the *Christian* was its video communication system from the bridge to other parts of the ship. Above the fireplace in each cabin was a small TV screen and this provided direct visual communication with the Captain at the wheel and with whatever other activity was going on there, giving as it did a view of almost the entire bridge. These sets could be switched *on* or *off*, but the first day they were left *on* before the passengers arrived, in order to spare anyone the embarrassment of not knowing what the new gimmick was. So that when passengers entered their cabins now they saw at once, there on the screen above the fireplace: the Captain at the wheel. Captain Klaus. And for this person, Guy Grand had engaged a professional actor, a distinguished silver-haired man whose every gesture inspired the deepest confidence. He wore a double row of service ribbons on his dark breast and deported himself in a manner both authoritative and pleasingly genial—as the passengers saw when he turned to face the screen, and this he did just as soon as they were all settled and under way.

He was filling his pipe when he turned to camera, but he paused from this to smile and touch his cap in easy salute.

"Cap'n Klaus," he said, introducing himself with warm informality, though certainly at no sacrifice to his considerable bearing. "Glad to have you aboard."

He casually picked up a pointer stick and indicated a chart on the nearby wall.

"Here's our course," he said, "nor' by nor'east, forty-seven degrees."

Then he went on to explain the mechanics and layout of the bridge, the weather and tide conditions at present, their prospects, and so on, using just enough technical jargon throughout all this to show that he knew what he was about. He said that the automatic-pilot would be used from time to time, but that he personally preferred handling the wheel himself, adding good-humoredly that in his opinion "a ship favored men to machines."

"It may be an old-fashioned notion," he said, with a wise twinkle, ". . . but to me, a ship is a woman."

At last he gave a final welcome-salute, saying again: "Glad to have you aboard," and turned back to his great wheel.

This contact with the bridge and the fatherly Captain seemed to give the passengers an added sense of participation and security; and, indeed, things couldn't have gone more smoothly for the first few hours.

It was in the very early morning that something untoward occurred, at about three A.M.—and of course almost everyone was sleep. They had watched their screens for a while: the Captain in the cozy bridge house, standing alone, pipe glowing, his strong eyes sweeping the black water ahead—then they had switched off their sets. There were a few people though who were still up and who had their sets on; and, of these few, there were perhaps three who happened to be watching the screen at a certain moment—when in the corner of the bridge house, near the door, there was a shadow, an odd movement . . . then suddenly the appearance of a sinister-looking person, who crept up behind the Captain, hit him on the head, and seized the wheel as the screen blacked out.

The people who had seen this were disturbed and, in fact, were soon rushing about, rousing others, wanting to go to the bridge and so on. And they did actually get up a party and went to the bridge—only to be met at the top of the ladder by the Captain himself, unruffled, glossing it over, blandly assuring them that nothing was wrong, nothing at all, just a minor occurrence. And, of course, back in the cabins, there he was on the screen again, Captain Klaus, steady at the helm.

Those three who had seen the outrage, being in such a hopeless minority, were thought to have been drunk or in some way out of their minds, and were gently referred to ship's doctor, the mental specialist, so the incident passed without too much notice.

And things went smoothly once more, until the next evening—when, in the exquisite gaming rooms just off the Marine Lounge, one of the roulette croupiers was seen, by several people, to be cheating . . . darting his eyes about in a furtive manner and then interfering with the bets, snatching them up and stuffing them in his pocket, that sort of thing.

It was such an unheard-of outrage that one old duke fainted dead away. The croupier was hustled out of the gaming room by Captain Klaus himself, who deplored the incident profusely and declared that the next dozen spins were on the house, losing bets to remain untouched for that time—gracious recompense, in the eyes of a sporting crowd, and applauded as such; still, the incident was not one easily forgotten.

Another curious thing occurred when some of the ladies went, individually, to visit the ship's doctor. For the most part they had simply dropped around to pick up a few aspirin, sea-sickness pills—or merely to have a reassuring chat with the amiable physician. Several of these ladies, however, were informed that they looked "rather queer" and that an examination might be in order.

"Better safe than sorry," the doctor said, and then, during

the examination, he invariably seemed to discover what he termed "a latent abrasion"—on the waist, side, hip, or shoulder of the woman—and though the abrasion could not be seen, the doctor deemed it required a compress.

"Nothing serious," he explained, "still it's always wise to take precautions." And so saying he would apply a *huge compress* to the area, a sort of gigantic Band-Aid about a foot wide and several inches thick, with big adhesive flaps that went halfway around the body. The tremendous bulk of these compresses was a nuisance, causing as they did, great deforming bulges beneath the women's smart frocks. They were almost impossible to remove. One woman was seen running about with one on her head, like a big white hat.

First lifeboat drill was scheduled for the following morning. Shortly before it, Captain Klaus came on the screen and smilingly apologized for the inconvenience and gave a leisurely and pleasantly informative talk about the drill and its necessity.

"Better safe than sorry," he said in a genial close to his little talk.

When the drill signal sounded, they all got into life jackets —which were the latest thing and quite unlike standard passenger-ship equipment—and then, grumbling good-naturedly, they started for their boat stations; but an extraordinary thing happened: two minutes after they had put them on, the life jackets began inflating in a colossal way. Apparently the very act of donning the jacket set off some device which inflated it. The extraordinary thing was that each one blew up so big that it simply obscured the person wearing it, ballooning out about them, above their heads, below their feet, and to a diameter of perhaps twelve feet—so that if they were in an open space, such as their cabins, the lounge, or on deck, they simply rolled or lolled about on the floor, quite hidden from view, whereas if they were in a corridor, they were hopelessly stuck.

In any event, almost no one escaped the effects of the faulty life jacket; so it was—after they deflated—with a good deal of annoyance that they came back to the cabins, quite ready to hear Captain Klaus' explanation of what had gone amiss.

Unfortunately though, the foghorn, which had been put to practice during the drill, was now evidently jammed. At any rate, it continued steadily during the Captain's after-drill talk and completely shut out his voice, so that it was like looking at someone talk behind several layers of glass. The Captain himself didn't seem to realize that he wasn't coming through, and he went on talking for quite a while, punctuating his remarks with various little facial gestures to indicate a whole gamut of fairly intense feelings about whatever it was he was saying.

The business with the foghorn was more serious than at first imagined; it continued, blasting without let-up, for the rest of the voyage.

Quite incidental to what was happening during the drill, fifty crew members took advantage of the occasion to go around to the cabins, lounges, and dining rooms, and to substitute a thin length of balsa wood for one leg of every chair, table, and dresser on ship.

When the Captain finished his lengthy and voiceless discourse, he smiled, gave an easy salute and left the bridge house. It was about this time that all the furniture began to collapse—in half an hour's time there wasn't one standing stick of it aboard the *Christian*.

Strange and unnatural persons began to appear—in the drawing rooms, salons, at the pool. During the afternoon tea dance, a gigantic *bearded-woman*, stark naked, rushed wildly about over the floor, interfering with the couples, and had to be forcibly removed by ship's doctor.

The plumbing went bad, too; and finally one of the *Christian's* big stacks toppled—in such a way as to give directly on to ship's dining room, sending oily smoke billowing through. And, in fact, from about this point on, the voyage was a veritable nightmare.

Large curious posters were to be seen in various parts of the ship:

SUPPORT MENTAL HEALTH

LET'S KEEP THE CLAP OUT
OF CHAPPAQUIDDICK

as well as rude slogans, vaguely political, scrawled in huge misshapen letters across walls and decks alike:

DEATH TO RICH!
BLOW UP U.S.!

Due to the strain of untoward events, more than one passenger sought solace and reassurance from the problem-counselor, the ship's distinguished doctor.

"Doctor, what *in the name of God* is going on here!" the frenzied passenger would demand.

The doctor would answer with a quizzical smile, arching his brows, only mildly censorious. "Fair-weather sailor?" he would gently chide, ". . . hmm? Cross and irritable the moment things aren't going exactly to suit you? Now just what seems to be the trouble?"

" '*Trouble*'!?!" exclaimed the outraged passenger. "Good Lord, Doctor, surely you don't think my complaint is an . . . an unreasonable one?"

The doctor would turn his gaze out to sea, thin fingers pressed beneath his chin in a delicate pyramid of contemplation, wistfully abstract for a moment before turning back to address the patient frankly.

"Deep-rooted and unreasonable fears," he would begin in a grand, rich voice, "are most often behind our anxieties . . ." and he would continue in this vein until the passenger fairly exploded with impatience.

"Great Scott, Doctor! I didn't come here for a lecture on *psychology*—I came to find out what *in the name of Heaven is going on aboard this ship*!"

In the face of these outbursts however, the doctor almost invariably retained his calm, regarding the patient coolly, searchingly, making a few careful notes on his pad.

"Now, you say that 'the life jacket *over inflated*,' and that you were 'stuck in the corridor'—that was your expression, I believe, '*stuck in the corridor*'—and at that moment you felt a certain *malaise*, so to speak. Now, let me ask you *this* . . ." Or again, on other occasions, he might behave eccentrically, his head craned far to one side, regarding the patient out of the corners of his eyes, a sly, mad smile on his lips which moved in an inaudible whisper, almost a hiss.

Finally, the patient, at the end of his tether, would leap to his feet.

"Well, in the name of God, Doctor, the least you can do is let me have some *tranquillizers*!"

But the doctor, as it turned out, was not one given to prescribing drugs promiscuously.

"Escape into drugs?" he would ask, wagging his head slowly. "Mask our fears in an artificial fog?" And there was always a trace of sadness in his smile, as he continued, "No,

I'm afraid the trouble is *in ourselves*, you see." Then he would settle back expansively and speak with benign countenance. "Running away from problems is scarcely the solution to them. I *believe* you'll thank me in years to come." And at last he would lean forward in quiet confidence. "Do you mind if I ask you a few questions about your . . . your *early childhood*?"

When Captain Klaus next appeared on the screen, he looked as though he had been sleeping in two feet of water. Completely disheveled, his ribbons dangling in unsightly strands, his open coat flapping, his unknotted tie strung loosely around his collar, he seemed somewhat drunk as well. With a rude wave of his hand he dismissed bridge personnel and lurched toward the video screen, actually crashing into it, and remained so close that his image was all distorted.

"We'll get the old tub through!" he was shouting at deafening volume, and at that moment he was attacked from behind by a ruffian type who was carrying a huge hypodermic and appeared to overpower the Captain and inject something into the top of his head, then to seize the wheel, wrenching it violently, before the screen went black.

Also, it was learned about this time that because of fantastic miscalculation on the part of the ship's-stores officer, the only food left aboard now was potatoes.

Thus did the *Christian* roar over the sea, through fair weather and foul.

Guy Grand was aboard of course, as a passenger, complaining bitterly, and in fact kept leading assault parties in an effort to find out, as he put it, "What the devil's going on on the bridge!"

But they were always driven back by a number of odd-looking men with guns and knives near the ladder.

"Who the deuce are those chaps?" Grand would demand as he and the others beat a hasty retreat along the deck. "I don't like the looks of this!"

Occasionally the communications screen in each of the cabins would light up to reveal momentarily what was taking place on the bridge, and it was fairly incredible. The bridge house itself now was a swaying rubble heap and the Captain was seen intermittently, struggling with various assailants, and finally with what actually appeared to be a gorilla—the beast at last overpowering him and flinging him bodily out of the bridge house and, or so it seemed, into the sea itself, before seizing the wheel, which he seemed then to be trying to tear from its hub.

It was about this time that the ship, which, as it developed, had turned completely around in the middle of the ocean, came back into New York harbor under full steam, and with horns and whistles screaming, ploughed headlong into the big Forty-Seventh Street pier.

Fortunately no one was injured on the cruise; but, even so, it went far from easy with Grand—he had already sunk plenty into the project, and just how much it cost him to keep clear in the end, is practically anyone's guess.

JOSEPH HELLER
from *Catch-22* (1961)

The time of *Catch-22* is World War II, the enemy the Germans, but the atmosphere is surreal enough to obviate any such distinctions. The atmosphere is, in fact, war itself, war anywhere and at any time. Heller thus focuses upon the ultimate madness of mankind, a traditional subject of satire. It is the ribald humor that rescues *Catch-22* from tradition, however; like any Black Humorist worth his definition, Heller knows too much about man to suppose that we can eradicate war simply by writing novels. The causes of aggression go too deep for that or anything else. Even in the most horrible moments of *Catch-22* there is the ambivalence of humor:

> There was only one catch and that was Catch-22, which specified that a concern for one's own safety in the face of dangers that were real and immediate was the process of a rational mind. Orr was crazy and could be grounded. All he had to do was ask; and as soon as he did, he would no longer be crazy and would have to fly more missions. Orr would be crazy to fly more missions and sane if he didn't, but if he was sane he had to fly them. If he flew them he was crazy and didn't have to; but if he didn't want to he was sane and had to. Yossarian was moved very deeply by the absolute simplicity of this clause of Catch-22 and let out a respectful whistle.
>
> "That's some catch, that Catch-22," he observed.
>
> "It's the best there is," Doc Daneeka agreed.
>
> Yossarian saw it clearly in all its spinning reasonableness. There was an elliptical precision about its perfect pairs of parts that was graceful and shocking, like

good modern art, and at times Yossarian wasn't quite sure that he saw it all, just the way he was never quite sure about good modern art or about the flies Orr saw in Appleby's eyes. He had Orr's word to take for the flies in Appleby's eyes.

No, Heller is not writing a simple-minded anti-war tract. If he were, if he were certain of the answer, his novel would not abound with wit and slapstick; it would make solemn proposals, in the manner of *All Quiet on the Western Front*. We laugh, someone once said, out of despair. The despair in *Catch-22* is profound, and that is why the book is so funny.

Catch-22 is a series of tragicomic vignettes built around various members of Captain Yossarian's doomed squadron, whose commanding officer, Colonel Cathcart, repeatedly increases the total number of bombing missions it must fly before returning home. After many desperate attempts to disable himself, Captain Yossarian, in this episode, is wounded and thus returns to the hospital for his epic confrontations, first with Nurse Duckett and then with Colonel Sanderson, a confrontation that will remind us of the meeting between K. and the Mayor in *The Castle*.

Yossarian flipped his eyes open in alarm and saw the totally unexpected bulging black puffs of flak crashing down in toward them from high up and Aarfy's complacent melon-round, tiny-eyes face gazing out at the approaching cannon bursts with affable bemusement. Yossarian was flabbergasted. His leg went abruptly to sleep. McWatt had started to climb and was yelping over the intercom for instructions. Yossarian sprang forward to see where they were and remained in the same place. He was unable to move. Then he realized he was sopping wet. He looked down at his crotch with a sinking, sick sensation. A wild crimson blot was crawling upward rapidly along his shirt front like an enormous sea monster rising to devour him.

He was hit! Separate trickles of blood spilled to a puddle on the floor through one saturated trouser leg like countless unstoppable swarms of wriggling red worms. His heart stopped. A second solid jolt struck the plane. Yossarian shuddered with revulsion at the queer sight of his wound and screamed at Aarfy for help.

"I lost my balls! Aarfy, I lost my balls!" Aarfy didn't hear, and Yossarian bent forward and tugged at his arm. "Aarfy, help me," he pleaded, almost weeping. "I'm hit! I'm hit!"

Aarfy turned slowly with a bland, quizzical grin. "What?"

"I'm hit, Aarfy! Help me!"

Aarfy grinned again and shrugged amiably. "I can't hear you," he said.

"Can't you see me?" Yossarian cried incredulously, and he pointed to the deepening pool of blood he felt splashing down all around him and spreading out underneath. "I'm wounded! Help me, for God's sake! Aarfy, help me!"

"I still can't hear you," Aarfy complained tolerantly, cupping his podgy hand behind the blanched corolla of his ear. "What did you say?"

Yossarian answered in a collapsing voice, weary suddenly of shouting so much, of the whole frustrating, exasperating, ridiculous situation. He was dying, and no one took notice. "Never mind."

"What?" Aarfy shouted.

"I said I lost my balls! Can't you hear me? I'm wounded in the groin!"

"I still can't hear you," Aarfy chided.

"I said *never mind*!" Yossarian screamed with a trapped feeling of terror and began to shiver, feeling very cold suddenly and very weak.

Aarfy shook his head regretfully again and lowered his obscene, lactescent ear almost directly into Yossarian's face. "You'll just have to speak up, my friend. You'll just have to speak up."

"Leave me alone, you bastard! You dumb, insensitive bastard, leave me alone!" Yossarian sobbed. He wanted to pummel Aarfy, but lacked the strength to lift his arms. He decided to sleep instead and keeled over sideways into a dead faint.

He was wounded in the thigh, and when he recovered consciousness he found McWatt on both knees taking care of him. He was relieved, even though he still saw Aarfy's bloated cherub's face hanging down over McWatt's shoulder with placid interest. Yossarian smiled feebly at McWatt, feeling ill, and asked, "Who's minding the store?" McWatt gave no sign that he heard. With growing horror, Yossarian gathered in breath and repeated the words as loudly as he could.

McWatt looked up. "Christ, I'm glad you're alive!" he exclaimed, heaving an enormous sigh. The good-humored, friendly crinkles about his eyes were white with tension and oily with grime as he kept unrolling an interminable bandage around the bulky cotton compress Yossarian felt strapped burdensomely to the inside of one thigh. "Nately's at the controls. The poor kid almost started bawling when he heard you were hit. He still thinks you're dead. They knocked open an artery for you, but I think I've got it stopped. I gave you some morphine."

"Give me some more."

"It might be too soon. I'll give you some more when it starts to hurt."

"It hurts now."

"Oh, well, what the hell," said McWatt and injected another syrette of morphine into Yossarian's arm.

"When you tell Nately I'm all right . . ." said Yossarian to McWatt, and lost consciousness again as everything went fuzzy behind a film of strawberry-stained gelatin and a great baritone buzz swallowed him in sound. He came to in the ambulance and smiled encouragement at Doc Daneeka's weevillike glum and overshadowed countenance for the dizzy second or two he had before everything went rose-petal pink again and then turned really black and unfathomably still.

Yossarian woke up in the hospital and went to sleep. When he woke up in the hospital again, the smell of ether was gone and Dunbar was lying in pajamas in the bed across the aisle maintaining that he was not Dunbar but *a fortiori*. Yossarian thought he was cracked. He curled his lip skeptically at Dunbar's bit of news and slept on it fitfully for a day or two, then woke up while the nurses were elsewhere and eased himself out of bed to see for himself. The floor swayed like the floating raft at the beach and the stitches on the inside of his thigh bit into his flesh like fine sets of fish teeth as he limped across the aisle to peruse the name on the temperature card on the foot of Dunbar's bed, but sure enough, Dunbar was right: he was not Dunbar any more but Second Lieutenant Anthony F. Fortiori.

"What the hell's going on?"

A. Fortiori got out of bed and motioned to Yossarian to follow. Grasping for support at anything he could reach, Yossarian limped along after him out into the corridor and down the adjacent ward to a bed containing a harried young man with pimples and a receding chin. The harried young man rose on one elbow with alacrity as they approached. A. Fortiori jerked his thumb over his shoulder and said, "Screw." The harried young man jumped out of bed and ran away. A. Fortiori climbed into the bed and became Dunbar again.

"That was A. Fortiori," Dunbar explained. "They didn't have an empty bed in your ward, so I pulled my rank and chased him back here into mine. It's a pretty satisfying experience, pulling rank. You ought to try it sometime. You ought to try it right now, in fact, because you look like you're going to fall down."

Yossarian felt like he was going to fall down. He turned to the lantern-jawed, leather-faced middle-aged man lying in the bed next to Dunbar's, jerked his thumb over his shoulder and said, "Screw." The middle-aged man stiffened fiercely and glared.

"He's a major," Dunbar explained. "Why don't you aim a little lower and try becoming Warrant Officer Homer Lumley for a while? Then you can have a father in the state legislature and a sister who's engaged to a champion skier. Just tell him you're a captain."

Yossarian turned to the startled patient Dunbar had indicated. "I'm a captain," he said, jerking his thumb over his shoulder. "Screw."

The startled patient jumped down to the floor at Yossarian's command and ran away. Yossarian climbed up into his bed and became Warrant Officer Homer Lumley, who felt like vomiting and was covered suddenly with a clammy sweat. He slept for an hour and wanted to be Yossarian again. It did not mean so much to have a father in the state legislature and a sister who was engaged to a champion skier. Dunbar led the way back to Yossarian's ward, where he thumbed A. Fortiori out of bed to become Dunbar again for a while. There was no sign of Warrant Officer Homer Lumley. Nurse Cramer was there, though, and sizzled with sanctimonious anger like a damp firecracker. She ordered Yossarian to get right back into his bed and blocked his path so he couldn't comply. Her pretty face was more repulsive than ever. Nurse Cramer was a goodhearted, sentimental creature who rejoiced unselfishly at news of weddings, engagements, births and anniversaries even though she was unacquainted with any of the people involved.

"Are you crazy?" she scolded virtuously, shaking an indignant finger in front of his eyes. "I suppose you just don't care if you kill yourself, do you?"

"It's my self," he reminded her.

"I suppose you just don't care if you lose your leg, do you?"

"It's my leg."

"It certainly is not your leg!" Nurse Cramer retorted. "That leg belongs to the U.S. government. It's no different than a gear or a bedpan. The Army has invested a lot of money to make you an airplane pilot, and you've no right to disobey the doctor's orders."

Yossarian was not sure he liked being invested in. Nurse Cramer was still standing directly in front of him so that he could not pass. His head was aching. Nurse Cramer shouted at him some question he could not understand. He jerked his thumb over his shoulder and said, "Screw."

Nurse Cramer cracked him in the face so hard she almost knocked him down. Yossarian drew back his fist to punch her in the jaw just as his leg buckled and he began to fall. Nurse Duckett strode up in time to catch him. She addressed them both firmly.

"Just what's going on here?"

"He won't get back into his bed," Nurse Cramer reported zealously in an injured tone. "Sue Ann, he said something absolutely horrible to me. Oh, I can't even make myself repeat it!"

"She called me a gear," Yossarian muttered.

Nurse Duckett was not sympathetic. "Will you get back into bed," she said, "or must I take you by your ear and put you there?"

"Take me by my ear and put me there," Yossarian dared her.

Nurse Duckett took him by his ear and put him back in bed.

Nurse Sue Ann Duckett was a tall, spare, mature, straight-backed woman with a prominent, well-rounded ass, small breasts and angular, ascetic New England features that came equally close to being very lovely and very plain. Her skin was white and pink, her eyes small, her nose and chin slender and sharp. She was able, prompt, strict and intelligent. She welcomed responsibility and kept her head in every crisis. She was adult and self-reliant, and there was nothing she needed from anyone. Yossarian took pity and decided to help her.

Next morning while she was standing bent over smoothing the sheets at the foot of his bed, he slipped his hand stealthily into the narrow space between her knees and, all at once, brought it up swiftly under her dress as far as it would go. Nurse Duckett shrieked and jumped into the air a mile, but it wasn't high enough, and she squirmed and vaulted and seesawed back and forth on her divine fulcrum for almost a full fifteen seconds before she wiggled free finally and retreated frantically into the aisle with an ashen, trembling face. She backed away too far, and Dunbar, who had watched from the beginning, sprang forward on his bed without warning and flung both arms around her bosom from behind. Nurse Duckett let out another scream and twisted away, fleeing far enough from Dunbar for Yossarian to lunge forward and grab her by the snatch again. Nurse Duckett bounced out across the aisle once more like a ping-pong ball with legs. Dunbar was waiting vigilantly, ready to pounce. She remembered him just in time and leaped aside. Dunbar missed completely and sailed by her over the bed to the floor, landing on his skull with a soggy, crunching thud that knocked him cold.

He woke up on the floor with a bleeding nose and exactly the same distressful head symptoms he had been feigning all along. The ward was in a chaotic uproar. Nurse Duckett was in tears, and Yossarian was consoling her apologetically as he sat beside her on the edge of a bed. The commanding colonel was wroth and shouting at Yossarian that he would not permit his patients to take indecent liberties with his nurses.

"What do you want from him?" Dunbar asked plaintively from the floor, wincing at the vibrating pains in his temples that his voice set up. "He didn't do anything."

"I'm talking about you!" the thin, dignified colonel bellowed as loudly as he could. "You're going to be punished for what you did."

"What do you want from him?" Yossarian called out. "All he did was fall on his head."

"And I'm talking about you too!" the colonel declared, whirling to rage at Yossarian. "You're going to be good and sorry you grabbed Nurse Duckett by the bosom."

"I didn't grab Nurse Duckett by the bosom," said Yossarian.

"*I* grabbed her by the bosom," said Dunbar.

"Are you both crazy?" the doctor cried shrilly, backing away in paling confusion.

"Yes, he really is crazy, Doc," Dunbar assured him. "Every night he dreams he's holding a live fish in his hands."

The doctor stopped in his tracks with a look of elegant amazement and distaste, and the ward grew still. *"He does what?"* he demanded.

"He dreams he's holding a live fish in his hand."

"What kind of fish?" the doctor inquired sternly of Yossarian.

"I don't know," Yossarian answered. "I can't tell one kind of fish from another."

"In which hand do you hold them?"

"It varies," answered Yossarian.

"It varies with the fish," Dunbar added helpfully.

The colonel turned and stared down at Dunbar suspiciously with a narrow squint. "Yes? And how come you seem to know so much about it?"

"I'm in the dream," Dunbar answered without cracking a smile.

The colonel's face flushed with embarrassment. He glared at them both with cold, unforgiving resentment. "Get up off the floor and into your bed," he directed Dunbar through thin lips. "And I don't want to hear

another word about this dream from either one of you.
I've got a man on my staff to listen to disgusting bilge
like this."

"Just why do you think," carefully inquired Major Sanderson, the soft and thickset smiling staff psychiatrist to
whom the colonel had ordered Yossarian sent, "that Colonel Ferredge finds your dream disgusting?"

Yossarian replied respectfully. "I suppose it's either
some quality in the dream or some quality in Colonel
Ferredge."

"That's very well put," applauded Major Sanderson, who
wore squeaking GI shoes and had charcoal-black hair that
stood up almost straight. "For some reason," he confided,
"Colonel Ferredge has always reminded me of a sea gull.
He doesn't put much faith in psychiatry, you know."

"You don't like sea gulls, do you?" inquired Yossarian.

"No, not very much," admitted Major Sanderson with a
sharp, nervous laugh and pulled at his pendulous second
chin lovingly as though it were a long goatee. "I think
your dream is charming, and I hope it recurs frequently
so that we can continue discussing it. Would you like a
cigarette?" He smiled when Yossarian declined. "Just why
do you think," he asked knowingly, "that you have
such a strong aversion to accepting a cigarette from me?"

"I put one out a second ago. It's still smoldering in your
ash tray."

Major Sanderson chuckled. "That's a very ingenious explanation. But I suppose we'll soon discover the true
reason." He tried a sloppy double bow in his opened shoelace and then transferred a lined yellow pad from his
desk to his lap. "This fish you dream about. Let's talk
about that. It's always the same fish, isn't it?"

"I don't know," Yossarian replied. "I have trouble recognizing fish."

"What does the fish remind you of?"

"Other fish."

"And what do other fish remind you of?"

"Other fish."

Major Sanderson sat back disappointedly. "Do you like
fish?"

"Not especially."

"Just why do you think you have such a morbid
aversion to fish?" asked Major Sanderson triumphantly.

"They're too bland," Yossarian answered. "And too bony."

Major Sanderson nodded understandingly, with a smile that was agreeable and insincere. "That's a very interesting explanation. But we'll soon discover the true reason, I suppose. Do you like this particular fish? The one you're holding in your hand?"

"I have no feelings about it either way."

"Do you dislike the fish? Do you have any hostile or aggressive emotions toward it?"

"No, not at all. In fact, I rather like the fish."

"Then you do like the fish."

"Oh, no. I have no feelings toward it either way."

"But you just said you liked it. And now you say you have no feelings toward it either way. I've just caught you in a contradiction. Don't you see?"

"Yes, sir. I suppose you have caught me in a contradiction."

Major Sanderson proudly lettered "Contradiction" on his pad with his thick black pencil. "Just why do you think," he resumed when he had finished, looking up, "that you made those two statements expressing contradictory emotional responses to the fish?"

"I suppose I have an ambivalent attitude toward it."

Major Sanderson sprang up with joy when he heard the words "ambivalent attitude." "You do understand!" he exclaimed, wringing his hands together ecstatically. "Oh, you can't imagine how lonely it's been for me, talking day after day to patients who haven't the slightest knowledge of psychiatry, trying to cure people who have no real interest in me or my work! It's given me such a terrible feeling of inadequacy." A shadow of anxiety crossed his face. "I can't seem to shake it."

"Really?" asked Yossarian, wondering what else to say. "Why do you blame yourself for gaps in the education of others?"

"It's silly, I know," Major Sanderson replied uneasily with a giddy, involuntary laugh. "But I've always depended very heavily on the good opinion of others. I reached puberty a bit later than all the other boys my age, you see, and it's given me sort of—well, all sorts of problems. I just know I'm going to enjoy discussing them with you. I'm so eager to begin that I'm almost reluctant to digress now to your problem, but I'm afraid I must. Colonel Ferredge would be cross if he knew we were spending all our time on me. I'd like to show you some ink blots now to find out what certain shapes and colors remind you of."

"You can save yourself the trouble, Doctor. Everything reminds me of sex."

"Does it?" cried Major Sanderson with delight, as though unable to believe his ears. "Now we're *really* getting somewhere! Do you ever have any good sex dreams?"

"My fish dream is a sex dream."

"No, I mean real sex dreams—the kind where you grab some naked bitch by the neck and pinch her and punch her in the face until she's all bloody and then throw yourself down to ravish her and burst into tears because you love her and hate her so much you don't know what else to do. *That's* the kind of sex dreams I like to talk about. Don't you ever have sex dreams like that?"

Yossarian reflected a moment with a wise look. "That's a fish dream," he decided.

Major Sanderson recoiled as though he had been slapped. "Yes, of course," he conceded frigidly, his manner changing to one of edgy and defensive antagonism. "But I'd like you to dream one like that anyway just to see how you react. That will be all for today. In the meantime, I'd also like you to dream up the answers to some of those questions I asked you. These sessions are no more pleasant for me than they are for you, you know."

"I'll mention it to Dunbar," Yossarian replied.

"Dunbar?"

"He's the one who started it all. It's his dream."

"Oh, Dunbar." Major Sanderson sneered, his confidence returning. "I'll bet Dunbar is that evil fellow who really does all those nasty things you're always being blamed for, isn't he?"

"He's not so evil."

"And yet you'll defend him to the very death, won't you?"

"Not that far."

Major Sanderson smiled tauntingly and wrote "Dunbar" on his pad. "Why are you limping?" he asked sharply as Yossarian moved to the door. "And what the devil is that bandage doing on your leg? Are you mad or something?"

"I was wounded in the leg. That's what I'm in the hospital for."

"Oh, no, you're not," gloated Major Sanderson maliciously. "You're in the hospital for a stone in your salivary gland. So you're not so smart after all, are you? You don't even know what you're in the hospital for."

"I'm in the hospital for a wounded leg," Yossarian insisted.

Major Sanderson ignored his argument with a sarcastic laugh. "Well, give my regards to your friend Dunbar. And you will tell him to dream that dream for me, won't you?"

But Dunbar had nausea and dizziness with his constant headache and was not inclined to co-operate with Major Sanderson. Hungry Joe had nightmares because he had finished sixty missions and was waiting again to go home, but he was unwilling to share any when he came to the hospital to visit.

"Hasn't anyone got any dreams for Major Sanderson?" Yossarian asked. "I hate to disappoint him. He feels so rejected already."

"I've been having a very peculiar dream ever since I learned you were wounded," confessed the chaplain. "I used to dream every night that my wife was dying or being murdered or that my children were choking to death on morsels of nutritious food. Now I dream that I'm out swimming in water over my head and a shark is eating my left leg in exactly the same place where you have your bandage."

"That's a wonderful dream," Dunbar declared. "I bet Major Sanderson will love it."

"That's a horrible dream!" Major Sanderson cried. "It's filled with pain and mutilation and death. I'm sure you had it just to spite me. You know, I'm not even sure you belong in the Army, with a disgusting dream like that."

Yossarian thought he spied a ray of hope. "Perhaps you're right, sir," he suggested slyly. "Perhaps I ought to be grounded and returned to the States."

"Hasn't it ever occurred to you that in your promiscuous pursuit of women you are merely trying to assuage your subconscious fears of sexual impotence?"

"Yes, sir, it has."

"Then why do you do it?"

"To assuage my fears of sexual impotence."

"Why don't you get yourself a good hobby instead?" Major Sanderson inquired with friendly interest. "Like fishing. Do you really find Nurse Duckett so attractive? I should think she was rather bony. Rather bland and bony, you know. Like a fish."

"I hardly know Nurse Duckett."

"Then why did you grab her by the bosom? Merely because she has one?"

"Dunbar did that."

"Oh, don't start that again," Major Sanderson exclaimed with vitriolic scorn, and hurled down his pencil disgustedly. "Do you really think that you can absolve yourself of guilt by pretending to be someone else? I don't like you, Fortiori. Do you know that? I don't like you at all."

Yossarian felt a cold, damp wind of apprehension blow over him. "I'm not Fortiori, sir," he said timidly. "I'm Yossarian."

"You're who?"

"My name is Yossarian, sir. And I'm in the hospital with a wounded leg."

"Your name is Fortiori," Major Sanderson contradicted him belligerently. "And you're in the hospital for a stone in your salivary gland."

"Oh, come on, Major!" Yossarian exploded. "I ought to know who I am."

"And I've got an official Army record here to prove it," Major Sanderson retorted. "You'd better get a grip on yourself before it's too late. First you're Dunbar. Now you're Yossarian. The next thing you know you'll be claiming you're Washington Irving. Do you know what's wrong with you? You've got a split personality, that's what's wrong with you."

"Perhaps you're right, sir," Yossarian agreed diplomatically.

"I know I'm right. You've got a bad persecution complex. You think people are trying to harm you."

"People *are* trying to harm me."

"You see? You have no respect for excessive authority or obsolete traditions. You're dangerous and depraved, and you ought to be taken outside and shot!"

"Are you serious?"

"You're an enemy of the people!"

"Are you nuts?" Yossarian shouted.

"No, I'm not nuts," Dobbs roared furiously back in the ward, in what he imagined was a furtive whisper. "Hungry Joe saw them, I tell you. He saw them yesterday when he flew to Naples to pick up some black-market air conditioners for Colonel Cathcart's farm. They've got a big replacement center there and it's filled with hundreds of pilots, bombardiers and gunners on the way home. They've got forty-five missions, that's all. A few with Purple Hearts have even less. Replacement crews are pouring in from the States into the other bomber groups. They want everyone to serve overseas at least once, even administrative personnel. Don't you read the papers? We've got to kill him now!"

"You've got only two more missions to fly," Yossarian reasoned with him in a low voice. "Why take a chance?"

"I can get killed flying them, too," Dobbs answered pugnaciously in his rough, quavering, overwrought voice. "We can kill him the first thing tomorrow morning when he drives back from his farm. I've got the gun right here."

Yossarian goggled with amazement as Dobbs pulled a gun out of his pocket and displayed it high in the air. "Are you crazy?" he hissed frantically. "Put it away. And keep your idiot voice down."

"What are you worried about?" Dobbs asked with offended innocence. "No one can hear us."

"Hey, knock it off down there," a voice rang out from the far end of the ward. "Can't you see we're trying to nap?"

"What the hell are you, a wise guy?" Dobbs yelled back and spun around with clenched fists, ready to fight. He whirled back to Yossarian and, before he could speak, sneezed thunderously six times, staggering sideways on rubbery legs in the intervals and raising his elbows ineffectively to fend each seizure off. The lids of his watery eyes were puffy and inflamed. "Who does he think," he demanded, sniffing spasmodically and wiping his nose with the back of his sturdy wrist, "he is, a cop or something?"

"He's a C.I.D. man," Yossarian notified him tranquilly. "We've got three here now and more on the way. Oh, don't be scared. They're after a forger named Washington Irving. They're not interested in murderers."

"Murderers?" Dobbs was affronted. "Why do you call us murderers? Just because we're going to murder Colonel Cathcart?"

"Be quiet, damn you!" directed Yossarian. "Can't you whisper?"

"I am whispering. I—"

"You're still shouting."

"No, I'm not. I—"

"Hey, shut up down there, will you?" patients all over the ward began hollering at Dobbs.

"I'll fight you all!" Dobbs screamed back at them, and stood up on a rickety wooden chair, waving the gun wildly. Yossarian caught his arm and yanked him down. Dobbs began sneezing again. "I have an allergy," he apologized when he had finished, his nostrils running and his eyes streaming with tears.

"That's too bad. You'd make a great leader of men without it."

"Colonel Cathcart's the murderer," Dobbs complained hoarsely when he had shoved away a soiled, crumpled khaki handkerchief. "Colonel Cathcart's the one who's going to murder us all if we don't do something to stop him."

"Maybe he won't raise the missions any more. Maybe sixty is as high as he'll go."

"He always raises the missions. You know that better than I do." Dobbs swallowed and bent his intense face very close to Yossarian's, the muscles in his bronze, rock-like jaw bunching up into quivering knots. "Just say it's okay and I'll do the whole thing tomorrow morning. Do you understand what I'm telling you? I'm whispering now, ain't I?"

Yossarian tore his eyes away from the gaze of burning entreaty Dobbs had fastened on him. "Why the goddam hell don't you just go out and do it?" he protested. "Why don't you stop talking to me about it and do it alone?"

"I'm afraid to do it alone. I'm afraid to do anything alone."

"Then leave me out of it. I'd have to be crazy to get mixed up in something like this now. I've got a million-dollar leg wound here. They're going to send me home."

"Are you crazy?" Dobbs exclaimed in disbelief. "All you've got there is a scratch. He'll have you back flying combat missions the day you come out, Purple Heart and all."

"Then I really will kill him," Yossarian vowed. "I'll come looking for you and we'll do it together."

"Then let's do it tomorrow while we've still got the chance," Dobbs pleaded. "The chaplain says he's volunteered the group for Avignon again. I may be killed before you get out. Look how these hands of mine shake. I can't fly a plane. I'm not good enough."

Yossarian was afraid to say yes. "I want to wait and see what happens first."

"The trouble with you is that you just won't do anything," Dobbs complained in a thick, infuriated voice.

"I'm doing everything I possibly can," the chaplain explained softly to Yossarian after Dobbs had departed. "I even went to the medical tent to speak to Doc Daneeka about helping you."

"Yes, I can see." Yossarian suppressed a smile. "What happened?"

"They painted my gums purple," the chaplain replied sheepishly.

"They painted his toes purple, too," Nately added in outrage. "And then they gave him a laxative."

"But I went back again this morning to see him."

"And they painted his gums purple again," said Nately.

"But I did get to speak to him," the chaplain argued in a plaintive tone of self-justification. "Doctor Daneeka seems like such an unhappy man. He suspects that someone is plotting to transfer him to the Pacific Ocean. All this time he's been thinking of coming to *me* for help. When I told him I needed *his* help, he wondered if there wasn't a chaplain *I* couldn't go see." The chaplain waited in patient dejection when Yossarian and Dunbar both broke into laughter. "I used to think it was immoral to be unhappy," he continued, as though keening aloud in solitude. "Now I don't know what to think any more. I'd like to make the subject of immorality the basis of my sermon this Sunday, but I'm not sure I ought to give any sermon at all with these purple gums. Colonel Korn was very displeased with them."

"Chaplain, why don't you come into the hospital with

us for a while and take it easy?" Yossarian invited. "You could be very comfortable here."

The brash iniquity of the proposal tempted and amused the chaplain for a second or two. "No, I don't think so," he decided reluctantly. "I want to arrange for a trip to the mainland to see a mail clerk named Wintergreen. Doctor Daneeka told me he could help."

"Wintergreen is probably the most influential man in the whole theater of operations. He's not only a mail clerk, but he has access to a mimeograph machine. But he won't help anybody. That's one of the reasons he'll go far."

"I'd like to speak to him anyway. There must be somebody who will help you."

"Do it for Dunbar, Chaplain," Yossarian corrected with a superior air. "I've got this million-dollar leg wound that will take me out of combat. If that doesn't do it, there's a psychiatrist who thinks I'm not good enough to be in the Army."

"I'm the one who isn't good enough to be in the Army," Dunbar whined jealously. "It was my dream."

"It's not the dream, Dunbar," Yossarian explained. "He likes your dream. It's my personality. He thinks it's split."

"It's split right down the middle," said Major Sanderson, who had laced his lumpy GI shoes for the occasion and had slicked his charcoal-dull hair down with some stiffening and redolent tonic. He smiled ostentatiously to show himself reasonable and nice. "I'm not saying that to be cruel and insulting," he continued with cruel and insulting delight. "I'm not saying it because I hate you and want revenge. I'm not saying it because you rejected me and hurt my feelings terribly. No, I'm a man of medicine and I'm being coldly objective. I have very bad news for you. Are you man enough to take it?"

"God, no!" screamed Yossarian. "I'll go right to pieces."

Major Sanderson flew instantly into a rage. "Can't you even do one thing right?" he pleaded, turning beet-red with vexation and crashing the sides of both fists down upon his desk together. "The trouble with you is that you think you're too good for all the conventions of society. You probably think you're too good for me too, just because I arrived at puberty late. Well, do you know what you are? You're a frustrated, unhappy, disillusioned, undisciplined, maladjusted young man!" Major Sanderson's disposition seemed to mellow as he reeled off the uncomplimentary adjectives.

"Yes, sir," Yossarian agreed carefully. "I guess you're right."

"Of course I'm right. You're immature. You've been unable to adjust to the idea of war."

"Yes, sir."

"You have a morbid aversion to dying. You probably resent the fact that you're at war and might get your head blown off any second."

"I more than resent it, sir. I'm absolutely incensed."

"You have deep-seated survival anxieties. And you don't like bigots, bullies, snobs or hypocrites. Subconsciously there are many people you hate."

"Consciously, sir, consciously," Yossarian corrected in an effort to help. "I hate them consciously."

"You're antagonistic to the idea of being robbed, exploited, degraded, humiliated or deceived. Misery depresses you. Ignorance depresses you. Persecution depresses you. Violence depresses you. Slums depress you. Greed depresses you. Crime depresses you. Corruption depresses you. You know, it wouldn't surprise me if you're a manic-depressive!"

"Yes, sir. Perhaps I am."

"Don't try to deny it."

"I'm not denying it, sir," said Yossarian, pleased with the miraculous rapport that finally existed between them. "I agree with all you've said."

"Then you admit you're crazy, do you?"

"Crazy?" Yossarian was shocked. "What are you talking about? Why am I crazy? You're the one who's crazy!"

Major Sanderson turned red with indignation again and crashed both fists down upon his thighs. "Calling me crazy," he shouted in a sputtering rage, "is a typically sadistic and vindictive paranoiac reaction! You really are crazy!"

"Then why don't you send me home?"

"And I'm going to send you home!"

"They're going to send me home!" Yossarian announced jubilantly, as he hobbled back into the ward.

"Me too!" A. Fortiori rejoiced. "They just came to my ward and told me."

"What about me?" Dunbar demanded petulantly of the doctors.

"You?" they replied with asperity. "You're going with Yossarian. Right back into combat!"

And back into combat they both went. Yossarian was enraged when the ambulance returned him to the squadron, and he went limping for justice to Doc Daneeka, who glared at him glumly with misery and disdain.

"You!" Doc Daneeka examined mournfully with accusing disgust, the egg-shaped pouches under both eyes firm and censorious. "All you ever think of is yourself. Go take a look at the bomb line if you want to see what's been happening since you went to the hospital."

Yossarian was startled. "Are we losing?"

"Losing?" Doc Daneeka cried. "The whole military situation has been going to hell ever since we captured Paris. I knew it would happen." He paused, his sulking ire turning to melancholy, and frowned irritably as though it were all Yossarian's fault. "American troops are pushing into German soil. The Russians have captured back all of Romania. Only yesterday the Greeks in the Eighth Army captured Rimini. The Germans are on the defensive everywhere!" Doc Daneeka paused again and fortified himself with a huge breath for a piercing ejaculation of grief. "There's no more Luftwaffe left!" he wailed. He seemed ready to burst into tears. "The whole Gothic line is in danger of collapsing!"

"So?" asked Yossarian. "What's wrong?"

"What's wrong?" Doc Daneeka cried. "If something doesn't happen soon, Germany may surrender. And then we'll all be sent to the Pacific!"

Yossarian gawked at Doc Daneeka in grotesque dismay. "Are you crazy? Do you know what you're saying?"

"Yeah, it's easy for to laugh," Doc Daneeka sneered.

"Who the hell is laughing?"

"At least you've got a chance. You're in combat and might get killed. But what about me? I've got nothing to hope for."

"You're out of your goddam head!" Yossarian shouted at him emphatically, seizing him by the shirt front.

"Do you know that? Now keep your stupid mouth shut and listen to me."

Doc Daneeka wrenched himself away. "Don't you dare talk to me like that. I'm a licensed physician."

"Then keep your stupid licensed physician's mouth shut and listen to what they told me up at the hospital. I'm crazy. Did you know that?"

"So?"

"Really crazy."

"So?"

"I'm nuts. Cuckoo. Don't you understand? I'm off my rocker. They sent someone else home in my place by mistake. They've got a licensed psychiatrist up at the hospital who examined me, and that was his verdict. I'm really insane."

"So?"

"So?" Yossarian was puzzled by Doc Daneeka's inability to comprehend. "Don't you see what that means? Now you can take me off combat duty and send me home. They're not going to send a crazy man out to be killed, are they?"

"Who else will go?"

PETER DE VRIES
from *The Blood of the Lamb* (1961)

The humor of Peter De Vries, which has darkened perceptibly over the years, here reaches it blackest hue. The circumstances are, of course, mitigating. The hero of *The Blood of the Lamb*, Don Wanderhope, has all alone nursed his only daughter through a long, discouraging onslaught of leukemia, which recedes just before the painful crash, here. All the same, two points seem worth our attention: first, the presence of wit and slapstick even at this moment, the kind of moment normally played quite straight, even by the greatest masters of literature; second, Black Humor is a mood, not a literary "school," a mood, as I have tried to say elsewhere, which we all share, on whatever level. In De Vries's case that black mood has been present in all of his work, even in *The Tunnel of Love*, hidden, or so it seems from most of the reviewers. Now it begins to predominate in novels like *Reuben, Reuben* and *Let Me Count the Ways*, and especially here, in a moment of great anguish and yet great farce, in *The Blood of the Lamb*.

Soldiers going into battle or embarking on missions of peril often reckon up their chances of coming out alive on the basis of odds that there is always some mathematician around to supply. Say twenty to one. Of this game there is a further refinement. Does luck in having emerged whole from previous dangers proportionately reduce the chances of doing so again? No, say the computers, the chances are the same each time: twenty to one.

Similarly does sickness make statisticians of us all, invokers of the laws of probability. When a relapsing marrow indicated that resistance had arisen to the first drug, and the beast after six months in chains was again abroad, the successor known as Methotrexate was hurled into the breach. It too had a fifty-fifty chance of being both effective and tolerable. Did luck with the 6-MP halve our odds on being lucky again? No, the average was the same. Indeed, the fact that the one drug worked indicated the second might.

The rise of the morbid cells in the marrow, which had gone from twenty per cent to forty to fifty, was checked, slowly reversed—thirty per cent, fifteen, five, till at last a normal marrow was drawn from that breast bone to which the healers so remorselessly helped themselves. "We're back in business again," said Dr. Scoville, turning his old-boy smile on me like a revolving lighthouse beacon. Then he ran to catch a plane for London.

That spring my father died, and when I flew to Chicago I took Carol with me, not because I thought children should attend funerals, but in order not to spend a day away from her.

I loitered a moment among the nearby graves. Doc Berkenbosch was there now in that colony of the dead Dutch, as was old Reverend Van Scoyen, who had performed so well over Louie's deathbed—and of course Louie. On my mother's headstone were chiseled the words, "Awaiting the resurrection of Our Lord." Your husband never saw your grave, *Moeke*; he was too steeped in melancholy to mourn you at the time, and we never brought him down for the funeral. *Melancholie*, as your ancestral tongue has it. Here is a branch of early lilac, and for you I always liked the old Dutch word for long-suffering: *lankmoedig*. I drop it on your grave like a sprig of fadeless syllables. That reminds me of a bright saying of your granddaughter's. She once wrote a theme for school which had to be a character sketch of some member of the family, and hers began, "My long, suffering father . . ." Of course that was long ago and she laughs at it now, as she did at Andy Biddle's story of the Hollywood secretary whose typescript of a dictated story synopsis began, "This is a swash, buckling story . . ."

Vaarwel, lankmoedig moeder, vaarwell. Melancholiek vader,

vaarwel. I leave you to the first flowers, and the tender stars of May.

One evening from the television room to which Carol had wandered in her nightgown with an orange on a plate, I began to hear a voice in a documentary: ". . . all medical science can to conquer it. The most fruitful source of study, and the best variation of the disease in which to try out certain new remedies, is that form in which it cruises in the bloodstreams of children under the name . . ." My mind spun helplessly like a wheel in a rut. Sick with horror, I strolled in and stood over her, bending down to help myself to an orange slice from the plate in her lap as on the TV screen a boy was put through familiar clinical tests for the instruction of the public. I should not have been surprised to see Dr. Scoville amble in. Were all my efforts to keep the truth from her, never to mention the name, the ceaseless censorship of word and tone, the hoarding of our secret from friends and neighbors, to collapse under this brutal mischance? "Lots of kids are worse off than you," I observed, striking a negligent pose against the wall. I patted my coat pockets. "Keep that, I want to get my pipe."

I shot on tiptoe to the kitchen, where I called Omar Howard. "Call Carol back. I'll explain later. Don't tell her I did this, but *call her back instantly and keep her on the telephone as long as you can.*"

"I understand, Mr. Wanderhope," said the young scholar, who was probably watching the same program. I think Omar knew.

Keeping the pre-teen-ager on the phone for an hour was no trick at all in view of the recent birthday presents she had to report. She had gotten a new bicycle, half a dozen dresses, three pairs of shoes, two new leotards for ballet school, a crate of storybooks, assorted jewelry, a kitten, what would probably be her last doll, since she was now twelve, and a tape recorder costing two hundred dollars. It had been Mrs. Brodhag who had reined the madman in. "For God's sake, Mr. Wanderhope, she'll surely get suspicious. Now don't buy her any more. In fact, take the tape recorder back, or say it's for yourself, which it is anyway. And while I'm at it, don't be so obvious about getting her piano pieces on it."

I was sitting in the television room when Carol returned, carrying the kitten. She hadn't much to say, or did I fancy that? There was a variety show on now anyway, on which a guest comedian was going strong.

Straight man: "Lew, your comedy is too primitive. Times have changed. People don't want that belly laugh and pratfall stuff any more, they want adult, *intellectual* amusement. The inward chuckle, the smile of appreciation."

Comedian: "Rolling 'em in the aisles is good enough for me."

"You missed a good program," I said.

She looked down at her plate, to which she had returned an uneaten segment of orange. "My gums sting again," she said.

"Well, fine! That's what we want. Just enough soreness to show the medicine is taking effect, like last time."

"I think I'll go to bed. Come on, kitty."

The nobility, the reticence and dignity of that royal child cannot always be reported of the father. Dead-drunk and cold-sober, he wandered out to the garden in the cool of the evening, awaiting the coming of the Lord. No such advent taking place, he shook his fist at the sky and cried, "If you won't save her from pain, at least let me keep her from fear!" A brown thrush began his evening note, the ever favored, unendurable woodsong. I snatched up a rock from the ground and stoned it from the tree.

Fear of leaving her to brood both on what she may have heard and on my absence, I went back into the house and to her bedroom. Each entrance there held its fear that a languid child would be found stretched out upon the bedclothes. I was glad to see her sitting up against the pillow, reading a book and stroking the puss for whom no name had as yet been found.

"Who's going to have a cup of cocoa with a man?"

She raised her eyes from the book. She put it aside. "O.K.," she said, getting up and into her pink robe.

Fixing the hot chocolate in the kitchen, I was happy to hear the piano begin in the parlor. It was a Chopin *Nocturne*, high among the pieces she had polished to perfection. Anxious to get it on tape, I stooped as unobtrusively as I could, after setting her cocoa on the piano, to switch on the nearby recorder. She glanced down at it and went on playing. I nodded to the cocoa steaming on a stack of sheet music, before wandering off to a chair.

After three months she reported headaches and trouble with her eyes. Here was noted also an increase in Dr. Scoville's charm. The slight complication was meningeal. "The disease can be kept at bay in the system while proliferating in the meninges, where for some reason the drug doesn't penetrate," he explained. "Why, we'll just leave her here in the hospital and take a spinal tap and see." The specimen extracted showed the ailment to be swirling richly in that sanctuary, into which massive doses of the Methotrexate had now to be injected directly.

So we were back in the Children's Pavilion, and there was again the familiar scene: the mothers with their nearly dead, the false face of mercy, the Slaughter of the Innocents. A girl with one leg came unsteadily down the hall between crutches, skillfully encouraged by nurses. Through the pane in a closed door a boy could be seen sitting up in bed, bleeding from everything in his head; a priest lounged alertly against the wall, ready to move in closer. In the next room a boy of five was having Methotrexate pumped into his skull, or, more accurately, was watching a group of mechanics gathered solemnly around the stalled machine. In the next a baby was sitting up watching a television set on which a panel show was in progress. Three experts were discussing the state of the contemporary theater. I paused in the doorway to listen. "I think writers like Tennessee Williams exaggerate the ugly side of life, the seamy side, it seems to me," observed a well-dressed female participant. "I fail to see what purpose is gained by that." A mother keeping watch at the next crib rose from her chair and turned the dial. There was a squawk of protest from the baby, who was evidently fascinated by the speaker's hat or the tone of her voice, or something else about the program, and the woman quickly tuned it back, making a comic face at me.

Among the parents and children, flung together in a hell of prolonged farewell, wandered forever the ministering vampires from Laboratory, sucking samples from bones and veins to see how went with each the enemy that had marked them all. And the doctors in their butchers' coats, who severed the limbs and gouged the brains and knifed the vitals where the demon variously dwelt, what did they think of these best fruits of ten million hours of dedicated toil? They hounded the culprit from organ to organ and joint to joint till nothing remained over which to practice their art: the art of prolonging sickness. Yet medicine had its own old aphorism: "Life is a fatal disease."

I rejoined in time the endless promenade of visitors pushing their treasures in wheel chairs. Among these was a beatnik adolescent trundling his younger sister. They were both very gay; one knew from their manner that she was going home soon. The youth was dressed in jeans and a black sweater. The beard was no doubt intended to be Bohemian but recalled, instead, the traditional figure of the hayseed. The pleasant spirit given off by their companionship made us join them, wheeling along side by side, up and down, back and forth, until some countertraffic forced us to break ranks. In one of these oncoming chairs was black-eyed Rachel Stein, propelled by her mother. The two girls instantly renewed the friendship begun the first time in, and it was obvious that they preferred now to be left together in the recreation room, where in any case a birthday party for another patient was in full swing. Mrs. Stein excused herself to dart after a disappearing doctor, and I looked around for Stein. As I neared the main lounge I heard voices raised in argument.

"These people who want to tell God how to run the universe," a man with a brick-red neck was saying, "they remind me of those people with five shares in some corporation who take up the entire stockholders' meeting telling the directors how to run their business."

I might have guessed who the object of the dressing down would be. Stein stood cornered behind the telephone booth, a carton of coffee in one hand and a smile on his face, obviously enjoying himself enormously. This was what he liked, proof of idiocy among the Positive Thinkers.

"I suppose you're going to tell me next I never met a payroll," he said, throwing me only the faintest sign of greeting so as not to interrupt the debate. Several visitors, mostly parents in various stages of vigil and dishevelment, listened or chimed in.

"You ought to be ashamed," a woman in an Easter bonnet told Stein. "Your race gave us our religion. It's a good thing the ancient prophets weren't like you or we wouldn't have any." Stein drank from his carton and waited; she had not yet delivered herself into his hands. "From ancient polytheism, the belief in lots of gods," the woman continued a little more eruditely, "the Hebrew nation led us on to the idea that there is only one."

"Which is just a step from the truth," said Stein, and dropped his carton into a wastebasket.

The woman began to show anger, squirming a bit on her leather chair. "We with our finite . . ."

"What baffles me is the comfort people find in the idea that somebody dealt this mess. Blind and meaningless chance seems to me so much more congenial—or at least less horrible. Prove to me that there is a God and I will really begin to despair."

"It comes down to submitting to a wisdom greater than ours," said the man who had been attempting to focus the problem in terms of a stockholders' meeting. "A plan of which we can no more grasp the whole than a leaf can the forest of which it is a rustling part, or a grain of sand the seashore. What do you think when you look up at the stars at night?"

"I don't. I have enough to occupy me here."

"The Lord giveth and the Lord taketh away. What do you think of that?"

"I think it's a hell of a way to run a railroad."

"You ought to be ashamed!" the woman repeated with a further rise in spirit, not noticing a four-year-old patient watching the argument from a tricycle in the doorway. "Have you ever read your Bible?"

I nearly laughed. Where did she think he had got his pessimism? On what had he nurtured his despair if not on "Vanity of vanities," "All flesh is grass," "My tears have been my meat day and night," and "Is there no balm in Gilead; is there no physician there?"

Stein left his persecutors to join me in the hall, sending little Johnny Heard off on his tricycle with a pat on the head. We stood a moment comparing notes. Rachel was in for the very same thing as Carol, after all these months of solid remission on Methotrexate and the 6-MP still to go. We sought out the girls in the recreation room, where they were getting on beautifully together. They didn't want any part of us. "How about a drink?" Stein proposed.

In my present need Stein might seem the last company I ought to seek. Yet in another sense he was precisely what I wanted at my side, the Devil's advocate off whom to bounce my speculations, the rock against which to hurl my yearnings and my thoughts, to test and prove them truly, an office that mealy-mouthed piety could not have performed. He was the goalkeeper past whom I must get my puck.

"There is so much we don't know," I said, walking down the street, we resumed the debate where we had left off last time. "Newton knew it, who told us so much we do know. We play like children on the shore—out there is the measureless sea. How do you explain—well, a thing like what happened on the road to Damascus?"

"Do I have to explain every case of hysterical blindness? How do we know it happened, anyway? It's related only in the Acts, which Luke wrote. Paul himself never mentions it, and him a man who talked about himself at the drop of a hat."

"He said Christ was revealed to him, as to a child born untimely. That may be what he's referring to. I think it's in Corinthians. And there's the incident of the viper and the fire."

"I'm told Orientals walk barefoot across hot coals with no ill effects."

"So such things happen." Something made me look up. I saw, her arms spread along the parapet of the second-story roof from which the mice were visible, the woman with the Easter bonnet, gazing up into the dirty spring evening. "Do you believe any of the miracles attributed to Christ?" I said quickly, perhaps because I had looked just in time to see her brush her eye, under the cheap pink veil.

Stein gave his snort, this time somewhat more finely shaded than usual. He jerked his head back toward the hospital. "Who do you expect to see take up his bed and walk in there?"

As we strolled along, for all the world like friends out taking the evening air rather than two men wringing each other's hearts like empty dishrags, we encountered a phenomenon that under the circumstances could hardly be ignored. A street-corner evangelist was hurling plangent metaphors rapidly into space.

"Would you like to call Heaven tonight? You can reverse the charges, you know. Oh, yes, brother, reverse the charges." He swung from his audience, a girl with a jump rope and a Chinese laundryman pausing in the gutter with his push-cart to eat a candy bar, toward us as we approached. "Oh, yes, brother, reverse the charges. *He'll* accept them. He's paid for your call with the ultimate price—His Son Jesus Christ! It's all paid for, all on the house, all for free! Just pick up the phone and tell the operator—that's the Holy Ghost, you know—'Get me Heaven, please. Put me through to God Almighty!' "

We shuffled on in silence. Stein had the grace not to smile at the ally I had picked up along the way. I observed after a moment:

"Someone has pointed out that nothing proves the validity of the Church so much as its ability to survive its own representatives. It's got to be divine to stand up against them."

"I have never been convinced by that argument—it's from one of the witty Catholics, isn't it? You might as well say it about the Ku Klux Klan."

"That's no analogy. In that case the members are no worse than the principles. In this, the principle is always supremely there for us to match up to or fall short of."

Stein shrugged and gave a grunt. I felt I had gotten past the goalkeeper and scored a point. We were passing a pushcart vendor selling sprigs of dogwood. I had brought plenty of that from the country this morning. I asked Stein, after another silence, whether he had ever heard the legend that the Cross had been made of dogwood and that supposedly explained the cross shaped vaguely into the grain of its heartwood, like that on the back of the Sardinian donkey for its having borne Our Lord into Jerusalem on his triumphal day. Stein said that he had never heard either of those things.

In the bar, I chided Stein for what he had said to the woman in the Easter hat, on the ground that Westminster Hospital was no place to pull rugs out from under mothers. He agreed, with the assurance that he never did that to mothers, or even to men unless they could take it, but informed me that the woman in this case was not the mother but an aunt—the mother was on another floor in the same hospital, having a malignancy edited from her foot. This brought Stein perilously close to his role of clown, and I could feel my shoulders threaten to shake in preparation for the only response possible to this eager trowel work with the Absurd. It didn't take much.

"Was the man who talked about stockholders' meetings the father?"

"No," said Stein, as though he had been waiting for me to ask that question, "the father is in a mental institution."

Stein watched me until my sobs of laughter had subsided, smiling uneasily as I gasped, "Have you no heart, man?" and brushing cigarette ashes from his horrible green sleeve.

Wiping my eyes, I asked whether he didn't think even aunts deserved to have their belief that those who mourned would be comforted, safeguarded from the scourge of intellect. Here I sensed a quiver of indignation as he launched a review of the Beatitudes aimed at finding one—"just one"— that held water when examined squarely in the light of reality. The poor in spirit would have to imagine for themselves any kingdom of heaven, as the pure in heart would any God for themselves; the merciful obtained no more mercy than the cruel; the meek would have to inherit anything they ever got, and so on. There was, however, one Beatitude with which one need not quarrel—could I guess which it was? It was not one of the official nine, having been delivered separately on the road to Calvary. I gave up. " 'Blessed are the wombs that never bare, and the paps that never gave suck,' " Stein said. "Could this be the Son of Man preparing himself for those final words against the black sky, the last, cosmic turn of the wheel of agony, the hoax at last seen through: 'My God, my God, why hast thou forsaken me?' "

"You mean you're not *sure*? Why, man, that's great! For the rest of us, who like to hug that little doubt we so desperately need today—what faith was to folk of another time—the ray of hope. Oh, how grateful we are for that uncertainty! Our salvation almost. Go thy way, thy doubt hath made thee whole. Bartender, two more!"

My spirits began to rise—genuinely, not in another spasm of unstable mirth. From nowhere, I had suddenly that conviction that we would beat the rap, that Carol and Rachel would be among those who were around when the Drug came. *Some* would; why not they? My mood continued to ascend. The wall-motto moralists quite rightly call bottom the place from which there is nowhere to go but up, the floor against which the swimmer kicks himself lightly toward the surface once again.

As we left the tavern, I remarked, "Well, we could go on arguing for hours, I suppose. As man has in fact for centuries about these things. There's as much to be said for one side as for the other. Fifty-fifty."

"Not quite. One charge can be brought against your point of view that can't against mine: wishful thinking. Believers believe what they want to believe. I would like to believe it, too, but deny that an honest man can. Unbelief is to that extent less suspect than faith."

We trudged along a moment longer, during which I debated with myself whether to say what I was thinking. I spoke up.

"One doubts that you don't enjoy thinking or saying what you do, at least a little, Stein. The side of man that loves to hate, to rub in the horrible, even revel in it. Psychiatrists have even got a name for it, I think. Algolagnia, or something like that."

We passed in due course the church of St. Catherine, from which a pair of people were contentedly emerging after their evening devotionals. Here a vibration of anger escaped Stein that was not put into words, but that I felt had given me a flash of illumination into his spirit—something that might even be held to confirm the theory of my friend to which I had been needled into giving audible expression. Stein resented the sedative power of religion, or rather the repose available to those blissfully ignorant that the medicament was a fictitious blank. In this exile from peace of mind to which his reason doomed him, he was like an insomniac driven to awaken sleepers from dreams illegitimately won by going around shouting, "Don't you realize it was a placebo!" Thus it seemed to me that what you were up against in Stein was not logic rampant, but frustrated faith. He could not forgive God for not existing.

When we returned to the Pavilion of Children, Mrs. Stein greeted us in the corridor. "You should see the two of them playing together," she said. "Come look."

We stood in the recreation room doorway. In a pandemonium of television noise, piano music being thumped out by a volunteer as youngsters banged drums and shook tambourines to its rhythm, Rachel and Carol sat side by side at a table, twisting into being paper flowers for children less fortunate. Mrs. Stein had quoted us that bit as we came down the hall with a surprising minimum of rue. "Aren't they just too sweet together?" she beamed in the doorway.

"Lifelong friends," said Stein, who gave, and asked, no quarter.

My conversations with Stein are almost all I am recalling of my relations with other parents because they were vital to my concerns, not because they—and the brief skirmish I overheard in the lounge—were typical of human intercourse there. Far from it. Airing the absolutes is no longer permitted in polite society, save where a Stein and a Wanderhope meet and knock their heads together, but I do not think this is due to apathy or frivolity, or because such pursuits are vain, though one pant for God as the hart after water-brooks. There is another reason why we chatter of this and that while our hearts burn within us.

We live this life by a kind of conspiracy of grace: the common assumption or pretense, that human existence is "good" or "matters" or has "meaning," a glaze of charm or humor by which we conceal from one another and per-haps even ourselves the suspicion that it does not, and our conviction in times of trouble that it is overpriced—some-thing to be endured rather than enjoyed. Nowhere does this function more than in precisely such a slice of hell as a Children's Pavilion, where the basic truths would seem to mock any state of mind other than rage and despair. Rage and despair are indeed carried about in the heart, but privately, to be let out on special occasions, like savage dogs for exercise, occasions in solitude when God is cursed, birds stoned from the trees or the pillow hammered in dark-ness. In the ward lounge itself, a scene in which a changing collection of characters are waiting for a new medicine that might as well be called Godot, the conversation is indistin-guishable from that going on at the moment in the street, a coffee break at the office from which one is absent, or a dinner party to which one could not accept an invitation. Even the exchange of news about their children has often the quality of gossip. An earful of it would be incredible to an uninvolved specatator, not to its principals. Quiet is re-quested for the benefit of the other parents. One holds his peace in obedience to a tacit law as binding as if it were framed on a corridor wall with a police officer on hand to see that it was enforced: "No fuss." This is all perhaps nothing more than the principle of sportsmanship at its highest, given in return for the next man's. Even Stein had it in no small degree, for all his seeming refusal to wish me good hunting in my spiritual quest. Perhaps he was trying to tell me in as nice a way as he could that there was no game in those woods. His grim little jokes on the barricades were in their way part of this call to courage. . . .

One time in that criminal winter, when the lights of Christmas sprouted in a thousand windows and the mercies of Methotrexate were drawing to a close, we went in for our fifth hospitalization. Now we were to have our horizons widened. Anterior bleeding is not so bad, but posterior calls for cauterization, as well as packing, back into the throat. "Oh, Daddy, I can't stand it," said my spattered burden as I carried her from the treatment room back to bed. It is one of the few cries of protest I ever heard from the thoroughbred, of whom I bear true and faithful witness. The stigmata were fresh: the wound in the breast from a new aspiration, the prints in the hands from the intravenous and transfusion needles to which the arms were once again spread as she watched television with a reassembled smile. On the screen were unfolding again a few reels of the dear old clowns. The comic for whom rolling 'em in the aisles had been sufficient was doing the narrating, only this time on the side of the intellectuals.

"You see, Daddy? How they wait for the pie, then take their time wiping it off and all? A ritual. He calls it that too."

Stein and his Rachel were not here this time, but the Great Debate went forward between two voices now scarcely for a moment silent in my brain.

"I ask, my Lord, permission to despair."

"On what grounds?"

"The fairy is now a troll. The spine is gone. She supports herself on her breastbone."

"Do you do as well?"

"Do you exist?"

"If I say yes, it will only be as a voice in your mind. Make me say it then, and be quiet."

"Are God and Herod then one?"

"What do you mean?"

"The Slaughter of the Innocents. Who creates a perfect blossom to crush it? Children dying in this building, mice in the next. It's all the same to Him who marks the sparrow's fall."

"I forgive you."

"I cannot say the same."

I awoke from a doze in the bedside chair that night remembering, for some reason, the occasion a few weeks before when I had taken Carol to the Blood Bank at the school she attended.

Wanderhope was being siphoned by the Red Cross, and she was watching, peeking through the curtain screening off the double line of donors. "Opium den," she said, exaggerating the words so as not to have to speak above a whisper. The conceit amused me no end. I finished out my gift in fantasies of myself and Mrs. Baldridge in the next bed, and the minister's wife next to her, lying in an opium trance, haggard devotees of the fix, lost in debaucheries beyond belief.

Seeing she was asleep, both arms spread to the trailers from the bottles overhead, I stole out to the lounge for a smoke. I had hopes of a drink from the flask I now carried regularly on my person, but I found a three-hundred-pound woman pacing there in a rumpled housedress, a cigarette with a sagging inch of ash hanging from her mouth.

"Boy, dis place," she said. "When me and my little girl come in here, she di'n't have nuttin' but leukemia. Now she's got ammonia." I listened, unbelieving. "Ammonia. Dat's serious. She's in a oxygen tent, and I can't smoke there. It's a tough break for her because, like I say, at first she di'n't have nuttin' but a touch of leukemia. I don't believe I ever heard of dat before. What is it?"

". . . Now have I permission to despair, my Lord?"

"How do you mean?"

"That woman. How ludicrous can grief become?"

"What else?"

"That birthday party in the playroom this afternoon for Johnny Heard. *Leukemic children with funny hats.* How slapstick can tragedy get? Is nobody seeing to the world? Is it run on no principles whatever? The children and next door the rats . . . "

"They are one to the Good Lord, who loves them all." Here a burst of mocking laughter suffices to express its alternative: the Voiceless Void, the bland stupor of eternity.

The Meticorten did only a third as well this time around, but home we went with the marrow only thirty per cent of normal, and a pocketful of a new drug. Glad we were to get out too, because an epidemic of staphylococcus was raging through the ward and half the innocents lay in oxygen tents. Two or three of the more fortunate had died, and the fat woman's girl, too, was released from harm by her pneumonia—the old man's friend, as we used to call it.

We had other blessings to be thankful for. Carol's gold hair began to come out by the handful, proof that the new drug was taking hold, for hair loss was one of its side effects. She was soon balder than her father. I tried to get her outside by suggesting she wear a scarf, without avail. Finally I got her into New York, where she was fitted for a wig—a transformation so perfect that she now willingly bound her head in a kerchief. Pending the next marrow test, we looked for other incidental signs that the drug was taking effect. One was a depressed white count. Carol's went down steadily, though not without its hazards since that left the patient wide open to infection—a delicate point of orchestration. One night I found her lying on the bed on her side, hugging a globe of the world for the pleasure of feeling its cool metal against her skin. I poked a thermometer into her mouth and found she had a temperature of a hundred and two. Dr. Cameron came and dosed her with his broad-spectrum antibiotics, but suggested she go into the hospital anyway for safety's sake.

I walked out past St. Catherine's to the bar and grill and back again so often through so many hospitalizations that I cannot remember which time it was that I stopped in the church on the way back to sit down and rest. I was dead-drunk and stone-sober and bone-tired, my head split and numbed by the plague of voices in eternal disputation. I knew why I was delaying my return to the hospital. The report on the morning's aspiration would be phoned up to the ward from the laboratory any minute, and what I died to learn I dreaded to hear.

I got up and walked to the center aisle, where I stood looking out to the high altar and the soaring windows. I turned around and went to the rear corner, where stood the little shrine to St. Jude, Patron of Lost Causes and Hopeless Cases. Half the candles were burning. I took a taper and lit another. I was alone in the church. The gentle flames wavered and shattered in a mist of tears spilling from my eyes as I sank to the floor.

"I do not ask that she be spared to me, but that her life be spared to her. Or give us a year. We will spend it as we have the last, missing nothing. We will mark the dance of every hour between the snowdrop and the snow: crocus to tulip to violet to iris to rose. We will note not only the azalea's crimson flowers but the red halo that encircles a while the azalea's root when her petals are shed, also the white halo that rings for a week the foot of the old catalpa tree. Later we will prize the chrysanthemums which last so long, almost as long as paper flowers, perhaps because they know in blooming not to bloom. We will seek out the leaves turning in the little-praised bushes and the unadvertised trees. Everyone loves the sweet, neat blossom of the hawthorn in spring, but who lingers over the olive drab of her leaf in autumn? We will. We will note the lost yellows in the tangles of that bush that spills over the Howards' stone wall, the meek hues among which it seems to hesitate before committing itself to red, and next year learn its name. We will seek out these modest subtleties so lost in the blare of oaks and maples, like flutes and woodwinds drowned in brasses and drums. When winter comes, we will let no snow fall ignored. We will again watch the first blizzard from her window like figures locked snug in a glass paperweight. 'Pick one out and follow it to the ground!' she will say again. We will feed the plain birds that stay to cheer us through the winter, and when spring returns we shall be the first out, to catch the snowdrop's first white whisper in the wood. All this we ask, with the remission of our sins, in Christ's name. Amen."

Mrs. Morganthaler was trundling the supper trays to the recreation room when I got back to the ward, for those who could eat there. Carol was asleep in bed. Her arms were spread to the perennial vessels, one white, one red, hanging above the bed. The special nurse rose from her corner chair and whispered that now might be a good time for her to slip out for a bite of supper. I nodded, and she left, carrying her magazine under her arm.

I stood a while over the quietly breathing child. She had her wig off, and now without her hair I could see how perfectly shaped her head was. Child of the pure, unclouded brow . . . The stigmata were more marked than ever, those in the hands dark and numerous from many needles, the wound in the breast fresh under its cotton pad. The short strip of adhesive tape over the cotton bore its usual gold star, given for good behavior and valor under fire.

As I stood there, I sensed the door being quietly opened. Turning, I saw the face of Dr. Romulo, the young Filipino resident, thrust shyly into the room. He beckoned me out into the corridor. He took my arm and led me off a few steps. His face had the solemn expression of one bearing important news.

"We just got the marrow report back," he said, "It's down to six per cent. Practically normal. Carol's in remission."

"The trouble with doubling recipes," said Mrs. Brodhag, "is that some ingredients do a little more than double when you put in twice as much of them. Matter of proportion. Like the fellow says about people being created equal, well, some are more equal than others."

I laughed extendedly at this, watching her complete her handiwork. From the pastry bag she squeezed eight green rosettes around the rim of the cake with meticulous care, then cleaned out the bag thoroughly for the eight red rosettes which were to alternate with them. The field of the frosting was white. Once again she washed out the bag to write, with a blue icing also separately mixed, Carol's name in her flawless Palmer Method. She had been up since dawn.

"See that she gets plenty but the other kids do too," Mrs. Brodhag said as she set the creation in my two hands. "It's not the kind of thing I like to see ice cream glopped on top of, but if that's what they want to do I guess we can't object. And tell her there'll be another ready for her when she comes home, though I don't imagine she has to be told that. Don't lay things on too thick, like I keep telling you."

After parking the car in New York, I picked the boxed cake up carefully from the seat and, pushing the door shut with my knee, carried it down the street. A short distance up ahead I could see Mrs. Morano, the night nurse, turn into the church of St. Catherine for her morning prayers. I shifted the package to one hand in order to open the door. I walked to the front of the church, which had its normal smattering of worshipers. I set the cake down on an empty pew and joined the kneeling figures.

When I rose, Mrs. Morano was standing at the edge of the chancel. We whispered together a moment in greeting as we moved up the aisle.

"You heard about Carol," I said.

"Yes, it's exciting. That's why I'm so sorry about this."

"What?"

"The infection. It's been going through the ward like wildfire. Half of the kids are in oxygen tents."

"Carol?"

She nodded. "They had me phone you this morning, but you'd left. The new drug does depress the white count so terribly, of course, and leave them wide open to infection. It's the old story—you can pick anything up in a hospital."

"Staph?"

"I don't know. They took a blood culture, but it takes a while for the organisms to grow out. They're putting Chloromycetin into her, I think. Maybe you'd better go up."

I hurried into the hospital. One look at Carol and I knew it was time to say good-by. The invading germ, or germs, had not only ravaged her bloodstream by now, but had broken out on her body surface in septicemic discolorations. Her foul enemy had his will of her well at last. One of the blotches covered where they were trying to insert a catheter, and spread down along a thigh. By afternoon it had traveled to the knee, and by the next, gangrened. Dr. Scoville could not have been kinder.

"Someone has ordered another tank of oxygen," he told me that afternoon in the corridor, "but I think you'll agree it won't be necessary. . . . Well, hello there, Randy, you're going home today." Up, up, my head, for the sake of that childhood whom there is none in heaven to love, and none to love on earth so much as you. Up, up! "I've left orders for all the morphine she needs. She'll slip away quietly. She doesn't know us now. It's just as well, because there isn't much in the new drug, if it's any consolation. We have a co-operative study on it, and the remissions are few and brief, and suspect because of the incidence of Meticorten administered with it. We can never be sure it wasn't the Meticorten in this case. It would only have meant another short reprieve—no pardon." He sighed and went his busy way, to the ends of the earth.

I went back into the room. The nurse was taking her blood pressure. "Almost none at all," she whispered. "It's just as well. Only a matter of hours now at the most." The wig was on a globe of the world on the table. The hands were free of needles now, spread out quietly on the counterpane, with their stigmata to which no more would be added. Her breathing slowed, each breath like a caught sob. But once she smiled a little, and, bending closer, I heard her call something to a comrade on another bicycle. They were flying home from school together, down the hill. "All her dreams are pleasant," the nurse murmured. I was thinking of a line of old poetry. "Death loves a shining mark." Now the flower-stem veins were broken, the flower-stalk of the spine destroyed. But through the troll I saw the fairy still, on her flying wheels, the sun in her hair and in the twinkling spokes. I had seen her practicing the piano in her leotard, there were so many things to do and so little time to do them in. I remembered how little labor the sprite had given her mother, so eager was she to be born, so impatient To Be.

The nurse stepped outside a moment, and I moved quickly from the foot of the bed around to the side, whispering rapidly in our moment alone:

"The Lord bless thee, and keep thee: The Lord make his face shine upon thee, and be gracious unto thee; The

Lord lift up his countenance upon thee, and give thee peace."

Then I touched the stigmata one by one: prints of the needles, the wound in the breast that had for so many months now scarcely ever closed. I caressed the perfectly shaped head. I bent to kiss the cheeks, the breasts that would now never be fulfilled, that no youth would ever touch. "Oh, my lamb."

The lips curled in another smile, one whose secret I thought I knew. I recognized it without the aid of the gaze, now sealed forever from mine, with which it had come to me so often throughout her childhood. It was the expression on her face when her homework was going well, the shine of pride at a column of figures mastered or a poem to spring successfully forged. It was the smile of satisfaction worn at the piano when a new composition had been memorized, on her bicycle when, gripping its vanquished horns, she had ridden past me on her first successful solo around the yard. Sometimes, as on that Saturday morning, she would turn the smile shyly toward me, taking added pleasure in my approval.

But this time the experience was not to be shared. She was going alone. Even without the eyes to help communicate it, there was a glow of the most intense concentration on her face, with that wariness of error or shortcoming that had always made it so complete and so characteristic. She had never seemed more alive than now, when she was gathering all the life within her for the proper discharge of whatever this last assignment might have been. Was it a sum of figures or a poem to nature she was undertaking in her dream? Or a difficult, delicate spray of notes, or the first ecstatic journey on the two-wheeler, with the promise of liberty on summer roads unfolding far ahead? I bent again to whisper a question in her ear, but there was no answer—only the most remote sense of flight upon the face. It shone like a star about to burst and, in bursting, yield me all its light at once—could I but bear the gift.

Even her wearied limbs had for the moment this tension, a vibrancy as of a drawn bow. But as the hours wore on, they seemed to slacken, and her features to relax as well. Perhaps the mission had been accomplished, and the hour of rest was at hand. Once, later that afternoon, the smile parted her lips again, this time widely enough to show that her gums were dripping. The enemy was pouring out of every crevice at last. The sight of these royal children pitted against the bestiality had always consumed me with a fury so blind I had had often to turn my face away. Now I was glad Carol could not see me standing there, alone, at last, on holy ground.

She went her way in the middle of the afternoon, borne from the dull watchers on a wave that broke and crashed beyond our sight. In that fathomless and timeless silence one does look rather wildly about for a clock, in a last attempt to fix the lost spirit in time. I had guessed what the hands would say. Three o'clock. The children were putting their schoolbooks away, and getting ready to go home.

After some legal formalities I went into the room once more to say good-by. I had once read a book in which the hero had complained, in a similar farewell taken of a woman, that it was like saying good-by to a statue. I wished it were so now. She looked finally like some mangled flower, or like a bird that had been pelted to earth in a storm. I knew that under the sheet she would look as though she had been clubbed to death. As for the dignity of man, this one drew forth a square of cloth, and, after honking like a goose, pocketed his tears.

The bartender had finished cleaning up after some last late lunchers and was polishing the glasses for the evening's trade. After I'd had six or seven drinks, he said to me, "No more. That must be the tenth muddler you've snapped in two." Perhaps he was hearing the voices too . . .

Passing the church of St. Catherine on the way to the car, I suddenly remembered the cake. I went inside, out of curiosity. It was still there on the pew, undisturbed. I picked it up and started out with it. An incoming worshiper took frowning note of my unsteady career through the lobby door.

Outside, I paused on the sidewalk, one foot on the bottom step. I turned and looked up at the Figure still hanging as ever over the central doorway, its arms outspread among the sooted stones and strutting doves.

I took the cake out of the box and balanced it a moment

on the palm of my hand. Disturbed by something in the motion, the birds started from their covert and flapped away across the street. Then my arm drew back and let fly with all the strength within me. Before the mind snaps, or the heart breaks, it gathers itself like a clock about to strike. It might even be said one pulls himself together to disintegrate. The scattered particles of self—love, wood thrush calling, homework sums, broken nerves, rag dolls, one Phi Beta Kappa key, gold stars, lamplight smiles, night cries, and the shambles of contemplation—are collected for a split moment like scraps of shrapnel before they explode.

It was miracle enough that the pastry should reach its target at all, at that height from the sidewalk. The more so that it should land squarely, just beneath the crown of thorns. Then through scalded eyes I seemed to see the hands free themselves of the nails and move slowly toward the soiled face. Very slowly, very deliberately, with infinite patience, the icing was wiped from the eyes and flung away. I could see it fall in clumps to the porch steps. Then the cheeks were wiped down with the same sense of grave and gentle ritual, with all the kind sobriety of one whose voice could be heard saying, "Suffer the little children to come unto me . . . for of such is the kingdom of heaven."

Then the scene dissolved itself in a mist in which my legs could no longer support their weight, and I sank down to the steps. I sat on its worn stones, to rest a moment before going on. Thus Wanderhope was found at that place which for the diabolists of his literary youth, and for those with more modest spiritual histories too, was said to be the only alternative to the muzzle of a pistol: the foot of the Cross.

BRUCE JAY FRIEDMAN
from *Stern* (1962)

Friedman is among the gentler Black Humorists; compared with Sebastian Dangerfield, for example, Stern is a virtual corporation man. Yet both are moved by the same vision. One day Stern's wife, Fabiola, is pushed by a rednecked neighbor who calls her a "kike." It is a long time before Stern recovers from this incident. The nervous breakdown recorded here shows his reaction in its most overt form. So far so good—good, liberal, and sensitive. But you will note that Stern's nervous breakdown corrects itself illogically, without reason. Note further that Stern is no moron and certainly no coward; his depression is metaphysical, not actual. A shrug of the shoulders, a few heated words, or a punch in the nose (in the end he does try the last, half-heartedly) would have satisfied even the idealists among us. Stern knows deep inside, however, that *kike* stands for an ineradicable darkness in the human soul. *In*eradicable.

It was a jangled, careening period that followed, and later he could remember it only as a black piece torn from his life rather than a number of days or weeks. He knew that it began trembling on the edge of a bed at midnight and he remembered how it ended, but he could pick out only single frenzied moments in between, as though it were all down on a giant mural he was examining in darkness with an unreliable flashlight. There was no good part of the day for him during this period, but it was the mornings that seemed the worst because there were always a giddy few minutes when it seemed he was going to be all right. But a dry, shriveling tremble would soon come over him, and it was then that he had to hold on to things, as though to keep himself on the ground. He held on to chairs and desks and he held on to himself, always keeping one fist buried deeply in his side, as though to nail himself down and join together the pieces of human spring that had snapped within him. Going to work was a stifled, desperate time, and there was at least one ride when, sealed up in the train, holding the bottom of his seat with all his might, he thought he was not going to be able to make it and said to the man next to him, "I'm in a lot of trouble. You may have to grab me in a second." He remembered that the man, who smoked a pipe and wore his hat down low, and hardly looked surprised and said, "I'll keep an eye on you," and then gone back to his *Times*.

He was certain, on these rides to the city, that he would lose his breath and begin to bite things so that heavy-set men, who'd been college athletes, would have to sit on him in mid-aisle, pressing his face to the floor, while conductors signaled on ahead to alert authorities. Each time the train pulled in, Stern would race gratefully to the street, sucking in hot blasts of summer air, stunned that he had made it.

In his office, on these mornings, a motor, powered by rocket fuels, ran at a dementedly high idle somewhere between his shoulder blades. He could not sit and he could not stand, and he remembered his narrow business room as a place to crouch and sweat and hope for time to pass. A film seemed to seal him off from the others around him. Unable to think, his mind an endless white lake, he touched papers and opened drawers and felt pencils, as though by physically going through remembered motions the work would get done. He did these things in short, frenzied bursts, holding on to a table with one hand; it seemed that someone was pulling him into the ground. At noon, his fist socked deep into his stomach, as though to seal it like a cork, he would run to a nearby park, where he would fling off his jacket, lie on his back, and stick his face in the sun, praying that he might sleep or disappear into the grass. Once he slept a long while in his office clothes, his face burning up in the heat. He awakened at a crazy, magical time of day, cool and grateful, the trembling stilled, and for a moment he thought it might be over. But then the motor turned over quietly and began to hum.

There was, too, during that period, a numb and choking fear of his boss, Belavista, that formed suddenly and oppressed Stern. He crouched within his office and gripped his desk and waited for the Brazilian to call. The man's confident morning steps in the hall sent Stern looking for a place to hide. The phone ring became a knife, and once, when it was late and Belavista summoned him, he flew first to the bathroom and locked the toilet stall. He could remember that later, in the front office, Belavista had stood for a long time without talking, his charred millionaire's face staring out of the skylight, while Stern died in his tracks. Turning finally, he had said, "How are things going in there?" And Stern, his tongue shriveling in his mouth, had said, "I just can't," and had run to put his face up to the park sun, grunting and squeezing his fists blood red, as though he could force and fight his way into a sleep.

His house, once he had screamed "Let's sell," became a dirty and infected place to Stern, and nights, returning home at a desperate clip, he could remember running lightly across the lawn, as though he did not want to make contact with the grass; lowering his head, so that he would not have to see the outside walls; and failing to touch the alien banister as he flew up to his bed, which was safe and clean and would go with him to the new place. He spent evenings on his bed, the cold sheets pacifying him, and he could remember a phone call after dark in which a man's voice had moaned out at him, "I saw your ad about the house. I don't want to know about anything but this: what kind of neighborhood is it? I mean, is it mixed? Oh, I don't want it to be all my kind, but it's got to be half and half, a little of everything. I can't tell you how important that part is." And Stern had moaned back, "Oh, I know; I really know," joining the man in tears.

There was a time when the house seemed the key to it all, an enemy that sucked oil and money and posted a kike-hating sentry down the street to await Stern's doom. But then Stern imagined himself on the twelfth story of a city apartment building, his house sold, sealed in now by new kike men, with different faces, occupying the three other apartments on his floor. He pictured himself high above the city at night, clawing at the windows. And during what must have been a weekend he told a solemn Swede who'd come to look the house over, "We have to stay here and have changed our mind."

The Swede, his head among a forest of basement pipes, hollered down, "Is it because I'm looking at the pipes?" And Stern said, "No, I'm too sick to move," and gave his wife the job of evicting the man.

Late at night, as he clutched his sheets in the darkness, ideas seemed to seize him by the throat, making him rock and cry and pray for sleep. The deep hot valleys of his wife's body frightened him now, and he could remember pulling her awake one night and saying, "You've got to get out of that dance thing. I know you don't go to bed with people, but the thought that you might is driving me crazy. I don't like to do this to you, but it'll just be for now, while I'm going through this thing."

"All right, I won't go to it any more."

"But that's not enough," he said. "What about every second I'm not with you? It would be easy for you to just pull up your skirt for someone. The second I leave the house. Or when you're just going alone somewhere. I'd never know."

"I'm not going to do anything," she said.

"I know, but you could. You could just flip up your skirt and open your legs and that would be it. It wouldn't take two minutes. And I don't want any man's thing in you. What would I do if that happened?"

"Well, then, what do you want me to do?"

"I don't know. But it's always going to be that way, all our lives." And he locked his hand around her wrist, as though only by holding her that way could he prevent her from flying out of the room in a desperate hunt for alien bodies.

He waited those nights for the trembling to stop, the engine to stop pumping. There had always been an end to bad things before—fevers dropped, homicidal dreams were chased by the dawn, and once, when he was a boy, his arm, heavy with a great infection, had suddenly fizzled and gone back to normal. But, now, it was as though he were an automobile with a broken horn, doomed to blare forever in a quiet residential neighborhood, all wiring experts having long been shipped out of the country. Sometimes, writhing and wet on the sheets at midnight, he would tell his wife,

"I'm touching bottom," but it wasn't really true. He seemed to be holding on to a twig, half-way down a sheer, rain-slick mountain. How nice it would be to let go. But he had only $800, and it would be eaten up quickly if he were put in a sanatorium. He imagined himself in such a place at the end of three days, the $800 gone, in a terrible panic, unable even to lie back and be crazy with the other patients. And so he held on to the twig and he clutched at people, too, pulling at men's lapels and woman's skirts on steaming city streets, telling them he was in bad trouble.

When it got so bad it seemed he'd have to smash himself against something to make the trembling stop, he would take some stranger's sleeve in the city and say, "I know this is going to sound crazy, but I'm pretty upset here and wish you would just talk to me a second." It amazed him that no one was perturbed by this. People seemed to welcome the chance to exchange wisdoms at midday with a strangulating young man. And Stern, no matter how banal their words, would attach great and profound significance to them, adopting each piece of advice as a slogan to live by. "I'm going to tell you something that's going to help you, fellow," an elderly gentleman said to him. "I was in trouble once, too, and I decided then and there never to give anyone more'n half a loaf. You remember that and you'll never go wrong again." And Stern said to him, "You know, that's right. I can see where, if you follow that, you'll always come out right." And he went off, determined to stop giving up entire loaves, convinced he had come up with the key to his trembling. A Negro ice-cream salesman told him, "You got to stop lookin' for things," and a retired jewelry executive, seized in a restaurant, advised him against "letting any person get hold of you." In both cases, Stern had said, "You know, you've really got it. I'm going to remember that."

He recalled being in many places and then running, choking, out of them. Once in a darkened, cavernlike restaurant, he ordered six lunchtime courses and thought to himself, "This is the end of it. I'm going to sit here like all the other men and eat, and when I leave this table it's all going to be over." But the service was slow, he lost his breath, and when the juice came, he gulped it down, threw out clumps of dollars, and flew from the pitlike restaurant, clawing for air. Another time, floundering across the hot city pavements, on an impulse he plunged into a physical

.culture studio and signed up for a six-year course. "I want to start right this minute," he said, and was shown to a locker. In shorts, he went into the gym, where the only person exercising was a great, bearlike man with oil-slick hair and huge, ballooning arms. He said to Stern, "Come here. Were you in the Army?"

"I was a flier," said Stern.

"I took a lot of crap from a drill sergeant in the Marines," said the man. "He'd stand out there, and the bullshit would come out of him in quart bottles, but do you know the only thing that saved me?"

"What's that?"

"His arms. They weren't even sixteens. I've got eighteens, myself. He'd stand there, and the shit would flow about how tough he was, but all you'd have to do is look at his arms and it didn't mean anything. How am I supposed to respect a man who doesn't have arms?"

"You can't," said Stern.

"Well, I'm going to do some arm work," the man said and began to curl a great dumbbell into his lap. Stern watched his arms expand and said, "I can't seem to get started today." He dressed and then ran, gasping and unshowered, for the daylight.

Once, when the sound of Belavista's slippered footsteps down the hall sent him spinning into the streets, he ran into a telephone booth and called Fabiola.

"This thing isn't getting any better," he said. "It's like I swallowed an anthill. I'm jumping through my ass. You've got to send me to someone."

"Psychiatry's up in the air," said Fabiola. "There's the cost too. Take a grain of pheno when you feel upset this way."

"I don't care about any expense. I don't think you know what's going on with me. It isn't the ulcer any more. I'd take a dozen of those compared to this new thing."

"All right, then," said Fabiola. "There's one good man. He's ten per session, and he *has* helped people."

"I really want to see him, then," said Stern.

The psychiatrist was a rail-thin man who talked with a lisp and whose office smelled musty and psychiatric. It bothered Stern that he had only one tiny diploma on the wall.

"Can it hurt me?" Stern asked.

"No," said the man. "Sometimes you dig down and come up with something very bad, but generally it helps."

"There's probably something lousy like that in me," said Stern. "How much is this going to cost?"

"Twenty a session."

Stern began to choke and said, "I heard ten. Oh God, I can't pay twenty." He gasped and sobbed and the man seemed to panic along with him.

"Maybe there's something about money," said the lisping psychiatrist. "Some people think it's dirty."

"No, no, it's the amount. Oh God, don't you just want to *help* people?" He got up, gasping, sucking in musty, psychiatric air, and the psychiatrist, gasping and white, too, said, "Maybe you think money has a smell. We could go into that."

"No, no," said Stern, "we're not going into anything. Imagine how you'd feel expecting ten and then hearing twenty." And with that he ran, crouching, through the door, with the panic-stricken psychiatrist hollering after him, "You've got a money neuroses."

One night, when for an hour or so there had been no gathering shriveling tremble inside him and it had seemed he might be done with it, he remembered being in a cramped and sultry theater with his wife, watching *Hedda Gabler*. He got through an act all right, but when Hedda tossed the writer's book manuscript into the furnace, he stood up in the stifling theater, shouted "Aye," and ran through the tiny exit, where he sat on the curb and waited for his wife.

Toward the end of it, he went everywhere with his arms folded tightly in front of him, as though he were naked in the snow. He bit down hard on things then, whatever was available—the drapes, a coffee cup, the corner of his desk—and yet there came over him, too, during this time, a kind of wild and gurgling courage he had never had before. Once, he ran with teeth clenched through a crowded train station, as though he were a quarterback going downfield, lashing out at people with his elbows, bulling along with his shoulders. One man said, "What do you think you're doing?" And Stern hollered back, "I didn't see you. You're insignificant-looking." When a cop stopped him for running through a stop sign, Stern heard himself saying, "Is this your idea of a crime?

With what's going on in this country—rape and everything?" It was a perspiring, released kind of feeling he had when he was at his most desperate, and it gave him courage one day to seize a girl in his building who had seemed unapproachable. Tall and blond, with horn-rimmed glasses, she had a tight-skirted, whiplike body and spoke with a shrill, slightly hysterical British accent. Stern saw her in elevators for the most part, talking to a girl friend, a book on some declining civilization always pressed against her high intellectual bosom. The word "problem" seemed to crop up in her every sentence.

"That's one of my problems."

"The man undoubtedly has a sexual problem."

Stern thought she was maddeningly intellectual and wanted to be with her in her small, book-lined apartment, kissing her hair as she discussed declining civilizations, spending long hours working out sick, tangled sexual problems.

One day outside the building, he took her arm and said, "This is crazy, but I don't know any other way to do it. I've seen you a lot in the elevator, and I'm in pretty bad trouble now, and I wonder if you'd mind my just walking along awhile with you."

"I have to meet someone," she said.

"I'm in pretty bad shape," Stern said, holding on to her arm. "I've got a whole bunch of problems and I have to just tell them to someone."

"Yes," she said, freeing herself with a shrill little laugh. "But I don't like men's hands on me."

At the tail end of it, with courage forming along the bottom of him like vegetable shoots, it pleased him to make detailed and shocking phone calls to his mother and sister.

"I actually chew on drapes," he told his mother at midnight, "I pull at my skin and I won't have my job for long. I expect to go into an institution and not come out of it."

"I haven't had that in my life?" she said. "I haven't had much worse? I've had the same thing. You can't scare me."

"How would you like to see your son peeled off the fender of a speeding car? It's going to happen, you know."

And to his sister, long-distance, he said, "Oh, it's a breakdown, all right. Dying doesn't scare me in the least. It'll be in about a week or so. They're going to find me in a tub. I'll bet you're amazed that I can discuss it so calmly.

Bet it really shakes you up to think it's happening to your own brother, who used to tell all those jokes."

He expected that if it ever did end, it would peter out, with a little less trembling and choking each day, but it surprised him by finishing up abruptly in a quite unexplainable way after a talk with a Polish woman who had come to clean his house.

Through it all, amazingly, he had never thought once of the kike man. Sliding down the mountain, he had been too busy casting about for things to clutch to think very much about who had pushed him. If the man had stopped him on the street, Stern, hunched over, fists planted in his waist to quiet the erupting, might have brushed on by and said, "I have no time to fool around."

On the night that it ended, his wife had gone to the movies, and Stern, a crawling, bone-deep shiver coming over him, had flicked off the television set and found the Polish woman on her knees in the broom closet. A small, pinched wrinkle of a woman, she seemed to have been made from a compound of flowered discount dresses, cleaning fluid, and lean Polish winters. She shook her head continually and muttered pieces of thoughts, finishing none of them. Stern talked to her for two hours and found her scattered, wise-sounding incantations soothing.

"You just can't," she said, rolling her head from side to side. "I mean you just don't go around. . . . You got to just . . . sooner or later. . . . I mean if a man don't. . . . This old world going to . . . When a fully grown man. . . . Rolling up your sleeves is what . . ."

To which Stern said, "Oh God, how I appreciate this. I think I'm going to be able to get hold of myself now. I really do. Sometimes you just get together with a certain person and it really helps. I think I'm going to be all right. And, you know, as long as I live, I'm never going to forget this and the help you've given me. I really think I'm going to be able to stop it tonight."

"Sure," said the woman, rolling her head from side to side. "Of course. I mean you just . . . you got to. . . . There comes a time . . ."

And that night, when Stern's wife came home, he said, "I think I'm out of it." In bed, he relaxed his grip on the headboard, and then, just as swiftly as it had come over him, it more or less disappeared.

He told someone in his office, "I had the mildest nervous breakdown in town. I didn't miss a day of work. It was pretty lousy, but all of a sudden you just come out of them." The two phrases "hanging on to desks" and "jumping through my tail" had great appeal to Stern, and he used them often to describe what had happened to him. He remembered a hairless boy with moonlike jowls who years back had worked for his company and had begun one afternoon to run into the water cooler. For two years, the boy had disappeared, taking mute and vacant vacations with his wife, renting clapboard houses and just sitting in them; Stern remembered seeing him on the street, looking white and clean as though someone had sponged him down. He looked up this boy's phone number now, called him, and said, "I just came out of one like yours. No water cooler, but I did a lot of hanging on to desks. I had to do it to keep from jumping through my tail. What are you doing with yourself these days?"

"Just sitting around," said the boy.

Stern had not thought of time or weather or clocks and dates and punctual changes of underwear, and he was certain that great clumps of dust had settled over his life; somehow, though, as he had choked and skidded and clutched at people's arms, he had managed to mail things, too, and pay dry cleaners. He expected to find his son making far-off, wistful comments about "new daddies" he would like to have, and yet the very first of the new evenings the boy tapped him on the shoulder and said, "Now can we play?"—as though he'd been waiting for Stern to finish tying a shoelace. "Yes," said Stern, falling to the floor. "I'm down here on the floor trapped and the only thing that can get me up is if someone touches a secret place on my ear three times and then taps me with a banana." The boy followed instructions delightedly, and Stern leaped up to shake his hand, saying, "Thank you for saving your daddy. I now owe you one hundred giraffe tails."

Stern looked at a calendar and saw that it had all worked out fine, ending on the first sharp and crackling day of October; now he would be able to draw winter down on himself and his family like a shade, huddling in his house and taking soups for strength. He had been too agonized and out of breath to think about his stomach, and it amazed him that it was not leaping with a fresh crop of ulcers; it seemed to be doing all right, the glue holding firm on a cracked china cup. Maybe that was the trick. Go into a tumbling, frenzied period and your stomach simply wouldn't have time to concentrate on ulcers. The idea was to set up small, diversionary troubles in other parts of your body, way out on your fingers or inside your head. But what if now, with things quieter, a new batch got underway?

He wanted to take the previous weeks in his hands, crush them down to snowball size, and examine them close to a light bulb so that he would understand them if they happened again. It seemed a time to talk, finally, about dramatic central things, death and wills and horrible, long-buried family crises from which lessons could be drawn. First he called his insurance man, who said, "Before we go any further, remember, you can't dictate from the grave." And then he called his mother, telling her, "I really want to have a talk now. You don't know what hell I've been through."

"I know what you've been through and, believe me, I could tell you a few things. I coud tell you things that would stand your hair on end."

"All right, tell me them then."

"Don't worry," she said. "I could tell you plenty. I could fill up books if you really wanted to listen."

"Meanwhile you haven't said anything."

"Someday, when you're ready, I'll say plenty. Then you won't wonder why I take an occasional drink. And then, years later, you'll tell people, 'I had some mother.' "

He met his father for dinner in the city, and much of the conversation had to do with the machinery of the meeting. "How long have you been waiting?" his father said, outside the restaurant. "I thought I'd take a cross-town bus, get myself a transfer, and then walk the extra two blocks over to Sixth. If I'd known you were going to be early, I'd have come all the way up by subway and the hell with the walking. How'd you get up here?"

"I just got here," said Stern. "I want to talk over some things with you."

Inside the restaurant, Stern's father kept grabbing the elbows of waiters and customers, turning to Stern, and saying, "You know how long I know this guy?" Stern would guess, and his father would say, "I know this guy for seventeen years" or "We go all the way back to 1933," bobbing his head up and down, as though to testify he was telling the truth, however astonishing the statement may have seemed.

During dinner, Stern said, "I went through a cruddy period. I don't know what in the hell hit me."

"I heard," said his father. "You know how I feel about you, though, don't you?"

After a while, his father said, "How do you plan on getting back? I think, in your situation, your best bet is to walk over west and catch a bus going downtown. Lets you off slightly north of the station. You can duck down and walk the rest of the way underground or, if you like, you can grab a cab. I haven't figured out how I'm going home myself. . . ."

ELLIOTT BAKER
from *A Fine Madness* (1964)

Samson Shillitoe is as close to the "hero" beloved of reviewers as Black Humor comes. He staggers through this
brilliant first novel clutching to his bedraggled poems as
if they were an absolute value. Not even a lobotomy erro-
neously performed upon him by a mental farm at the end
of the book can stop him. In his stand against the world,
however, he reminds us of Binx Bolling and Sebastian Dangerfield and Cabot Wright, and even—in the selection
included earlier—Guy Grand. The Black Humorists are
no friends of *Kultur*, and Grand would have loved Shillitoe's performance as guest poet for the literary ladies. You
should also know that "Gaye Litmus," a prostitute, is an
old friend whom Samson meets in a bar on the way to the
reading, which had been arranged for him by another friend,
Rollie Butler, and that "Rhoda" is the lady with whom
he currently resides. "Lydia Wren" is the wife of the
psychiatrist who—later on—will attempt to "cure" Shillitoe.

Mrs. Fitzgerald was sitting on the front stoop, holding a
sheet of aluminum foil under her chin and poking her face
at the sun. As Shillitoe came out he patted her shoulder.

"Have a nice *coup de soleil*, Mrs. Fitz'."

It was half hour before Rollie Butler was due to call for
him. But Shillitoe's nerve ends were sputtering and he thought
that walking the seventy-three blocks to Da Vinci Hall might
deaden them enough for him to go through with the reading.

The thick tweed suit was suffocating. The thin copy of *Hellebore* in the pocket banged its forewarning against his hip. The shirt collar, appropriately enough, felt like a noose. If that lunkhead didn't stop starching everything, he'd starch her. He tried to pile other grievances on Rhoda, to build a case against her so he could blame her for what he was about to do. But he had never been able to volley responsibility for his actions over to others and the poetry reading was no exception. He had been conscious when he agreed to do it. He could even recall being titillated by visions of high finance. He deserved everything he was about to get.

This might, he realized, exceed his most hideous expectations. Shillitoe had never read one of his own poems aloud to anyone. Once transferred from him to paper and complete they held little interest for him. As for reading to an audience, that was for the octogenarians with their fluffy white crowns making personal appearances to prove that one could have a soul and still survive. But, in a little while, it would be he who was on the stage, staring at a room full of "kulcher" chasers, clearing his throat and . . . And what?

What would he do? How would he begin? He could tell a joke, except he hated jokes and never remembered any. He could let loose a few metaphors that would creep up their skirts. That's what they really wanted. But why should he give them what they wanted? They'd like him to wear a black turtle-necked sweater. That was why he'd put on the starched collar and his one and only suit even though it was Harris tweed and stunk of naphthalene. They'd also like plenty of exhibitionism. So he'd open his book, read for twenty minutes in a monotone and scram as soon as he collected the hundred bucks.

This decision strengthened his steps for another few blocks. Then, gradually, he became increasingly aware of the bars he was passing. As the heat shortened and slowed his stride, the cool, dark doorways beckoned more seductively. Shillitoe gritted his teeth and trudged on. He might have made it all the way if Gaye Litmus hadn't come around the corner.

"Shillitoe!" she rasped happily.

"Hello, Gaye. How's the whoring?"

"I got a problem, Shillitoe. Let's have a drink and I'll tell you."

"No thanks."

"Jesus, that's a good one."

The nearest place was a cocktail lounge. The round cushions of the bar stools gasped as they sat down. Vikings pitchforked mermaids on the frosted mirror and muted dance music seemed to come from the cash register. The bartender approached them suspiciously.

"Beer," said Shillitoe.

"I'm paying," said Gaye.

"The best Scotch you've got," said Shillitoe.

"That's my Samson." Gaye pounded him on the back. "I still got that poem you wrote for me. I framed it and hung it right over my bed. It got lots of laughs."

"Which poem's that?"

"You know. 'Up lad, when the journey's over there'll be time enough to sleep.' "

"Not me," he said. "Housman."

"I never worked in a house, you pimp!"

"Forget it," he said. "Tell me your problem."

"It's this guy. He does certified public accounting. He's got me paying income tax." Gaye's laugh sounded like it was being sucked through a straw. Shillitoe looked her over. She was developing the hump on her shoulders that so many women raised in their forties. Her features had spread as her face had become more bloated and her heavy makeup didn't completely hide the pitted skin. When she raised her hands to smooth her fluffy bleached hair he saw the dark splotches under her arms. Simultaneously, the odor hit him.

"Christ, haven't you taken a bath yet?"

"Destroys the natural oils."

"I don't know how in hell you make a living."

"Applegarth doesn't complain."

"Who's Applegarth?"

"I told you. The accountant. It's been steady with him now for almost two months."

"Love?"

"Yeah. I really got it for him."

"And how does he feel?"

"He don't say. He just likes to do a certain thing. You know."

"Urolagnia?"

"What the hell's that?" She nodded as he put it into more colloquial terms. "Yeah. That's my Applegarth."

"Sounds like the basis of a happy marriage."

"That's the problem," said Gaye sadly. "I think a girl should only go so far before she's married."

"Popular ethics," said Shillitoe and ordered another two drinks.

"The only thing is, he's got three sons and a crummy wife. She don't appreciate him."

"Maybe he's never experimental at home."

"Don't be such a wise-guy," she snapped. "This is important to me. What am I supposed to do?"

Shillitoe pondered the question for several seconds. "For one thing, stop doing what Applegarth wants."

"And what if he starts looking for somebody else? I really got it for him, Shillitoe."

"The rules of free enterprise distinctly state that no man shall pay for what he receives free. Nobody knows this better than the maker of poetry. But he has no choice."

"Aw, shove the sermon."

Shillitoe signaled the bartender again. "What do you want me to do?"

Tears began to extend her mascara. "I don't know. But I thought you'd do something. I thought at least you were my friend."

"I am your friend."

"I kept you going, how many years?"

"About six months."

"And I never asked you any favors, did I?" Shillitoe agreed that she hadn't. "So when I finally ask you for one thing, one pimpin' little thing . . ."

"What thing?"

"I told you. I really got it for Applegarth. I ain't getting any younger, Shillitoe. It's time I got married again. If you were so smart you could think of something."

"I'll think of something," said Shillitoe.

"The hell you will."

"I told you I'll think of something. That's a promise. Now have another drink."

When the mermaids on the frosted glass began to wiggle their tails, Shillitoe asked the bartender the time.

"Three-thirty."

Three-thirty? Where was he supposed to be at three-thirty? The dance music from the cash register kept repeating the same four notes, dum-dum-de-dum, da-dum-de-hall, da-vin-chi-hall.

"Gotta' beat it," he said to Gaye, wavering off the stool.

"Where's the fire?"

"Gotta' read poetry."

Gaye clung to his arm, telling him how much she liked poetry, especially, "Up lad, when the journey's over there'll be time enough to sleep."

The sun had stretched the street and tilted it at a crazy angle. Hundreds of automobiles blockaded every crossing but they squeezed by, swearing back at the bilious faces and skipping arm-in-arm to the next barricade. Then they were in a booming stone entrance hall and groups of women in peacock and sunflower dresses were huddling around and conspiring against them.

"Your invitations, please?"

It came from a mouth like a mail slot. Shillitoe felt in his pockets for tickets to drop between the even rows of teeth. All he could find was his library card.

"Oh, Mr. Shillitoe. The chairman was just looking for you. And is this person with you?"

He explained that Gaye was the literary editor of *The Manchester Guardian*.

"The Manchester Guardian," squeaked the teeth. "Do you know Alistair Cooke?"

"Sure," said Gaye. "Up lad, when the journey's over . . ." She finished the line over her shoulder as Shillitoe dragged her inside.

"Find yourself a seat," he said. "I gotta' report to somebody."

"Anything I can do?" asked Gaye.

"Just keep out of the way. And when they introduce me, stand up and yell 'bravo.' "

"Bravo, bravo," rehearsed Gaye as she stumbled down the aisle.

Shillitoe retraced his steps to the wide mouth and spoke in to it until it told him how to get backstage where he would find the chairman.

When the woman with the terrible body odor took the aisle seat, Lydia Wren moved along to the middle of the row. She had accepted, as had Mr. Czolgacz's other pupils, his invitation to have iced coffee with him after the recital. He had mentioned that there would be others on the program, but had done so in such a way as to make it clear that they were simply preliminaries to his appearance.

The mimeographed program told her otherwise. Underneath the listing of Mr. Czolgacz's harp selections it said, *S. Shillitoe, reading from his published poetical works.* Lydia felt a vague need to move back closer to the aisle. But the foul-smelling woman was there and the auditorium was filling up fast. The inertia Lydia had been experiencing more and more lately kept her where she was.

The program also told her that she was a guest of The Silver Horn Society. Studying the members' hairdos and dresses, Lydia placed the organization somewhere near Fifth Avenue and Ninetieth Street. She wondered if any of them could tell she wasn't a Silver Horner, and decided they probably couldn't. She lived twenty blocks down from them and further east, but she had become an obvious type, too—wife of a professional man, children in private school, dabbler in the arts; nothing that would make her stand out in this crowd.

The chairman, horsey, sporting an enormous orchid and nervously doing an abbreviated Charleston, eventually hushed the hall and introduced the first guest. He was an art critic Lydia had never heard of, his subject for today was Suprematism and he had a high roof to his mouth so that all *L* sounds came out like horses' hoofs on cobblestones. Lydia knew little about Suprematism except that it had derived from Cubism and that the "White Square on Black" at the Merivale Gallery was an example of it. Sneaking glances at the attentive profiles flanking her, she wondered how much the audience really understood about what was being said. Most of it sailed over her head and she had studied art for almost two years.

Mr. Czolgacz's harp provided a welcome change of pace. His choice of the Attaignant piece and Dussek's Sonata was, she knew, deliberate. The egotistical snob *would* play things with which his audience wasn't familiar. She could feel the women nearest her relax as he moved on to Bach and she too felt more comfortable with the familiar sonorous sounds.

Czolgacz acknowledged the applause with perfunctory little bows and it was then that Lydia realized her mistake. Hers was the seventh folding chair in from the aisle. To make her move during the applause would incur Czolgacz's wrath for weeks. Waiting meant she'd have to inch her way past the line of chubby knees during S. Something's reading of his published poetry. Not knowing what to do, she did nothing.

The horsey chairman again, this time doing a sort of mambo. Then a tall, rangy, fierce-looking man in a bulky brown tweed suit wavered to the center of the platform, shielded his eyes and peered at the audience as if sighting land. Some handclapping greeted him. Lydia decided to try to get out before it died and half rose from her chair. But the reeking woman on the aisle suddenly stood up and started shouting "bravo." Lydia sat down again and waited, ready to make her escape as soon as she could summon up enough impervious nerve. Then she heard the first line of her favorite poem.

"How do I love thee? Let me count the ways."

He spoke the words with a solemnity which made them ring out more hauntingly than ever before. Then he paused. Lydia wanted to call out to him to go on, to recite the rest of it. "I love thee to the depth and breadth and height my soul can reach." But he wouldn't. He just stood there looking slowly across the rows of women, his eyes gliding past her own for a flimsy second. Then he started muttering and she had to strain to hear.

"That's probably the kind of lullaby you want me to sing. But can't do it. Neither sickly nor feminine. Never found out why, when a woman thinks about love she always starts counting. Nothing against Lizzie, though she probably dimmed old Browning's lambent flame. Can't turn out a poem when you're horizontal. She tried to write poetry. Can't be written. Got to be formed, like a gallstone, only opposite direction. Still, what she did was better than any of you will do if you live to be three hundred and five. Just mention that so you'll know your place."

There was a scraping of chairs as several members of The Silver Horn excused their way past others and headed for the exit. Lydia knew this was her chance to leave, but now she wanted to stay. She consulted her program again. *S. Shillitoe*, and a footnote, *Mr. Shillitoe is from Indiana*. She cheered him on silently. "Go on, S. Shillitoe from Indiana. This is priceless."

"Shame," said the poet. "Shame that we should have to meet this way, you bribing me to show you some fully dimensioned slides of the real world. Give you lots of credit. Don't know how the hell you can drag yourself through day after night where you are. Cruel of me to tell you about places you'll never see. But that's my reason and the reason of the composers who were just screwed by your banjo player."

Banjo player? Lydia prayed that Czolgacz had heard it.

"And you are paying me one hundred dollars and I am sworn to read to you from my blood. Almost as drunk when I made the deal as I am now. Immoral of you to hold me to it, but that never stopped you. Where was I?"

He looked straight at Lydia as if she was his prompter, nodded at her and continued.

"Right. Facts spread their madness in overlapping circles. Sensation of progress is nothing but currents of air passing between two equal minds holding different information. So you should revive when poetry spins tornadoes through your windows. Why don't you? I don't know. People being more reflective than shadows, makes a shadow wonder about substance. Bedlam's in my pocket, rats are in your beds, welcome all easy-to-spell conditions. Any questions?" He waited as if expecting some. "None? Won't anyone ask me if what is might be preferable to what she thinks it is?"

The woman next to her poked Lydia and motioned toward the aisle. Czolgacz hunched there, impatiently waving at her to come out. Lydia got up.

"Ah!" came the delighted shout from the platform. "One woman not yet lost."

Lydia stared at him in horror. What had he asked that her standing up was an answer to? She felt all the smirking little faces around her and saw Czolgacz signaling her again. Dropping "excuse me" on each lap and crunching on several toes, she stumbled toward him.

"Not that way! Up here!"

Czolgacz seemed unaware that the voice from the platform was aimed at her. Why didn't he hurry?

"Up here, Pocahontas! This way!"

Everyone was looking at her and the exit seemed miles away. She didn't realize she'd been sitting so far down front.

> *"When the juggler failed to stop the show*
> *She changed her seat to another row*
> *And snubbed agility."*

He chanted it in rhythm to her step. Rotten Greenwich Village character making fun of her. How dare he? He probably sold socks at Macy's. As Czolgacz held the door open for her, the socks salesman was addressing himself to the whole audience.

"Looking at your faces, I know you are all sincerely interested in poetry. Or else my fly's open."

Then she was in the lobby with Czolgacz's other students and the harpist was probing them for compliments.

A sudden invasion of Boy Scouts from Harrisburg, Pennsylvania, most of whom wanted grilled cheese, kept Rhoda on the sandwich block an extra hour. By the time she reached the lobby of Da Vinci Hall the women were stampeding from the auditorium.

"Most disgusting thing I've ever heard."

"People like that should be put away."

"He obviously isn't a poet at all."

Rhoda swung her handbag at the last one, but a new wave of women from the auditorium pushed her target out of range. Rhoda turned and faced the tide, rolling and bumping against it until she was through the door.

"When putty and ungainly strings resolved to join in me."

She recognized the line from *Hellebore* but it seemed to come from the acrobats on the platform. Then she realized that the center of the acrobatics was Samson's winter suit. Rollie Butler was clinging to its right arm for dear life, a woman with a big orchid was pulling on the back of the collar and Samson was inside. Another woman in a tight satin dress reached across the edge of the platform and tried to snare one of Rollie's ankles. Rollie jumped out of the way, his mouth and eyes open like he'd stepped into some ice water. Then he saw Rhoda.

"Mrs. Shillitoe! Help!"

Rhoda, already halfway down the aisle, shouted at them to get their hands off Samson's suit.

"An apparition, scratching off the crust of sleep," proclaimed Samson, waving his free hand at her.

The first one she reached was the ankle grabber. Rhoda sunk her fingers into the bulging back and pulled. Regaining her balance, she looked down at her two handfuls of damp satin.

"Not her, you idiot," called Samson.

The ankle grabber had become a contortionist, twisting her head around and pawing at the openings in the back of her dress. Rhoda vaulted up onto the platform.

"So the soul is chased deviously."

"Please, Mr. Shillitoe," panted the orchid lady.

"Tail with snapping teeth."

"Let go of him," ordered Rhoda and tried to pry open the fingers gripping the Harris tweed.

"That's his wife," panted Rollie, still hanging on Samson's arm.

"Oh." The orchid lady let go. Samson, suddenly free of his anchor, spun around like a discus thrower and heaved Rollie into the front row of folding chairs.

"Dear lonely import house," intoned Samson to the empty auditorium.

"Please tell him to stop," the orchid lady begged Rhoda. "The program's over. They'll never let me be chairman of anything again." She seemed about to cry.

"Busy with micrometers. Boasting of tolerances."

"That's enough, baby," said Rhoda.

"Advertising Africans with brogues in haciendas."

"I said that's enough."

"He ruined everything," sobbed the orchid lady. Rhoda felt like sitting down and having a good cry with her. Then the ankle grabber crawled up on the platform.

"Somebody tore my dress."

"Rhoda," said Samson, "this is Gaye."

Rhoda felt jealousy heating her face.

"You been at it again?"

"No, no. Gaye goes back more than a dozen years. She charges." . . .

"Who's gonna' pay for this dress?" screamed Gaye.

"Mr. Applegarth," said Samson.

The orchid lady, crying openly now, was salvaging Rollie from the folding chairs.

"You pimps!" yelled Gaye. "What about my good dress?"

"Rollie," said Samson, "give her two bucks out of my hundred."

"Your hundred?" shrieked Rollie, freeing his leg from a chair. "Do you expect to get paid for what you've done?"

"Look at this. Look at it!" demanded Gaye, tearing the back of her dress more to emphasize the holes. Then she beat at the sides of Samson's head until he grabbed her hands and both of them tumbled to the floor. Rhoda started to pull them apart, then saw Rollie limping up the aisle with the orchid lady. She jumped down from the platform and caught up with them.

"What did he do wrong?" asked Rhoda.

The orchid lady gasped and rolled her eyes.

"What didn't he do?" said Rollie. "He didn't wait for me to pick him up. I spent an hour looking in every saloon on Second Avenue. By the time I got here, he'd emptied the hall."

"He . . . he . . ." The orchid lady was getting her speech back. "He made all kinds of pubic references."

"How long did he recite?"

"He didn't recite a single poem," said the orchid lady.

"How long did he stand up there?"

"When I found your apartment empty, I almost died," said Rollie.

"How long?"

"Half an hour at least, making all kinds of pubic references," said the orchid lady.

"You said a hundred dollars for twenty minutes," persisted Rhoda.

"But he didn't read a single poem," said the orchid lady.

"Everything he says is a poem," said Rhoda, holding out her hand.

"Don't pay her." Rollie started to pull the orchid lady away, but Rhoda clamped onto her arm.

"No!" cried the orchid lady. "I can't go through that again." She produced a sealed envelope with the saw-edged outline of a check showing through.

"It's indecent of you to accept it," sneered Rollie.

"Just look at him up there," said the orchid lady.

"Just look," echoed Rollie. "Portrait of a poet."

Rhoda looked where they pointed. Gaye and Samson had separated on the platform. She had reached her hands and knees and was making an effort to get to her feet. But Samson just sat there, one leg twisted under him, staring blankly. . . .

WARREN MILLER
from *The Siege of Harlem* (1964)

Here is Black Humor at its blackest, literally speaking. Harlem decides to break away from the United States and function as an independent country. Washington is prevented by world opinion from exercising military force against the insurgents. But psychology, sabotage, and economic pressure are still part of the game. In this selection the speaker, an elderly Negro living now in an established, independent Harlem, recalls for a group of youngsters how Harlem in its rebel days stood on the brink of failure. "Grandpa," the speaker, was a guardsman then, engaged with other young bloods in attempting to solve a mysterious series of street murders. Again, as in Southern, the tone is cool, and the most absurd events are related in the same matter-of-fact voice with which the press not long ago reported the antics of Jack Ruby.

High living? Nights of forgetfulness at Miss Susan's bar and grill? That was over and finished with and I personally was glad to see the ending of it; for that wasn't gaiety, that was desperation pure and simple. We had just laid around and fooled around in our sorrow, and that's no way for grown men to behave. Now don't get me wrong. I'm not saying anything against Miss Susan Brune or her bar and grill, but that place was a hotbed of loyalty and patriotism, they treated us Guardsmen like heroes, and this gave us a picture of ourselves that was untrue. Things like that going on, some men get the feeling they are hot stuff and the chosen of the earth. But what were we? What were we? I'll tell you what we were: except for Captain Stack Purdy we were youngsters just coming up, still untried and unproven.

"Well, children, here's how it was: once Action became the number for the day, things changed up considerable. Art Rustram, Stack Purdy, and yours truly, we got to be as close as brothers ever get. We shared risk and we shared danger and that brings men really close together, as you know as good as me. We had always called each other brother, true; but it wasn't until the Time of the Bad Nights that we became brothers. I mean we were close, really close.

"Since our work kept us up all night we slept till way up in the day, and this meant that for nearly two weeks I missed my classes up at Columbia U; yes, and those classes were really dear to me. One of the first acts of our new government was to sign what is called a Concordat with Columbia and also with City College, both of which are within our country's boundaries. We gave them permission to continue their good works and in return they provided classes for us in African History and Culture, and other courses of interest to us, as well as library facilities which we needed bad and at least as much as food, as Lance said.

"Some citizens said, 'Lance, you know they are going to infiltrate spies through Columbia and City; don't do it, baby,' et cetera. But Lance simply replied, Education is dear to us and they are going to infiltrate spies anyway.

"You children don't know what it is, I am happy to say, you don't know the thrill of having an armload of books in your arms at the age of fifteen for the first time in your life. I would gladly have given up food, sleep and all to get the learning which I wanted so bad.

"Four months after the founding of Harlem the first of us started going to college, young men and women from the militia, and yours truly among them. I enrolled in the classes of African History and The History of Revolutions from George Washington to Fidel Castro. Ask me anything and I'll give you the particulars including the date. When it comes to people like Danton, Robespierre, and Camillo Cienfuegos, I can tell you their lives and actions to a T. I mean I really know my stuff in that regard.

"Well, you should have seen the faces of those Privileged People's students that first day we walked in to Columbia U. The absence of black must have been bugging them something awful, and when we entered in our uniforms they gave us a big hand and a warm welcome, for you know how youth are. Being members of the exploitative Western Civilization had not taken its toll of their consciences yet; I mean they were still striving to be good and their hands were not yet red.

"Before the week was out some of them were asking could they come over and join the militia. I had to tell them we had all the people we could use; I was polite about it, you know, but I let them know which way the wind was blowing. They were young and my they did get upset. 'I'm going to leave this country before I go insane,' one of them said to me; and I believe it. I believe it for there are decent people everywhere and those who lived within the iron cage were having a really rough time. They could not stand to see what was happening and worried how it was all going to end. They looked over the wall at us in our freedom and they were full of a longing. Like those youth at Columbia U, they were saying, 'My home's not here, it's up there with you.'

"No, children, they are not all devils; some of them are really men and love freedom as we do up here. Well, they're living in a country which just can't reach their case anymore and I am sorry for them from my heart, aren't you? Yes, it's unfortunate.

"Now where was I up to?—Columbia U. Columbia U is where I was at and I won't go into all the ramifications but will only tell you one incident. I'll just allude to it briefly, to give you an idea of the conditions up there and how things had run down without us.

"The coaches were desperate. That's a fact. They lacked men. Not a day passed that one of them did not bug our people with offers: 'Come out for the team,' they say, 'and we'll put you in a place where you don't have to worry anymore. You can do yourself a real good deal, fella.' I mean they were really up the creek.

"Things got so bad that Lance had to write a letter to the president of the U. Lance called in Jim Hardison and says, Jim, send off a letter to Columbia U and tell those people once and for all that for now and ever after on our children will run only for themselves. You can't sell us to Mississippi anymore, says, and we're not going to be bought by Princeton or Cornell either. Tell them those days are gone forever, Jim.

"After that the coaches stole away home and tried to make out with the stuff they had. And what they had wasn't very stylish, as we saw for ourselves just two years later. That was when the first summer Olympics was held at our stadium out on Riker's Island. Our youth brought home nearly every laurel there was, for when it comes to style and endurance, our people just can't be beat; I mean we'll take the cake everytime. But it's just as dear old Lance once said, They want us to prove it too many times because they don't really believe it.

"Now what was I telling you? Where was I up to? Am I out on the street with Stack and Art, or where?"

Sekou said, "You have been missing your classes at Columbia U due to the fact that your work kept you up all night and you been sleeping till way up in the day."

"You have really got it, honey," the old man said. "That's just the way it was. Slept till way up in the day, then met in the map room to read the reports of the night before. Art and Stack, and with my help too, we worked it out that the invaders were following a pattern, hitting a certain neighborhood one night and concentrating some other place on the next. The problem was to figure out where they were going to hit, then to be waiting there, and fix them good.

"No use of talking, it was just guess work and for nine nights Stack and I stood by while dear Art Rustram offered himself to the would-be killers. He was the decoy, the sitting duck, just as Lance said he'd be. Art picked a spot, you see, he picked a spot—you following me, honey?—as for example he's pretend to be all juiced up and with a bottle in his hand he'd flop on some stoop and lay there stoned. I hid myself in the entrance-way above; Stack hid below the stoop, there in the shadows; and all night long we waited and watched and strived never to blink an eye.

"That was the trap. Art Rustram was the bait. Stack and yours truly, we were the teeth, ready to bite any rat that sauntered in.

"Rats was what they were and rats is how they acted. We figured they were tunneling through from the Other Side for we knew they could not get past our lines. What kind of manner of men could they be? That is what we kept asking ourselves. To do the things they did, crawl under the ground, and then kill those who had never raised a hand against them? They were using every trick in the book: strangulation by wire and outright killing with knives and silencer pistol.

"It was our common belief that they were coming through by way of a tunnel. It was a guileful thing and we were really up tight. Before Lance sent the three of us out on that dangerous assignment, our militia people had checked the cellars of all the houses along both frontiers, north and south. We did not find a trace; no, not sign number one. And meanwhile, death stalked the streets by night.

"Come up and sit here beside me, honey, and don't you worry about a thing.

"I will now pursue the tale.

"By the time night would fall on the streets of Harlem you could see no human soul except for the militia patrols, which were out in large numbers; and by the time night fell Art would decide what our area for the night was going to be. Message goes out to militia headquarters; militia told to stay out of there. That neighborhood then was ours, all ours; it was our kingdom for the night. Any intruders came into our sight we'd know they were from the Other Side.

"Too bad for them. They come from the far shore and on bad business they got to take their chances. That was how I reasoned on those terrible dark nights, waiting in some entrance-way, peering into shadows, watching dear Art Rustram offer himself to a bullet or to cold steel. I wasn't a natural warrior like some; no, I had to work myself up to it and let me tell you it took some doing. And I don't mind confessing it.

"I never shall forget those nights. It was around the end of winter but it was still cold—oh that wind from the river—and it was a-drizzling rain. Streets were slick and shiny as mirrors; there were street lights above and street lights below, each one had another mirrored on the shiny street. But it still wasn't light enough, let me tell you. And it was eerie.

"And by that time there were no buses, no public transportation of any kind; they had all broke down and spare parts were unobtainable. Majority People said No to that. Later, of course, our supply system and repair depots got going and friends on the Outside saw to it that we got what we needed. But in those early days of Harlem's first year to which I am now alluding, you had to walk, walk everywhere. Rationing notwithstanding, we became a healthy people; exercise and purpose made us hardy. The Minister of Health and Welfare had nothing but good to report on that score. Also, everybody trimmed down considerable and heavy-hipped women went completely out of style. Thin but strong—that was the order of the day in those times.

"For my particular use, it could not have made less difference I want to say. I was in love from head to foot with your sainted grandmother and I could not have cared less whether she was on the heavy or the thin side. In those days you would hear any number of men saying things like, 'My woman's a little on the austere side, but what she's got is what it takes.' I personally never went in for that kind of talk and I advise you against it.

"Well, that's enough of this fancy ta-doo stuff. Let's get back to the scene. Now where are we up to now? I have told you about our studies in the map room and all the guess work we put our minds to and about the weather in the streets at that time. Now here's what we'd do.

"We took no chances; we did not take chance number one when there was a question of human life involved, especially a life so precious to us as Art Rustram's. And since we did not know but what these men from the Other Side might not be roaming around by day as well—keeping an eye on things, you know, and spying out the lay of the land—we figured, you see, that they had dyed their skin and were passing the other way—oh yes, that's been known, that has been known.

"So what we'd do we'd dress up carefully in clothes of a nondescript nature; I mean suits that were neither here or there. We could have been anything at all, representing any calling from the lower ranks of life's various callings and professions.

"So around ten o'clock at night we'd slip out the back door of headquarters and stroll to the neighborhood of our choice, rain falling on us, chatting about this and that in a friendly fashion, with yours truly striving in the worst way to hush the banging of my heart. I tell you, children, after the seventh night of nights like that my nerves were beginning to weaken down.

"We'd wander through the chosen neighborhood until we found some likely place: some stoop or the doorway of a store such as a hardware store, and Art would say, 'This looks good to me, brothers.' Then he'd point out Stack's post and mine, where we were to lie in wait.

"We marked the spot in our minds, never stopping, no, not for a minute, for that would have given the game away and we were taking no chances. Then we'd continue strolling and by this time, it being around eleven o'clock, we'd repair to some local bar and grill, pretending we were after beer and a quiet corner.

"During that period which I am now touching on, most bars and grills were closed up tight by nightfall, due to a combination of two circumstances: a lack of beer, which was rationed, and a lack of customers, most people not finding the streets very inviting at that time.

"Many nights we'd be the only customers present after eleven o'clock, the others having retired to their rooms and their teevees. It was awful the way the citizens hurried home—I mean they did not stroll—to chain and double-lock their doors. I tell you it did our hearts no good at all to see that happening, for it meant we were no longer in control. Come night, and we lost our edge. We were soldiers, Guardsmen at that, vanguard of the Army of Harlem, and we knew what this meant.

"What did it mean? I'll tell you what it meant. It meant the government did not have the power to protect our citizens. The Majority People were just waiting for an excuse like that so as to step in and try to take over. Show me a government that can't protect its own and I'll show you a government that don't deserve to be up there. No two ways about it. . . ."

"And on the ninth night it came, the big chance for which we had been waiting for through all those lonely cold and miserable nights.

"There was Art Rustram—get the picture now—there was Art, all sprawled out over the stoop, an empty pint near his right side, and singing in a hapless way as some do when they have had far too much. Stack was underneath the steps, standing in the shadow of a column of empty garbage cans, darker of hue than the shadow itself. He was an extra darkness there, a wonder to see.

"And yours truly, where was I? In the vestibule above, no lights, leaning up against the mailboxes, thinking of names. I mean there they were, all those rows of names right behind my shoulder blades, and in my boyish way I imagined those names inhabiting the apartments over my head. I tell you it was something, it really was: whole families worrying their hearts out about the troubles we were having, some of them so sick of soul they thought they heard the sound of the picks tunneling under Harlem. And maybe they could so, I could not say; I never heard it myself but the nights were then so awful quiet that a lot of citizens were certain they really heard it for sure. Well, rumors were rife and that kind of thing has got to be expected.

"Don't you worry, though. For all the imaginings and the worry going on in my head, I was alert, I really was. I knew my duty—we all did in those times when alertness and danger was the order of the day—and needed no reminding, no. I knew we were right down to the nitty gritty, to where it counted, really counted, and I kept my eye directly on Art and was careful not to come too near the glass of the door; for my breath would have got it all steamed up. It was in the month of March I'm talking about now but that's how cold it still was. Talk near a glass and you left a mark. Children, doesn't it seem to you that whenever there's trouble it's winter outside?

"Well, it does seem so to me; and now here it is, I won't keep you waiting any longer. Let me tell you how it went. Before my mind had ever taken it in, children— I mean the sight of him, the would-be murderer now ap-

THE SIEGE OF HARLEM / 205

proaching Art's supine form—snuggle closer, honey—I found my hand reaching for the Colt in my belt.

"I was good to go as soon as my mind knew what my body was up to, and I made my move. Yes, it's a funny thing how the human system works. Art had his hand on the murderer's throat and that was the start of the fight. The situation was pretty well in hand as Stack and yours truly snapped the trap shut.

"Old Art says, 'Careful, brothers, let's don't damage our prize. . . .'

"We put him in the back of the big command car which had been sent for us and Stack propped him up on the seat like a bale of hay and clapped a gang of chains around his wrists. He then whipped out his little old pocket flash and shone it on the prisoner's face.

"You can imagine our astonishment at what we saw! 'I'll be double damned,' Stack simply said and ripped open the man's shirt, saying, 'Just want to see if he's as black underneath as he is outside.'

"There were three militiamen with us plus the man driving and they were all stuck by what they saw, believe it. General sadness hit bottom. It was too hard to believe. That man was one of our own, no getting around it, children; he had turned against us and was doing the dirty deeds for the Other Side.

"Stack wrung his hands. He was all shook up. Well, I knew just how he felt. Said, 'Brothers, I have never in my life felt so forlorn,' Stack said.

"I knew it, for I was feeling that way too. I sat there on the jump-seat, I looked at that man's face, and I secretly mourned.

"All this is a great long while back, children, but I remember the feeling as if I felt it only yesterday or no longer than week before last. Along in those times, because of the actions I witnessed and the things I heard, I was one of the saddest persons you would ever want to see. I mean I was really far down for a while there. The thing is, it hits you hardest when you are young at a certain age."

It is now the next day. Prisoner's in the cooler and my how he did sing. Those types always do. No undue pressure was brought down on him; he was willing and eager: told us everything touching on where the tunnel was, and also how many men had been employed, who trained them, et cetera and so on and on. He incriminated practically the entire human race except only himself, for whom he begged mercy.

"Children, you should have seen that guard-room: militiamen and plain ordinary citizens coming from the length and breadth of Harlem to have a look at that fella. He was of the long slender type and dressed in a one-piece dark green jump-suit. It had the biggest pockets I have ever seen. Well, he needed roomy pockets to carry all the junk they gave him.

"His masters sent him out loaded to the gills. He had a complete drugstore in one of the pockets, including a hypo containing stuff to be used in killing himself painlessly in case of capture. But he wasn't the kind to turn go of life for any principle, for he didn't have any in the first place and was just a businessman engaged in the business of murder. And in his other pocket he carried a complete armory. You should have seen it. It was awesome.

"Oh no doubt about it, he was well equipped in the way of accoutrements, but inside himself he was lacking totally in what it takes. We stripped him down to his skin first of all and examined him every whichawhere for any hidden implements of whatever kind. Then we gave him pants without a belt, not being desirous of taking any chances; shoe laces also, we took them away. Put four men to guard him, two inside the cell, two outside. We cared for him like a baby. He was our prize and he was our evidence.

"Yes, you would have witnessed an astonishing sight if you could have seen how the citizens lined up by the hundreds to get a glimpse of that man. They clamored to see him. It was something. Lance said, Let the people in. And they came every day to take a look and satisfy themselves as to the prisoner's true color.

"I was reminded of this event many years later; something happened then to put me in mind of it and raise it in my recollection. It was twenty years later it occurred, or maybe thirty; I don't remember distinctly—but it was at the time the Privileged People got a hold of a young woman of our race.

"Don't ask me where they found her. Some say she was the daughter of a cook who worked for a family so far out in the suburbs that she never did hear what was going on in Harlem; she didn't receive the call and therefore stayed put and raised her daughter in ignorance. That's the way it must have been.

"Or maybe it was some other way. But the fact is some Privileged hustler discovered her and put that poor child on exhibition. She was at that time going on eighteen years of age as I remember. They put her in a nightclub and charged fancy prices to see her. Majority People came from miles around for a glimpse of the girl; they had not seen skin like that for more years than they could count and they were hungry for the sight of it.

"Proposals of marriage poured in by the dozens; artists painted her; poems were written; and all she did was stand on a revolving stage in a glittery gown that must have cost ten dollars a yard and let them glimpse her beauty while the hustler made his spiel. You'd see her pictures in all the magazines which came in from the Other Side, and in full color, too, saying things like *Miss Milicent's Favorite Perfume Is Lover-Be-Good*. Or they'd have her saying: 'My skin is too delicate for ordinary soaps and that is why I only use *Bland*, the soap of the stars.'

"She just didn't know. Privileged People kept her in a condition of total ignorance; never let her see a newspaper and held her in a gilded cage. It was terrible. She thought she was alone in the world and the only one of her kind. How was she to know? By that time—this was around thirty years after the founding of Harlem—there was not Negro number one left in Manhattan, and elsewhere they were growing rarer every day, some coming to us here and some going to the original home in dear old Africa. I mean the Majority People were in a really bad way when it comes to variety. Sameland the land of Sameness, that is what we came to call it and that is what it is.

"Well, you can imagine; we were stunned for a minute there, but our government soon lodged a strong protest. Old Jim Hardison, he was still alive and kicking, he wrote it and it really wailed. Did no good. No good at all. So we got some friends to put in a complaint at the UN; we took it all the way up to the Human Rights people.

"Mister Eddie's successor at the UN said, 'This is free enterprise at work and an internal matter purely. You tell one hustler what he can and cannot do and you'll have Socialism creeping over the land faster than you can say John Maynard Keynes!'

"Oh dear," Sekou said.

"You said a mouthful, honey," the old gentleman replied. "And poor Miss Milicent—Miss Milicent Hodge was her name now that I come to think of it—she finally died of loneliness before that year was out, and you can't call that a natural death but that is purely what it was: death by loneliness. She pined away for her own kind and never even knew what ailed her. Children, I can't imagine a more miserable way to go than that, can you?

"The thought of that poor girl has bugged me for years. And that hustler would not turn go of her; no, not even after she was dead and gone. Death himself could not soften that man's heart. He had Miss Milicent embalmed; he placed her in a glass case; and he put her on view in a store on Times Square. Fifty cents admission and he's still collecting; parents bringing their children for a look, standing there hushed at the sight of her. Little sign says: *A Negro Woman, Last of her Race to live in Freedom*."

"Oh my."

"Yes, it's sad but that's how it went and that's how it goes. Now where was I up to?"

"Citizens coming for a glimpse of the prisoner." Diego said.

"From far and wide they came, honey, far and wide; and as the days went by, more and more of the people showed up, and not less and less as you might think. Why was this? I'll tell you why. It was because the citizens of Harlem just could not believe he was one of our own. They believed he had been dyed and that if we kept him in the cooler long enough he'd fade back to his original whiteness.

"But such was not the case; no, it was not to be.

"And you would hear any number of well-meaning citizens say, 'That poor lad, they must have brainwashed him good.' And other statements to that effect.

"Lance himself came down to the guard room. He took one

direct look at the boy and he said, Brothers, I know the type: whiter than white.

"Lance took the tape recording of the prisoner's long confession and he played out the whole spool on radio station WEBDuBois. Afterwards, he made one of the most memorable chats it has ever been my pleasure to hear and you know I have been casting a shadow for a long long time.

"He was in fine voice that night; the people were in the streets again—the tunnels having been found and blocked up—and a general air of jubilation reigned. Since the capture there had not been a single act of violence, except for a neighborly quarrel here and there; but no hand had been raised against another human soul.

"Well, there was Lance at the microphone and there was yours truly, right at his side, back at my old post. Lance was fiddling around with the electric wire in that famous way he had, saying, Brothers and Sisters, you've heard it all and I hope you'll now stop tormenting yourselves, says. This boy is not one of ours, he is one of *theirs*. He is a plastic man! and he was manufactured by the Privileged People!

"And that is how this came to be known as The Time of the Plastic Men. For as Lance said, these men weren't men at all, no; they were products! Products is what they were and they had been made sick to their souls by their mechanical condition. They were wind-up men and they were the last of their kind for we don't breed them like that anymore and the Majority do not have the power to manufacture them anymore.

"So Lance says, Now what are we ever going to do with this boy? Says, We have abolished capital punishment and we are not going to bring it back for *him*! Such barbarities have been banned forever in *this* part of the world, Lance says.—Oh yes, he rubbed it in a little; he took the occasion to give the Majority People a nudge for their backward ways.—He says, And I see no point in housing and feeding this plastic creature for the rest of his un-natural life.

"So what we going to do? Lance asked the citizens. It beats me, he says. It's a problem and we're just going to have to sit on it for a while. You know, he says, when Napoleon invaded Spain, our Spanish brothers traded French prisoners for pigs. Maybe that's what *we* ought to do, he says, trade this boy for a few tons of the best ham.

"Well, he raised a big laugh with that line but the Majority People took him seriously. Well, you see, that's the whole thing in a nutshell: when we cracked a joke, they never knew to laugh; and when we were dead serious they always thought we were joking. It was a sad sad situation, let me tell you, and no good for anybody's health.

"Mister Tom Man, who was at that time the Majority's president down in Washington, he got on the teevee and said, 'Now naturally the whole world knows we don't have thing number one to do with the recent alleged events up in Harlem; but in accordance with the spirit and letter of our humane traditions, I am going to form a committee of private citizens to raise hams and ransom that poor innocent boy.'

"Mister Tom kept right on saying he did not have a thing to do with the nocturnal activities we had been suffering, and the opposition congressman said, 'Tom honey, we *know* you didn't have a thing to do with it and that your hands are clean but you should have sent in air support.' It was one big mix-up, let me tell you, and there were a lot of red faces down there, as they say.

"Also at the dear old UN there were many friendly countries who got seized by the notion of lending us a helping hand and they came down hard on poor Mister Eddie. Oh my, that boy did more coughing than was good for him; he showed photos of the tunnel and said, 'Look here at this sloppy workmanship; that proves it couldn't have been done by us. We got too much technical know-how to build any tunnel as sloppy as that!'

"So they formed this committee containing a football coach and a retired admiral in the time-honored way, and Lance sent Josea Boutwell to meet with them. Lance picked a number out of a hat in a manner of speaking and said to Josea, Tell those people we want a hundred tons of the best ham in return for that boy of theirs.

"Josea met them at the border and I went along for the ride and to witness history in the making; I had got a taste for it, you know. I was down on Robeson Boulevard, formerly Second Avenue, at the southern frontier, and Josea says to them, 'A hundred tons of Grade A ham and that boy of yours will be delivered whole into your hands.'

"The retired admiral says, 'Now, son, you know that boy ain't none of ours but we just want to do the humane thing.'

" 'Un-hunh,' Josea says.

"Admiral replied, 'Tell you what we'll do, we'll give you fifty tons. I think that's a very generous offer, son, all things considered.'

" 'I didn't come here to bargain,' Josea says. 'The number is one hundred and if you call me *son* just one more time I will double it.'

"Coach says to the admiral, says, 'Admiral, let's retire to the locker room and talk this over with the alumnae association in a manner of speaking.'

"Coach and the admiral, they step back a little ways behind the barrier and carry on talk of an agitated nature. The admiral got all angerly and we could hear him say, 'I turn the twenty-inch guns on this whole land mass and reduce it to rubble if it wasn't that we owned it all.'

"Coach says, 'We used to, admiral sir, we used to but they broke through our service and nationalized everything we had right down to the cleats in our boots. Now what I say is let's get in there and fight, fight, fight, for the old Statue of Liberty play don't work anymore.'

" 'Why won't that boy let me call him *son?*' admiral says; oh my but he was all aggrieved over that. 'I don't know whichaway is up anymore,' admiral says. Says, 'Did you tell these people who I used to be?'

"Coach says, 'Admiral sir, the flying wedge is out, was outlawed since way back and gone. Now let's get out there, play hard and play clean and make them an offer of seventy-five tons.'

" 'I won't give an inch,' admiral says, 'and you know how dangerous I am when aroused. I wasn't called Bulldog for nothing!'

"Coach takes him by the elbow and leads him back to our lines where Josea Boutwell is smoking a Corona just as cool as can be.

" 'First and three, admiral,' coach says, 'and we're on our own ten, remember that.'

" 'Let's offer them seventy-five,' admiral says.

" 'Good idea,' says coach, fiddling with the whistle around his neck. 'Boutwell,' coach says, 'you got the wind in your favor but I know you are going to play like gentlemen. We're offering seventy-five and I know you'll accept that in the same generous spirit in which it was offered.'

" 'I have got my instructions,' Josea says, 'and I didn't

come here to dicker. One hundred is still the number for today.'

"Coach says to the admiral, 'Baby, it's the old squeeze play and good sportsmanship is not to be expected. Why, they ain't even members of the conference.'

"Well, children, I won't keep you waiting; the long and short upshot of it all was that the Privileged People gave what we demanded and delivered one hundred tons of Grade A ham in one week's time. The Great African & Pan-Islamic co-op stores were bulging at the seams. Extra rations were declared and our spirits received a real lift.

"On receipt of the hams we turned over to them the prisoner, all sound of body and limb and broken in spirit; good for nothing. Well, I don't need to tell you, dears, it does not take much to break a plastic man. He covered his face whenever our cameramen strived to get a shot of him; he had just enough humanity left in him to feel a little shame, I guess.

"Our people saw him in the newsreels and some began to feeling sorry for him again, saying things like, 'Well, that boy probably could not help himself,' and 'He must have been thoroughly brainwashed to do a thing like that,' and 'Maybe he had no Mother to guide him.' Et cetera and so on.

"Lance wouldn't hear of it; he wasn't having any of that, no. On his very next radio chat he took the occasion to have the final word on the matter. I'm not telling you to hate that boy, Lance said; no, I am not telling you to do anything of the kind. I'm just telling you how I feel myself, says, and this is the way I feel: if you *force* yourself to love somebody, you give birth to a murderer in your own body!"

"One of Lance's most profound utterances," Sekou said.

"Tooby sure it was, honey," the old gentleman said. "It was a companion utterance to another famous saying of his, I mean the one about anybody walking a mile with a heart full of false sympathy is walking to the funeral of the whole human race."

"It is graven on his statue," Ahmed said.

"You do know your facts, honey," the old man said and prepared to rise from his chair. "Children, right now I am off to the Veterans of the First Day Lodge. Tomorrow if I'm still casting a shadow I will project the tale of Art Rustram's life and death struggle at Harlem Hospital and of how with the help of others he caught new courage and came back out of death."

THOMAS PYNCHON
from *The Crying of Lot 49* (1966)

Thomas Pynchon's great comic masterpiece is *V*, but there are superb qualities also in *The Crying of Lot 49*, and it is less widely known. In this scene from the early part of the novel, Oedipa Maas, a Kinneret, California, housewife (married to an LSD addict named Mucho), drives down to San Narciso, where a large fortune has been left to her by a former lover, Pierce Inverarity. Pynchon is seen here at his exuberant best, seemingly inveighing against everything at once: motels, California, freeways, television, rock 'n' roll, cosmetics—all within a dreamlike world that moves from one minute to the next remorselessly, carelessly, quickly. *O lente, lente....*

She left Kinneret, then, with no idea she was moving toward anything new. Mucho Maas, enigmatic, whistling "I Want to Kiss Your Feet," a new recording by Sick Dick and the Volkswagens (an English group he was fond of at that time but did not believe in), stood with hands in pockets while she explained about going down to San Narciso for a while to look into Pierce's books and records and confer with Metzger, the co-executor. Mucho was sad to see her go, but not desperate, so after telling him to hang up if Dr. Hilarius called and look after the oregano in the garden, which had contracted a strange mold, she went.

San Narciso lay further south, near L.A. Like many named places in California it was less an identifiable city than a grouping of concepts—census tracts, special purpose bond-issue districts, shopping nuclei, all overlaid with access roads to its own freeway. But it had been Pierce's domicile, and headquarters: the place he'd begun his land speculating in ten years go, and so put down the plinth course of capital on which everything afterward had been built, however rickety or grotesque, toward the sky; and that, she supposed, would set the spot apart, give it an aura. But if there was any vital difference between it and the rest of Southern California, it was invisible on first glance. She drove into San Narciso on a Sunday, in a rented Impala. Nothing was happening. She looked down a slope, needing to squint for the sunlight, onto a vast sprawl of houses which had grown up all together, like a well-tended crop, from the dull brown earth; and she thought of the time she'd opened a transistor radio to replace a battery and seen her first printed circuit. The ordered swirl of houses and streets, from this high angle, sprang at her now with the same unexpected, astonishing clarity as the circuit card had. Though she knew even less about radios than about Southern Californians, there were to both outward patterns a hieroglyphic sense of concealed meaning, of an intent to communicate. There'd seemed no limit to what the printed circuit could have told her (if she had tried to find out); so in her first minute of San Narciso, a revelation also trembled just past the threshold of her understanding. Smog hung all round the horizon, the sun on the bright beige countryside was painful; she and the Chevy seemed parked at the centre of an odd, religious instant. As if, on some other frequency, or out of the eye of some whirlwind rotating too slow for her heated skin even to feel the centrifugal coolness of, words were being spoken. She suspected that much. She thought of Mucho, her husband, trying to believe in his job. Was it something like this he felt, looking through the soundproof glass at one of his colleagues with a headset clamped on and cueing the next record with movements stylized as the handling of chrism, censer, chalice might be for a holy man, yet really tuned in to the voice, voices, the music, its message, surrounded by it, digging it, as were all the faithful it went out to; did Mucho stand outside Studio A looking in, knowing that even if he could hear it he couldn't believe in it?

She gave it up presently, as if a cloud had approached

the sun or the smog thickened, and so broken the "religious instant," whatever it might've been; started up and proceeded at maybe 70 mph along the singing blacktop, onto a highway she thought went toward Los Angeles, into a neighborhood that was little more than the road's skinny right-of-way, lined by auto lots, escrow services, drive-ins, small office buildings and factories whose address numbers were in the 70 and then 80,000's. She had never known numbers to run so high. It seemed unnatural. To her left appeared a prolonged scatter of wide, pink buildings, surrounded by miles of fence topped with barbed wire and interrupted now and then by guard towers: soon an entrance whizzed by, two sixty-foot missiles on either side and the name YOYODYNE lettered conservatively on each nose cone. This was San Narciso's big source of employment, the Galactronics Division of Yoyodyne, Inc., one of the giants of the aerospace industry. Pierce, she happened to know, had owned a large block of shares, had been somehow involved in negotiating an understanding with the county tax assessor to lure Yoyodyne here in the first place. It was part, he explained, of being a founding father.

Barbed wire again gave way to the familiar parade of more beige, prefab, cinderblock office machine distributors, sealant makers, bottled gas works, fastener factories, warehouses, and whatever. Sunday had sent them all into silence and paralysis, all but an occasional real estate office or truck stop. Oedipa resolved to pull in at the next motel she saw, however ugly, stillness and four walls having at some point become preferable to this illusion of speed, freedom, wind in your hair, unreeling landscape—it wasn't. What the road really was, she fancied, was this hypodermic needle, inserted somewhere ahead into the vein of a freeway, a vein nourishing the mainliner L.A., keeping it happy, coherent, protected from pain, or whatever passes, with a city, for pain. But were Oedipa some single melted crystal of urban horse, L.A., really, would be no less turned on for her absence.

Still, when she got a look at the next motel, she hesitated a second. A representation in painted sheet metal of a nymph holding a white blossom towered thirty feet into the air; the sign, lit up despite the sun, said "Echo Courts." The face of the nymph was much like Oedipa's, which didn't startle her so much as a concealed blower system that kept the nymph's gauze chiton in constant agitation, revealing enormous vermilion-tipped breasts and long pink thighs at each flap. She was smiling a lipsticked and public smile, not quite a hooker's but nowhere near that of any nymph pining away with love either. Oedipa pulled into the lot, got out and stood for a moment in the hot sun and the dead-still air, watching the artificial windstorm overhead toss gauze in five-foot excursions. Remembering her idea about a slow whirlwind, words she couldn't hear.

The room would be good enough for the time she had to stay. Its door opened on a long courtyard with a swimming pool, whose surface that day was flat, brilliant with sunlight. At the far end stood a fountain, with another nymph. Nothing moved. If people lived behind the other doors or watched through the windows gagged each with its roaring air-conditioner, she couldn't see them. The manager, drop-out named Miles, maybe 16 with a Beatle haircut and a lapelless, cuffless, one-button mohair suit, carried her bags and sang to himself, possibly to her:

MILES'S SONG

Too fat to Frug,
That's what you tell me all the time,
When you really try'n' to put me down,
But I'm hip,
So close your big fat lip,
Yeah, baby,
I may be too fat to Frug,
But at least I ain't too slim to Swim.

"It's lovely," said Oedipa, "but why do you sing with an English accent when you don't talk that way?"

"It's this group I'm in," Miles explained, "the Paranoids. We're new yet. Our manager says we should sing like that. We watch English movies a lot, for the accent."

"My husband's a disk jockey," Oedipa trying to be helpful, "It's only a thousand-watt station, but if you had anything like a tape I could give it to him to plug."

Miles closed the door behind them and started in with the shifty eye. "In return for what?" Moving in on her. "Do you want what I think you want? This is the Payola Kid here, you know." Oedipa picked up the nearest weapon, which happened to be the rabbit-ear antenna off the TV in the corner. "Oh," said Miles, stopping. "You hate me too." Eyes bright through his bangs.

"You *are* a paranoid," Oedipa said.

"I have a smooth young body," said Miles, "I thought you older chicks went for that." He left after shaking her down for four bits for carrying the bags.

That night the lawyer Metzger showed up. He turned out to be so good-looking that Oedipa thought at first They, somebody up there, were putting her on. It had to be an actor. He stood at her door, behind him the oblong pool shimmering silent in a mild diffusion of light from the nighttime sky, saying, "Mrs. Maas," like a reproach. His enormous eyes, lambent, extravagantly lashed, smiled out at her wickedly; she looked around him for reflectors, microphones, camera cabling, but there was only himself and a debonair bottle of French Beaujolais, which he claimed to've smuggled last year into California, this rollicking lawbreaker, past the frontier guards.

"So hey," he murmured, "after scouring motels all day to find you, I can come in there, can't I?"

Oedipa had planned on nothing more involved that evening than watching *Bonanza* on the tube. She'd shifted into stretch denim slacks and a shaggy black sweater, and had her hair all the way down. She knew she looked pretty good. "Come in," she said, "but I only have one glass."

"I," the gallant Metzger let her know, "can drink out of the bottle." He came in and sat on the floor, in his suit. Opened the bottle, poured her a drink, began to talk. It presently came out that Oedipa hadn't been so far off, thinking it was an actor. Some twenty-odd years ago, Metzger had been one of those child movie stars, performing under the name of Baby Igor. "My mother," he announced bitterly, "was really out to kasher me, boy, like a piece of beef on the sink, she wanted me drained and white. Times I wonder," smoothing down the hair at the back of his head, "if she succeeded. It scares me. You know what mothers like that turn their male children into."

"You certainly don't look," Oedipa began, then had second thoughts.

Metzger flashed her a big wry couple rows of teeth. "Looks don't mean a thing any more," he said. "I live inside my looks, and I'm never sure. The possibility haunts me."

"And how often," Oedipa inquired, now aware it was all

words, "has that line of approach worked for you, Baby Igor?"

"Do you know," Metger said, "Inverarity only mentioned you to me once."

"Were you close?"

"No. I drew up his will. Don't you want to know what he said?"

"No," said Oedipa, and snapped on the television set. Onto the screen bloomed the image of a child of indeterminate sex, its bare legs pressed awkwardly together, its shoulder-length curls mingling with the shorter hair of a St. Bernard, whose long tongue, as Oedipa watched, began to swipe at the child's rosy cheeks, making the child wrinkle up its nose appealingly and say, "Aw, Murray, come on, now, you're getting me all wet."

"That's me, that's me," cried Metzger, staring, "good God."

"Which one?" asked Oedipa.

"That movie was called," Metzger snapped his fingers, "*Cashiered.*"

"About you and your mother."

"About this kid and his father, who's drummed out of the British Army for cowardice, only he's covering up for a friend, see, and to redeem himself he and the kid follow the old regiment to Gallipoli, where the father somehow builds a midget submarine, and every week they slip through the Dardanelles into the Sea of Marmara and torpedo the Turkish merchantmen, the father, son, and St. Bernard. The dog sits on periscope watch, and barks if he sees anything."

Oedipa was pouring wine. "You're kidding."

"Listen, listen, here's where I sing." And sure enough, the child, and dog, and a merry old Greek fisherman who had appeared from nowhere with a zither, now all stood in front of phony-Dodecanese process footage of a seashore at sunset, and the kid sang.

BABY IGOR'S SONG

'Gainst the Hun and the Turk, never once do we shirk,
My daddy, my doggie and me.
Through the perilous years, like the Three Musketeers,
We will stick just as close as can be.
Soon our sub's periscope'll aim for Constantinople,
As again we set hopeful to sea;
Once more unto the breach, for those boys on the beach,
Just my daddy, my doggie and me.

Then there was a musical bridge, featuring the fisherman and his instrument, then the young Metzger took it from the top while his aging double, over Oedipa's protests, sang harmony.

Either he made up the whole thing, Oedipa thought suddenly, or he bribed the engineer over at the local station to run this, it's all part of a plot, an elaborate, seduction, *plot*. O Metzger.

"You didn't sing along," he observed.

"I didn't *know*," Oedipa smiled. On came a loud commercial for Fangoso Lagoons, a new housing development west of here.

"One of Inverarity's interests," Metzger noted. It was to be laced by canals with private landings for power boats, a floating social hall in the middle of an artificial lake, at the bottom of which lay restored galleons, imported from the Bahamas; Atlantean fragments of columns and friezes from the Canaries; real human skeletons from Italy; giant clamshells from Indonesia—all for the entertainment of Scuba enthusiasts. A map of the place flashed onto the screen, Oedipa drew a sharp breath, Metzger on the chance it might be for him looked over. But she'd only been reminded of her look downhill this noontime. Some immediacy was there again, some promise of hierophany: printed circuit, gently curving streets, private access to the water, Book of the Dead. . . .

Before she was ready for it, back came *Cashiered*. The little submarine, named the "Justine" after the dead mother, was at the quai, singling up all lines. A small crowd was seeing it off, among them the old fisherman, and his daughter, a leggy, ringletted nymphet who, should there be a happy ending, would end up with Metzger; an English missionary nurse with a nice build on her, who would end up with Metzger's father; and even a female sheepdog with eyes for Murray the St. Bernard.

"Oh, yeah," Metzger said, "this is where we have trouble in the Narrows. It's a bitch because of the Kephez minefields, but Jerry has also recently hung this net, this gigantic net, woven out of cable 2½ inches thick."

Oedipa refilled her wine glass. They lay now, staring at the screen, flanks just lightly touching. There came from the TV set a terrific explosion. "Mines!" cried Metzger, covering his head and rolling away from her. "Daddy," blubbered the Metzger in the tube, "I'm scared." The inside of the midget sub was chaotic, the dog galloping to and fro scattering saliva that mingled with the spray from a leak in the bulkhead, which the father was now plugging with his shirt. "One thing we can do," announced the father, "go to the bottom, try to get *under* the net."

"Ridiculous," said Metzger. "They'd built a gate in it, so German U-boats could get through to attack the British fleet. All our E class subs simply used that gate."

"How do you know that?"

"Wasn't I there?"

"But," began Oedipa, then saw how they were suddenly out of wine.

"Aha," said Metzger, from an inside coat pocket producing a bottle of tequila.

"No lemons?" she asked, with movie-gaiety. "No salt?"

"A tourist thing. Did Inverarity use lemons when you were there?"

"How did you know we were there?" She watched him fill her glass, growing more anti-Metzger as the level rose.

"He wrote it off that year as a business expense. I did his tax stuff."

"A cash nexus," brooded Oedipa, "you and Perry Mason, two of a kind, it's all you know about, you shysters."

"But our beauty lies," explained Metzger, "in this extended capacity for convolution. A lawyer in a courtroom, in front of any jury, becomes an actor, right? Raymond Burr is an actor, impersonating a lawyer, who in front of a jury becomes an actor. Me, I'm a former actor who became a lawyer. They've done the pilot film of a TV series, in fact, based loosely on my career, starring my friend Manny Di Presso, a one-time lawyer who quit his firm to become an actor. Who in this pilot plays me, an actor become a lawyer reverting periodically to being an actor. The film is in an air-conditioned vault at one of the Hollywood studios, light can't fatigue it, it can be repeated endlessly."

"You're in trouble," Oedipa told him, staring at the tube, conscious of his thigh, warm through his suit and her slacks. Presently:

"The Turks are up there with searchlights," he said, pouring more tequila, watching the little submarine fill up, "patrol boats, and machine guns. You want to bet on what'll happen?"

"Of course not," said Oedipa, "the movie's made." He only smiled back. "One of your endless repetitions."

"But you still don't know," Metzger said. "You haven't seen it." Into the commercial break now roared a deafening ad for Beaconsfield Cigarettes, whose attractiveness lay in their filter's use of bone charcoal, the very best kind.

"Bones of what?" wondered Oedipa.

"Inverarity knew. He owned 51% of the filter process."

"Tell me."

"Someday. Right now it's your last chance to place your bet. Are they going to get out of it, or not?"

She felt drunk. It occurred to her, for no reason, that the plucky trio might not get out after all. She had no way to tell how long the movie had to run. She looked at her watch, but it had stopped. "This is absurd," she said, "of course they'll get out."

"How do you know?"

"All those movies had happy endings."

"All?"

"Most."

"That cuts down the probability," he told her, smug.

She squinted at him through her glass. "Then give me odds."

"Odds would give it away."

"So," she yelled, maybe a bit rattled, "I bet a bottle of something. Tequila, all right? That you didn't make it." Feeling the words had been conned out of her.

"That I didn't make it." He pondered. "Another bottle tonight would put you to sleep," he decided. "No."

"What do you want to bet, then?" She knew. Stubborn, they watched each other's eyes for what seemed five minutes. She heard commercials chasing one another into and out of the speaker of the TV. She grew more and more angry, perhaps juiced, perhaps only impatient for the movie to come back on.

"Fine then," she gave in at last, trying for a brittle voice, "it's a bet. Whatever you'd like. That you don't make it. That you all turn to carrion for the fish at the bottom of the Dardanelles, your daddy, your doggie, and you."

"Fair enough," drawled Metzger, taking her hand as if to shake on the bet and kissing its palm instead, sending the dry end of his tongue to graze briefly among her fate's furrows, the changeless salt hatchings of her identity. She wondered then if this were really happening in the same way as, say, her first time in bed with Pierce, the dead man. But then the movie came back.

The father was huddled in a shellhole on the steep cliffs of the Anzac beachhead, Turkish shrapnel flying all over the place. Neither Baby Igor nor Murray the dog were in evidence. "Now what the hell," said Oedipa.

"Golly," Metzger said, "they must have got the reels screwed up."

"Is this before or after?" she asked, reaching for the tequila bottle, a move that put her left breast in the region of Metzger's nose. The irrepressibly comic Metzger made crosseyes before replying,

"That would be telling."

"Come on." She nudged his nose with the padded tip of her bra cup and poured booze. "Or the bet's off."

"Nope," Metzger said.

"At least tell me if that's his old regiment, there."

"Go ahead," said Metzger, "ask questions. But for each answer, you'll have to take something off. We'll call it Strip Botticelli."

Oedipa had a marvellous idea: "Fine," she told him, "but first I'll just slip into the bathroom for a second. Close your eyes, turn around, don't peek." On the screen the "River Clyde," a collier carrying 2000 men, beached at Sedd-el-Bahr in an unearthly silence. "This is it, men," a phony British accent was heard to whisper. Suddenly a host of Turkish rifles on shore opened up all together, and the massacre began.

"I know this part," Metzger told her, his eyes squeezed shut, head away from the set. "For fifty yards out the sea was red with blood. They don't show that." Oedipa skipped into the bathroom, which happened also to have a walk-in closet, quickly undressed and began putting on as much as she could of the clothing she'd brought with her: six pairs of panties in assorted colors, girdle, three pairs of nylons, three brassieres, two pairs stretch slacks, four half-slips, one black sheath, two summer dresses, half dozen A-line skirts, three sweaters, two blouses, quilted wrapper, baby blue peignoir and old Orlon muu-muu. Bracelets then, scatter-pins, earrings, a pendant. It all seemed to take hours to put on and she could hardly walk when she was finished. She made the mistake of looking at herself in the full-length mirror, saw a beach ball with feet, and laughed so violently she fell over, taking a can of hair spray on the sink with her. The can hit the floor, something broke, and with a great outsurge of pressure the stuff commenced atomizing, propelling the can swiftly about the bathroom. Metzger rushed in to find Oedipa rolling around, trying to get back on her feet, amid a great sticky miasma of fragrant lacquer. "Oh, for Pete's sake," he said in his Baby Igor voice. The can, hissing malignantly, bounced off the toilet and whizzed by Metzger's right ear, missing by maybe a quarter of an inch. Metzger hit the deck and cowered with Oedipa as the can continued its high-speed caroming; from the other room came a slow, deep crescendo of naval bombardment, machine-gun, howitzer and small-arms fire, screams and chopped-off prayers of dying infantry. She looked up past his eyelids, into the staring ceiling light, her field of vision cut across by wild, flashing over-flights of the can, whose pressure seemed inexhaustible. She was scared but nowhere near sober. The can knew where it was going, she sensed, or something fast enough, God or a digital machine, might have computed in advance the complex web of its travel; but she wasn't fast enough, and knew only that it might hit them at any moment, at whatever clip it was doing, a hundred miles an hour. "Metzger," she moaned, and sank her teeth into his upper arm, through the sharkskin. Everything smelled like hair spray. The can collided with a mirror and bounced away, leaving a silvery, reticulated bloom of glass to hang a second before it all fell jingling into the sink; zoomed over to the enclosed shower, where it crashed into and totally destroyed a panel of frosted glass; thence around the three tile walls, up to the ceiling, past the light, over the two prostrate bodies, amid its own whoosh and the buzzing, distorted uproar from the TV set. She could imagine no end to it; yet presently the can did give up in mid-flight and fall to the floor, about a foot from Oedipa's nose. She lay watching it.

"Blimey," somebody remarked. "Coo." Oedipa took her teeth out of Metzger, looked around and saw in the doorway Miles, the kid with the bangs and mohair suit, now multiplied by four. It seemed to be the group he'd mentioned, the Para-noids. She couldn't tell them apart, three of them were carry-

ing electric guitars, they all had their mouth open. There
also appeared a number of girls' faces, gazing through arm-
pits and around angles of knees. "That's kinky," said one
of the girls.

"Are you from London?" another wanted to know: "Is
that a London thing you're doing?" Hair spray hung like
fog, glass twinkled all over the floor.

"Lord love a duck," summarized the boy holding a pass-
key, and Oedipa decided this was Miles. Deferent, he began
to narrate for their entertainment a surfer orgy he had
been to the week before, involving a five-gallon can of kidney
suet, a small automobile with a sun roof, and a trained seal.

"I'm sure this pales by comparison," said Oedipa, who'd
succeeded in rolling over, "so why don't you all just, you
know, go outside. And sing. None of this works without mood
music. Serenade us."

"Maybe later," invited one of the other Paranoids shyly,
"you could join us in the pool."

"Depends how hot it gets in here, gang," winked jolly
Oedipa. The kids filed out, after plugging extension cords
into all available outlets in the other room and leading them
in a bundle out a window.

Metzger helped her stagger to her feet. "Anyone for Strip
Botticelli?" In the other room the TV was blaring a commercial for a Turkish bath in downtown San Narciso, wher-
ever downtown was, called Hogan's Seraglio. "Inverarity
owned that too," Metzger said. "Did you know that?"

"Sadist," Oedipa yelled, "say it once more, I'll wrap the
TV tube around your head."

"You're really mad," he smiled.

She wasn't, really. She said, "What the hell didn't he own?"

Metzger cocked an eyebrow at her. "You tell me."

If she was going to she got no chance, for outside, all
in a shuddering deluge of thick guitar chords, the Paranoids
had broken into song. Their drummer had set up precar-
iously on the diving board, the others were invisible. Metzger
came up behind her with some idea of cupping his hands
around her breasts, but couldn't immediately find them because of all the clothes. They stood at the window and heard
the Paranoids singing.

SERENADE

As I lie and watch the moon
On the lonely sea,
Watch it tug the lonely tide
Like a comforter over me,
The still and faceless moon
Fills the beach tonight
With only a ghost of day,
All shadow gray, and moonbeam white.
And you lie alone tonight,
As alone as I;
Lonely girl in your lonely flat, well, that's where it's at,
So hush your lonely cry.
How can I come to you, put out the moon, send back the tide?
The night has gone so gray, I'd lose the way, and it's dark
   inside.
No, I must lie alone,
Till it comes for me;
Till it takes the sky, the sand, the moon, and the lonely sea.
And the lonely sea . . . etc. [FADE OUT.]

"Now then," Oedipa shivered brightly.

"First question," Metzger reminded her. From the TV set the St. Bernard was barking. Oedipa looked and saw Baby Igor, disguised as a Turkish begger lad, skulking with the dog around a set she took to be Constantinople.

"Another early reel," she said hopefully.

"I can't allow that question," Metzger said. On the doorsill the Paranoids, as we leave milk to propitiate the leprechaun, had set a fifth of Jack Daniels.

"Oboy," said Oedipa. She poured a drink. "Did Baby Igor get to Constantinople in the good submarine 'Justine'?"

"No," said Metzger. Oedipa took off an earring.

"Did he get there in, what did you call them, in an E Class submarine."

"No," said Metzger. Oedipa took off another earring.

"Did he get there overland, maybe through Asia Minor?"

"Maybe," said Metzger. Oedipa took off another earring.

"Another earring?" said Metzger.

"If I answer that, will you take something off?"

"I'll do it without an answer," roared Metzger, shucking out of his coat. Oedipa refilled her glass, Metzger had another snort from the bottle. Oedipa then sat five minutes watching the tube, forgetting she was supposed to ask questions. Metzger took his trousers off, earnestly. The father seemed to be up before a court-martial, now.

"So," she said, "an early reel. This is where he gets cashiered, ha, ha."

"Maybe it's a flashback," Metzger said. "Or maybe he gets it twice." Oedipa removed a bracelet. So it went: the succession of film fragments on the tube, the progressive removal of clothing that seemed to bring her no nearer nudity, the boozing, the tireless shivaree of voices and guitars from out by the pool. Now and then a commercial would come in, each time Metzger would say, "Inverarity's," or "Big block of shares," and later settled for nodding and smiling. Oedipa would scowl back, growing more and more certain, while a headache began to flower behind her eyes, that they among all possible combinations of new lovers had found a way to make time itself slow down. Things grew less and less clear. At some point she went into the bathroom, tried to find her image in the mirror and couldn't. She had a moment of nearly pure terror. Then remembered that the mirror had broken and fallen in the sink. "Seven years' bad luck," she said aloud. "I'll be 35." She shut the door behind her and took the occasion to blunder, almost absently, into another slip and skirt, as well as a long-leg girdle and a couple pairs of knee socks. It struck her that if the sun ever came up Metzger would disappear. She wasn't sure if she wanted him to. She came back in to find Metzger wearing only a pair of boxer shorts and fast asleep with a hardon and his head under the couch. She noticed also a fat stomach the suit had hidden. On the screen New Zealanders and Turks were impaling one another on bayonets. With a cry Oedipa rushed to him, fell on him, began kissing him to wake him up. His radiant eyes flew open, pierced her, as if she could feel the sharpness somewhere vague between her breasts. She sank with an enormous sigh that carried all rigidity like a mythical fluid from her, down next to him; so weak she couldn't help him undress her; it took him 20 minutes, rolling, arranging her this way and that, as if she thought, he were some scaled-up, short-haired, poker-faced little girl with a Barbie doll. She may have fallen asleep once or twice. She awoke at last to find herself getting laid; she'd come in on a sexual crescendo in progress, like a cut to a scene where the camera's already moving. Outside a fugue of guitars had begun, and she counted each electronic voice as it came in, till she reached six or so and recalled only three of the Paranoids playing guitars; so others must be plugging in.

Which indeed they were. Her climax and Metzger's, when it came, coincided with every light in the place, including the TV tube, suddenly going out, dead, black. It was a curious experience. The Paranoids had blown a fuse. When the lights came on again, and she and Metzger lay twined amid a wall-to-wall scatter of clothing and spilled bourbon, the TV tube revealed the father, dog and Baby Igor trapped inside the darkening "Justine," as the water level inexorably rose. The dog was first to drown, in a great crowd of bubbles. The camera came in for a close-up of Baby Igor crying, one hand on the control board. Something short-circuited then and the grounded Baby Igor was electrocuted, thrashing back and forth and screaming horribly. Through one of those Hollywood distortions in probability, the father was spared electrocution so he could make a farewell speech, apologizing to Baby Igor and the dog for getting them into this and regretting that they wouldn't be meeting in heaven: "Your little eyes have seen your daddy for the last time. You are for salvation; I am for the Pit." At the end his suffering eyes filled the screen, the sound of incoming water grew deafening, up swelled that strange '30's movie music with the massive sax section, in faded the legend THE END.

Oedipa had leaped to her feet and run across to the other wall to turn and glare at Metzger. "They didn't make it!" she yelled. "You bastard, I won."

"You won me," Metzger smiled.

"What did Inverarity tell you about me," she asked finally.

"That you wouldn't be easy."

She began to cry.

"Come back," said Metzger. "Come on."

After awhile she said, "I will." And she did.

WALKER PERCY
from *The Last Gentleman* (1966)

Walker Percy's *The Moviegoer* dwelled upon the life and mind of Binx Bolling, a man in search of meaning, who haunted movie houses where life gained a sense of authenticity it lacked outside. *The Last Gentleman* concentrates upon two men—Will Barrett, a young Southerner frequently subject both to despair and amnesia, and Sutter Vaught, M.D., a brilliant, enigmatic physician who delights in both Christian Existentialism and pornography. Barrett pursues Dr. Vaught throughout the novel, sure that the pornographer can tell him what to do with his life. At long last, Barrett corners him; the dialogue that results needs close attention, but in it there is a kind of desperate resolution characteristic of Black Humor in its metaphysical mood.

"Jamie" is Dr. Vaught's ailing younger brother, whose care has been entrusted to Barrett. "Val," a nun, is Dr. Vaught's sister, with whom he frequently debates the value of orthodox religion. "Kitty," another Vaught girl, is Barrett's intended. The setting is deep in the southeastern United States, where Barrett has come in search of Vaught.

The next morning Jamie was even better. His fever was gone, but he was tired and wanted to sleep. For the first time he spoke seriously of going home, no, not home but to the Gulf Coast, where they could lie in the sand dunes and get in shape for the next semester. "I have the strongest hunch that the combination of cold salt water and the warm sunny dunes would be great!"

The engineer nodded. Sure enough it might.

Would the engineer take him?

"Let's go," said the latter rising.

Jamie laughed and nodded to signify that he knew the other meant it. "But I'll leave tomorrow, no kidding," he said as the engineer cranked him flat for his nap.

"We can make it in three days," the engineer told him. "Your monk's pad is still on the upper berth."

Jamie said no more about calling Val.

But for the present it was the engineer who lay in the upper berth and read:

Christ should leave us. He is too much with us and I don't like his friends. We have no hope of recovering Christ until Christ leaves us. There is after all something worse than being God-forsaken. It is when God overstays his welcome and takes up with the wrong people.

You say don't worry about that, first stop fornicating. But I am depressed and transcendent. In such a condition, fornication is the sole channel to the real. Do you think I am making excuses?

You are wrong too about the sinfulness of suicide in this age, at least the nurtured possibility of suicide, for the certain availability of death is the very condition of recovering oneself. But death is as outlawed now as sin used to be. Only one's own suicide remains to one. My "suicide" followed the breakdown of the sexual as a mode of reentry from the posture of transcendence.

Here is what happened. I became depressed last summer when I first saw Jamie's blood smear, depressed not because he was going to die but because I knew he would not die well, would be eased out in an oxygen tent, tranquilized and with no sweat to anyone and not even know what he was doing. Don't misunderstand me: I wasn't thinking about baptism.

The depression made me concupiscent. On a house call

to the Mesa Motel to examine a patient in diabetic coma (but really only to collect blood for chemistry—I was little more than a technician that summer). Afterwards spied a chunky blonde by the pool, appraised her eye, which was both lewd and merry. She 41, aviatrix, winner of Powder Puff Derby in 1940's, raced an old Lockheed P-38 from San Diego to Cleveland. We drank two glasses of straight whiskey. I spoke in her ear and invited her to her room. Afterwards very low. Went to ranch, shot myself, missed brain, carried away cheek.

Recovery in hospital. The purity of ordeal. The purity of death. The sweet purity of the little Mexican nurse. Did Americans become lewd when they banished death?

I saw something clearly while I had no cheek and grinned like a skeleton. But I got well and forgot what it was. I won't miss next time.

It was the last entry in Sutter's casebook. When he finished reading, the engineer left the Trav-L-Aire and threw the pad into the trashburner of Alamogordo Motor Park. As he watched it burn, glowering, his head sinking lower and lower, mouth slack and drying, he became aware that someone was speaking to him. It was a fellow Trav-L-Aire owner, a retired fire inspector from Muncie. He and his wife, the man had told him, were in the midst of their yearly swing from Victoria, B.C., to Key West, They kept just ahead of winter on the way down and just behind spring going north. It was a courtesy of the road that camper owners show their rigs to each other. The engineer invited him in. The Hoosier was polite enough—the engineer's was the most standard of all Trav-L-Aires—but it was obvious that the former had a surprise in store. After showing off his cabin, which had a tinted sun-liner roof, he pressed a button. A panel above the rear door flew open and a contraption of aluminum spars and green netting unhinged in six directions. With a final grunt of its hidden motor the thing snapped into a taut cube of a porch big enough for a bridge game. "You take off your screen door and put it here," the Hoosier told him. "It's the only thing for west Florida, where you're going to get your sand flies."

"Very good," said the engineer, nodding, and thrusting his hand through his pocket, for his knee had begun to leap.

Returning to his own modest camper, he became at once agitated and lustful. His heart beat powerfully at the root of his neck. The coarsest possible images formed themselves before his eyes. But this time, instead of throwing a fit or lapsing into a fugue as he had done so often in the past, he became acutely conscious of the most insignificant sensations, the slight frying sound of the Servel refrigerator, the watery reflection on the Formica table, which seemed to float up the motes of dust. His memory, instead of failing, became perfect. He recalled everything, even a single perception years ago, one of a thousand billion, so trivial that it was not even remembered then, five minutes later: on a college field trip through the mangy Jersey woods looking for spirogyra, he had crossed a utility right-of-way. When he reached the farther woods, he had paused and looked over his shoulder. There was nothing to see: the terrain dipped, making a little swale which was overgrown by the special forlorn plants of rights-of-way, not small trees or bushes or even weeds exactly but just the unclassified plants which grow up in electric-light-and-power-places. That was all. He turned and went on.

Desolate places like Appomattox and cut-over woods were ever the occasion of storms of sexual passion. Yet now when he rushed out into the abstract afternoon to find a maid (but who?) he forgot again and instead found himself picking through the ashes of the trashburner. What was that last sentence? It had a bearing. But the notebook was destroyed.

Jumping into the cab of the G.M.C., he tore out of the poplar grove, forgetting his umbilical connections until he heard the snappings of cords and the shout of the Hoosier.

"What the—" yelled the latter like an astounded comic-strip character, Uncle Walt (so that's where the expression "What the—" comes from—Indiana).

"I'm going over to Albuquerque," shouted the engineer as if this were an explanation and as quickly changed his mind, stopped, and strode past the still-astounded

Hoosier. "Pardon," he said, "I think I'll call Kitty—" and nodded by way of further explanation to a telephone hooked contingently to a telephone pole. Could he call Kitty from such a contingent telephone?

Perhaps if he could talk to a certain someone he would stop hankering for anyone and everyone, and tender feelings of love would take the place of this great butting billygoat surge which was coming over him again. He clung to the pole, buffeted by an abstract, lustful molecular wind, and might even have uttered a sound, brayed into the phone, for the Hoosier looked astounded again and rushed into his deluxe Sun-Liner.

"I remember everything now, Dr. Vaught," he said calmly, no longer agitated. "You said I was to come and find you. Very well, here I am. What was it you wished to tell me?"

So distracted had been the engineer in his headlong race across the desert that he had noticed not a single thing on the way and could not have said how he found his way here. Only now as Sutter sighed and sank into himself could he spare time to take a breath and see where he was.

Sutter was sitting in a sheriff's chair on the front porch of Doc's cottage. Doc's was one of a hundred or more such cottages fronting on a vast quadrangle of rich blue-green winter grass bordered by palm trees, a rectangular oasis in a scrabbly desert of mesquite. The evening rides were over and it was almost suppertime. Doors slammed as the dudes, mostly women, began the slow promenade to the chuck wagon. The sun was already down behind Sandia Mountain but the sky was bright and pure and empty as map space. The dudes smiled and nodded at Doc as they passed but the latter sat slumped and unresponsive, his dried-up Thom McAn shoes propped on the rail and Curlee pants hitched halfway up his skinny legs.

Sutter didn't seem to hear him. He slumped further and gazed at the bare mountain. The material of his trousers bunched up between his legs like curtain drapes.

"Then you have nothing to tell me," the engineer asked him again.

"That is correct. Nothing."

"But, sir, you wrote many things in—"

"In the first place I didn't write them to you. In the second place I no longer believe a word of it. Did you ever read the great philosopher Wittgenstein?"

"No sir," said the other gloomily.

"After his last work he announced the dictum which summarized his philosophy. He said: Whereof one cannot speak, thereof one should keep silent. And he did. He stopped teaching and went to live in a hut and said no more."

"And you believe that?"

"No, I don't even believe that."

They watched the women for a while. Presently the engineer said, "But you told me to come out and find you."

"I did?"

"Therefore you at least owe me the explanation of what happened to make you change your mind."

"What has happened?" Sutter looked puzzled.

"What has happened to you?"

"Nothing has happened."

From the chair beside him, where he must have held it all along and out of the other's sight, Sutter raised the Colt Woodsman and sighted it at an airliner which sparkled like a diamond in the last of the sunlight.

"But Val told me that you—"

"Val." Sutter smiled as he tracked the airliner.

"Oh, I know you don't agree with Val."

"Oh, but I do agree with her."

"You do?"

"Oh yes, in every respect. About what has happened to the world, about what God should be and what man is, and even what the Church should be."

The engineer sighed. "Yes sir. That is very interesting, but I think you know why I am here."

"You see, Barrett, Val had a dream of what the Church should come to. (And I agree! Absolutely!) For example, she did not mind at all if Christendom should be done for, stove in, kaput, screwed up once and all. She did not mind that the Christers were like everybody else, if not worse. She did not even mind that God shall be gone, absent, not present, A.W.O.L., and that no one noticed or cared, not even the believers. Because she wanted us to go the route and be like Sweden, which is not necessarily bad, but to go the route, to leave God out of it and be happy or miserable, as the case might be. She believes that then, if we go the route and run out of Christendom, that the air would be cleared and even that God might give us a sign. That's how her own place makes sense, you see, her little foundation in the pines. She conceived herself as being there with her Delco and her butane tanks to start all over again. Did you notice how much it looked like one of those surviving enclaves after the Final War, and she's probably right: I mean, who in the hell would want to bomb South Alabama? But yes, I agree with her. Absolutely! It's just that nothing ever came of it."

"Dr. Vaught. Excuse me, but—"

"Don't you see? Nothing happened. She got all dressed up for the bridegroom and the bridegroom didn't come. There she sits in the woods as if the world had ended and she was one of the Elected Ones Left to keep the Thing going, but the world has not ended, in fact is more the same than usual. We are in the same fix, she and I, only I know it and she doesn't. Here I sit in Sweden—most of those women are Swedes, spiritual Swedes, if you will notice—but I do not wait for a sign because there is no sign. I will even agree with her that when I first came to the desert I was waiting for a sign, but there was no sign and I am not waiting for one now."

"Yes sir. That is very interesting. But the reason I came, if you will recall, is that you told me—"

"But she changed, you see, and that was when we parted company. I could make some sense of her notion of being the surviving remnant of her Catholic Thing (which has to prevail, you see, in spite of all, yes, I don't mind that) set down back there in that God-forsaken place. That was fitting. But she changed, you see. *She became hopeful.* She goes to confraternity meetings in Mobile. She has dealings with the Methodist preacher, even the Baptists. She corresponds with scientists. She begs from the Seven-Up man and slips him a K.C. pamphlet

('How many churches did Christ found?'). She talks the Klonsul into giving her a gym. In short, she sold out. Hell, what she is is a Rotarian."

"Yes sir, very true, but what I want to—"

"Barrett."

"Sir?"

"Which is the best course for a man: to live like a Swede, vote for the candidate of your choice, be a good fellow, healthy and generous, do a bit of science as if the world made sense, enjoy a beer and a good piece (not a bad life!). Or: to live as a Christian among Christians in Alabama? Or to die like an honest man?"

"I couldn't say," said the engineer. He was bitterly disappointed by Sutter's refusal to take him seriously.

"How is Jamie?" asked Sutter.

"Better," said the other absently. "I am on my way there now. If you will answer my question, I'll leave."

"What question?"

"The last time I saw you you said you had something to tell me. What was it?"

"I don't remember."

The engineer, who had been pacing the tiny porch, which abutted Wells Fargo on one side and the O.K. Corral on the other, paused and fixed Sutter with a lively clairvoyant expression. Now at last he remembered everything, knew what he knew and what he didn't know and what he wished to know. He even remembered every sentence in Sutter's notebook.

"I want to know what it was you discovered while you were in the, ah, hospital out here last summer."

"What?" said Sutter, coming down hard on all four legs of the captain's chair.

The engineer was not disconcerted. "I've finished your casebook. I wish to know whether you meant only that when you're in a bad way things look better than they do ordinarily."

"Oh," said Sutter, replacing his feet. "That. I don't remember. That was a long time ago and, as I told you, I attach no importance to that stuff. It was written to be rid of it, excreta, crap, and so intended."

"I just finished speaking to Kitty." The engineer drew up another sheriff's chair. "We spoke for two hours. It cost twenty-four dollars. I had to reverse the charges."

"Good Lord. I can't imagine talking to Kitty for five minutes."

"We settled a great many things," said the engineer, frowning—who in hell was Sutter to patronize Kitty?

"Are you getting married?" asked Sutter politely, turning his chair a few degrees but keeping his pale eyes fixed on the brown schematic mountain.

"Yes. After—things are more settled. But that is not why I drove out here this afternoon. I want to know this," he said, leaning over and grabbing the rim of Sutter's chair so hard that his knuckles turned white. "I want to know why you brought Jamie out here."

Sutter tried to tear his eyes from the mountain. "You're right. It didn't work, did it?"

"Right? What do you mean? What didn't work?"

Sutter shrugged. "Jamie's little idea of a vacation."

"Jamie's? But according to what you wrote, it was your idea too. What did you expect him to do?"

"It's not what I expected."

"Then he expected something?"

"Yes."

"What?"

"He expected something to happen."

"What? Not get well?"

Sutter shrugged.

"But you brought him out. You must have hoped for something."

"Only that he might get a little better."

"Get better?" He watched the other like a hawk. "No, you mean die better, don't you?"

Sutter shrugged and said nothing.

"You didn't answer," said the engineer after a moment.

Again Sutter's feet hit the floor. "Goddamn it, Barrett, what do you mean by requiring answers from me? Why should I answer you? What are you to me? Christ, if you recall I never solicited your company in the first place."

"I am asking nevertheless," said the engineer cheerfully.

"Why me, for Christ's sake?"

"I don't know."

"What do you take me for, some pissant wise man, ole rebel Sutter whom the yokels back home can't stand and who therefore by your peculiar logic must be onto something just because they're not? You know something, Barrett? There's one thing I've never been able to get the straight of, and that is what it is you want of me. I suspect it is one of two things. You either want me to tell you to fornicate or not to fornicate, but for the life of me I can't tell which it is."

"Then tell me," said the engineer smiling.

"I will not tell you."

"Tell me to be chaste and I will do it. Yes! I will do it easily!" he said, striking the rail softly with his fist. "All you have to do is tell me."

"I will not tell you."

"Then tell me not to be chaste."

"I will not."

"Why not?"

"Barrett, since when is failure, my failure, a badge of wisdom?"

"I did not think of it that way," said the engineer, frowning. Suddenly he did see Sutter for the first time as the dismalest failure, a man who had thrown himself away. He marveled at his, the engineer's, being here.

"I know you don't," said Sutter, not unkindly. "But maybe you better start. For both our sakes. Be done with me. Go stay with Jamie."

"That's what I'm trying to do," said the other absently.

"What?"

"Be done with you."

"I fervently wish you success."

"Yes," said the engineer, cheering up. "Yes! You're right. There is no reason why I can't just get up and go about my business, is there?"

"No reason."

"To answer your earlier question: yes, Kitty and I are getting married."

"You mentioned it."

"We spoke of many things."

"Good."

"And settled a fair proportion of them."

"Good."

"It turns out we see eye to eye on most things."

"Excellent."

"It seems that Mr. Vaught has made Lamar a vice-president and that he is going to offer me the position of personnel manager. I actually feel I might do well at it."

"I have no doubt of it."

"For the first time I feel fairly certain of what I want to do."

"I'm glad to hear it."

"We even have a house in mind. Cap'n Andy Mickle's place on South Ridge. Do you know it?"

"Very well indeed."

"You've been there?"

"A dozen times."

"Why? Oh. You mean to treat Cap'n Andy?"

"A colossal bore. He bored himself to death. But that's no reflection on the house. An ideal spot. The best view on the ridge."

The Engineer frowned, thinking of the buzzards circling the doleful plain and Cap'n Andy striding the "bridge." But he quickly brightened. "We've even agreed on the same denomination."

"The same *what?*"

"Denomination. Church. Kitty has become quite religious. She is convinced of the wisdom of our having the same church home, to use her expression." The engineer laughed tolerantly, shaking his head at the ways of women, and wiped a merry tolerant little tear from his eye.

"Jesus," muttered Sutter.

"Eh?" The other cocked his good ear.

"Nothing."

"You don't fool me, Dr. Vaught. Don't forget that I've read your casebook. Though I do not pretend to understand everything, that part didn't escape me."

"What part?"

"Your awareness of the prime importance of the religious dimension of life."

"The religious dimension of life?" Sutter looked at him suspiciously. "Barrett, are you putting me on?"

"No sir."

"Then if you're not, you're doing something worse."

"Sir?" asked the engineer politely.

"Never mind."

"Dr. Vaught," said the engineer earnestly. "There is one more thing. Then I will leave."

"What is that?"

"Dr. Vaught, Kitty and I are getting married. I am going to take a good position with your father, settle down on the South Ridge, and, I hope, raise a family."

"Yes," said Sutter after a pause.

"I think I'm going to be a pretty fair member of the community. God knows the place could use even a small contribution of good will and understanding."

"Beyond a doubt. Good will and understanding. Yes. Very good."

"Well?"

"Well what?"

"What's wrong with that?"

"Nothing. I think you'll be very happy. In fact I'll go further than that. I don't think you'll have any more trouble with your fugues. And I take it back: I don't think you are kidding me."

"I see. Dr. Vaught."

"What?"

"I know you think there is something wrong with it."

"You do?"

"Yes. I know you think there is everything wrong with it."

"Nonsense." Sutter laughed. "Would you rather join me here?"

"No, but—"

"But what?"

"But nothing." The engineer rose. "There is nothing wrong with it. Truthfully I see now there is nothing wrong with such a life."

"Right!"

"It is better to do something than do nothing—no reflection, sir."

"No reflection."

"It is good to have a family."

"You are quite right."

"Better to love and be loved."

"Absolutely."

"To cultivate whatever talents one has."

"Correct."

"To make a contribution, however small."

"However small."

"To do one's best to promote tolerance and understanding between the races, surely the most pressing need before the country."

"Beyond question the most pressing need. Tolerance and understanding. Yes."

The engineer flushed. "Well, isn't it better?"

"Yes."

"Violence is bad."

"Violence is not good."

"It is better to make love to one's wife than to monkey around with a lot of women."

"A lot better."

"I am sure I am right."

"You are right."

The engineer gazed gloomily at the chuck wagon, a large red dining cottage across the quadrangle. Cookie, a Chinese with a black cap and a queue, came out and seizing the branding iron rang it around the iron triangle.

"You know, Dr. Vaught, I have lived a rather abnormal and solitary life and have tended to get things backwards. My father was a proud and solitary man. I had no other family. For a long time I have had a consuming desire for girls, for the coarsest possible relations with them, without knowing how to treat them as human beings. No doubt, as you suggested, a good part of my nervous condition stems from this abnormal relationship—or lack of relationship—"

"As I suggested? I never suggested any such goddamn thing."

"At any rate," the engineer went on hurriedly, looking down at the other, "I think I see for the first time the possibility of a happy, useful life."

"Good. So?"

"Dr. Vaught, why was that man screaming?"

"What man?"

"The man you told me about—the Deke from Vanderbilt —with the lovely wife and children—you know."

"Oh, Scotty. Christ, Barrett, for somebody with fugues, you've got quite a memory."

"Yes sir."

"Don't worry about Scotty. You won't scream. I can assure you, you will not scream."

"Then it is better not to?"

"Are you asking me?"

"Yes."

Sutter shrugged.

"You have nothing more to tell me?"

"No, Barrett, nothing." To his surprise, Sutter answered him quietly, without making a face or cursing.

The engineer laughed with relief. "For the first time I think I really might live like other men—rejoin the human race."

"I hope you'll all be happy. You and the race, I mean."

"Oh, I forgot something. It was something Kitty said to tell you. God, I'm selfish."

"But in the future you're going to be unselfish."

"What? Oh. Yes," said the engineer, smiling. He declined to conspire with Sutter's irony. "Kitty said to tell you Lamar was going to take a special course in management at the Harvard Business School."

"Good Lord, what do I care what Lamar does?"

The engineer kept a wary eye on him. "And that while he is in Boston, Myra is going to stay with Rita in New York."

"Myra Thigpen? I see. Do you want to know something? It figures."

"Rita is already gone. Myra is leaving after—afterwards."

"So Rita is gone." Sutter gazed into the empty sky, which instead of turning rosy with sunset was simply going out like a light.

As the other watched him, Sutter began idly picking off dudes, sighting the Colt at one after another of the passing women, idly yet with a regardlessness which was alarming. It was a very small thing, no more than that Sutter did not take pains to conceal the pistol from the women, but for some reason the engineer's heart began to pound against his ribs.

"On the other hand," Sutter was saying between shots, "it is also possible to die without significance and that is hardly an improvement of one's state of life. I knew a man once, not my own patient I am glad to say, who was sitting with his family one Sunday evening watching Lassie, who had befriended a crippled duck and was protecting him from varmints. During the commercial he got up and got out his old army forty-five. When his family asked him what he intended to do, he told them he was going outside to shoot a varmint. So he went outside to the garage and got into the family's second car, a Dodge Dart, and blew the top of his head off. Now that's a lot of damn foolishness, isn't it?"

"Yes sir," said the engineer, who was now more irritated than frightened by Sutter's antics with the pistol. Nor did he any longer believe Sutter's dire little case histories. "The other thing I want to tell you is that—" he said as Cookie rang second call with the branding iron, "Kitty said to tell you that the, ah, legal difficulties in your case have been cleared up and that—"

"You mean the coast is clear."

"Yes sir."

"Poppy has fixed things up and Doc Holliday can come back home to Valdosta."

"Sir, you have an enormous contribution to make—" began the engineer.

Sutter rose so suddenly that the younger man was afraid he'd made him angry again. But Sutter's attention was elsewhere.

Following his eye, the engineer alighted upon one of the guests who had left the O.K. Corral next door and was presently coming abreast of Doc's cottage. To judge from her Levis, which were stiff and blue, she was a new arrival. The old civil sorrowful air of the East still clung to her; she walked as if she still wore a dress. Though she had hooked her thumbs into her pockets, she had not yet got into the way of making herself free of herself and of swinging her legs like a man. She even wore a cowgirl hat, not at all the thing here, which had fallen down her back and was supported by a string at her throat. But she was abstracted and did not care, and instead of ambling along with the others, she went musing alone, tongue set against her teeth and hissing a solitary little tune. There was about her the wryness and ruefulness of a twenty-eight-year-old who has been staggered by a not quite mortal blow and has her own woman's way of getting over it and in fact has already done so. She knew how to muse along a path and hiss a little tune and keep herself to herself.

Sutter rose creakily but cheerfully and rubbed his dry

reedy hands together. "I do believe it is time to eat. Will you join me?"

"No sir. I promised Jamie I'd be back by seven."

To his relief, Sutter left the Colt in his chair and had, apparently, forgotten about it.

"I'll be in by nine."

"Yes sir."

"Barrett, I think you'd better call the family."

"But I just—"

"Tell them they'd better get out here."

"Yes sir."

"Tell them I said so."

"All right."

"Somebody will have to be here to take care of things after Jamie's death."

"I'll be here."

"Some member of the family."

"You'll be here."

"No, Barrett, I'll not be here."

"Why not?" asked the other angrily—he had had enough of Sutter's defections.

"Barrett," said Sutter as cheerfully as ever, craning his neck to keep track of the new guest, "if you know anything at all—and, what with your peculiar gifts, you know a good deal more than that—you ought to know why not."

"I don't," said the engineer, at a total loss. He had lost his intuition!

"If I do outlive Jamie," said Sutter, putting on his Curlee jacket (double breasted!), "it will not be by more than two hours. What in Christ's name do you think I'm doing out here? Do you think I'm staying? Do you think I'm going back?"

The engineer opened his mouth but said nothing. For the first time in his life he was astonished.

"You won't join me, Barrett?"

"What? No. No, thanks."

Sutter nodded cheerfully, dropped the pistol in the side pocket of the jacket, and hurried down the path after the last of the dudes.

Perhaps this moment more than any other, the moment of his first astonishment, marked the beginning for the engineer of what is called a normal life. From that time forward it was possible to meet him and after a few minutes form a clear notion of what sort of fellow he was and how he would spend the rest of his life.

Part III

Four Endings

Black Humor tends to the apocalyptic conclusion. I have selected three which reach a particularly raucous pitch and, for contrast, a fourth that is almost effeminate in its tone, being meditative in nature rather than explosive—yet disclosing, on that level, what prompts the others. The first three conclude Charles Wright's *The Wig*, James Purdy's *Cabot Wright Begins*, and William Burroughs's *Nova Express*; the last is from John Barth's *The Floating Opera*. The center of Wright's novel is Lester Jefferson, a young Negro who dons a blonde wig, assuming that the wig alone will insure him a place in the Great Society. He meets nothing but failure until the very end, when he seduces a rich, beautiful girl eager for his permanent company. But Jefferson unaccountably leaves her, falls into the hands of the mysterious Mr. Fishback, the *eminence noir* (or should I say *blanche*?) of the novel, hears that his real love, The Deb, is dead, and proceeds with Fishback to a grotesque resolution in his parlor.

Cabot Wright Begins and *Nova Express* literally defy summary; for that very reason, paradoxically, they can be read easily in excerpt, for context is never a factor. Like *The Wig*—and many similar works, *Catch-22* and *The Magic Christian* prominent among them—*Cabot Wright Begins* piles episode upon episode, building a tower of absurdity with a straight face. It is the story of a production-line rapist, Cabot Wright, who "rapes out of boredom," a boredom not unlike that suffered by Binx Bolling and Will Barrett, a boredom based on an inability to find meaning of any sort in modern life. Here at last, imprisoned after committing more than 300 rapes, he comes to a new understanding. . . . *Nova Express* can only be read as a kind of modern *Paradise Lost*, where in the last few pages

Burroughs projects an appalling vision of a universe engulfed in technological madness.

John Barth's *The Floating Opera* seemingly ends on a note of hope. Todd Andrews, the speaker, manages to convince himself that he need not carry out the suicide toward which he has been moving all day in careful, premeditated action. If there is no reason why he should go on living, Todd reasons, there is also no reason why he should die. But I caution you to think carefully about the pale affirmation reached here. For all of the congeniality of Barth's tone, his metaphysics are no less stark than the grotesque parabolas of Wright, Purdy, and Burroughs. To repeat Wylie Sypher once again, any renewal of humanism proceeding from this base must surely find its renewal in a universe indifferent, at best, to the doings of mankind.

CHARLES WRIGHT
from *The Wig* (1966)

. . . The sky was clear and blue. A glazed sun highlighted the Harlem skyline. Looking at that skyline, I remembered what Mr. Fishback had once said to me. "Lester Jefferson," Mr. Fishback had said—it was on my sixteenth birthday—"you're almost a man. It's time you learned something. That Harlem skyline is the outline of your life. There is very little to discover by looking at the pavement."

I didn't know what he meant then, and I didn't know now. If I asked him—and I had asked—he'd just say, "You're on your own for now. *My presence won't be required until . . .*"

As if I wasn't aware that he was always, always around, hovering over me. He was a prime mover of people, a black magician. But it was the first of April, and too many things had happened, and Mr. Fishback was in Spain, or somewhere. Perhaps I didn't need him as yet. . . .

By the time I reached Central Park and 96th Street, four Puerto Ricans stopped me.

"Español?"

"No," I laughed, trying to break a gut string. I understood. It was The Wig. I realized that many Puerto Ricans wanted to lose their identity. Many of them pretended to be Brazilians. It was not only safer, it was chic. Puerto Ricans had inherited the dog trough vacated by the Negroes.

Burnished-red-golden-haired Puerto Ricans were extremely rare, as were burnished-red-golden-haired Negroes, I sadly reflected, crossing at 72nd Street and Central Park.

I walked along, magnificently Bewigged, shoulders erect, firm hands jammed in my blue jeans, jingling nickels and pennies, calm and a little lonely.

Suddenly I wanted to talk to someone; hoped someone

would say, "Good morning. What lovely weather we're having." "Yes. Isn't it?" I'd reply. "I think we'll have an early spring." "I hope so," the other party would say. "Of course, you never can tell." "That's right," I'd say. Corny human stuff like that.

I was rehearsing the imaginary dialogue when I smiled at a middle-aged woman with a face that looked as if it had stared too long at the walls of too many furnished rooms. The middle-aged woman's tiny pink eyes went from my smiling face to The Wig. She leaned back on the bench, opened her mouth, and shut her eyes tight.

Well, I thought moving on, she is not accustomed to beauty.

An elderly couple were eying me. I heard the man mutter to his wife: "It's all right, Wilma. Times are changing. Remember the first automobile? World War One? We can't escape what we've never dreamed because we've always believed it was impossible. Wilma? Please don't cry. We'll be dying soon. *And then we won't have to look at such sights.*"

He meant me.

The sight went calmly on, smiling at a fat Negro who carried a shopping bag with Silky Smooth printed on the side. The fat Negro woman spat tobacco juice at my shoes, and a blond Alice-in-Wonderland type urinated in a plastic sand bucket and tried to splash me. Her mother applauded.

I was beginning to get a little sore. I felt like saying, "Nothing, nothing—do you hear me—nothing can stop me." Who the hell did they take me for? Was I the young man who had ground three hundred pounds of chopped meat out of the bodies of seventy blind people? Or the young man who had rescued a pregnant mother and her five children from their burning home, and then single-handed built them a ranch house overnight? Was I the champion rod who had respectively screwed wife, husband, mother-in-law, part-time maid, twelve-year-old daughter, fourteen-year-old son, white parrot, and family collie pup?

No! I was the celebrated chicken man, and none of them knew it. Ten hours a day, five and a half days a week, crawling on my hands and knees all over Manhattan. And I'd been a target for such a long time. Five-feet-ten, naked without shoes, normal weight one hundred and forty pounds. Boyish, with a rolling non-nautical gait, my face typically mixed: chamber-pot-simmered American, the result of at least five different pure races copulating in two's and three's like a game of musical chairs.

Following my own shadow, it seemed that I was taking a step in *some* direction and that The Wig was my guide. Progress is our most important product, General Electric says, and I had progressed to the front door of hell when all I had actually been striving for was a quiet purgatory. And I did not find it strange that hell had a soft blue sky, a springlike air, music, dust, laughter, curses.

I only wished I could see a friendly face.

Up ahead I saw a girl wearing what seemed to be a white mink coat. I checked my stride. A trick of nature or a goddam trick of my eyes? I neared the girl. My blood began to percolate. She was different. Blue-black shiny hair. Complexion: light brown, or did it have an Oriental cast, or was it a trick of the light? The girl's dark eyes were heavily lidded. The lips might have belonged to a beautiful woman of any race. But what was her actual nationality? Mulatto? American Indian? East Indian? Italian?—she had a mustache of moisture on her upper lip and I had been schooled in the folklore of Italian women by printed matter. There was a hint of warmth in her marvelous dark eyes; so it was extremely possible that she was a beauty from North Africa. She might even be Jewish, I thought, remembering that beautiful Jewish girl on West 87th Street.

I would die if the girl was simply a dark Gentile.

I was about ten paces from her, when the sun blazed forth. Traffic around the circle was jammed.

The girl said, "I've been waiting for you."

"And I've been waiting too," I found myself saying.

"I've been waiting for someone exactly like you."

"You're beautiful. You don't have to wait for anyone."

The girl smiled warmly. "No. You're wrong," she said. "Are you coming with me?"

I nodded doubtfully but I took the girl's arm. "All right. I'm game. Where are we going?"

"Just keep in step with me. I've been so lonely," she said, "I feel like I'm living in the desert, though actually I'm living in a great city with millions of people."

"I've often felt like a hermit, too," I said. Was this chick stoned? She didn't look it.

"I know. I know. Now it'll be different for us. I've got

a lifetime of love to give and I couldn't give it to just anyone. Understand?"

"Yeah," I replied, beginning to relax. Man, The Wig was
really working! "I know what you mean."

"Most people are not very nice, are they?"

"No. Most people are not very nice."

Then we were silent. We danced arm in arm across Central
Park West and up the five steps of a very respectable
brownstone, just as the siren, like a proclamation, announced
twelve o'clock.

The girl's two-rooms-and-kitchenette was very clean. There
were no cockroaches, rats, mice, no leeches, no tigers.

Softly feminine, the girl said, "Relax, baby."

Then she came over and tried to rip the button-down shirt
from my body.

"Take it easy, baby," I said, biting her neck. "We have
all the time in the world."

"I know, I know," she said contritely, "but I must have
this release."

She elbowed me so hard that I fell backward onto a big
brass bed, where she proceeded to remove my loafers, socks,
and blue jeans. I wore no shorts because the chicken cos-
tume was very warm.

The girl kissed the soles of my feet.

"Come on up here," I said, feeling my kingly juices.

"You have beautiful strong legs."

I kicked her lightly on the chin, she fell back on the floor.
I jumped off the bed. Ready, at attention. She whimpered.
I mounted her right on the floor. She sighed and patted my
forehead. I sighed. Irritable, I also frowned. "Let's cut the
James Bond bit. Let's get this show on the road."

The girl sank her teeth into my right shoulder. I slapped
her hard and carried her to the bed. She whimpered again.
I fell on top of her. Her tongue was busy in my left ear.
I whimpered. Her right hand, like a measuring tape, grabbed
my penis.

With my right hand I cupper her chin and thrust my
tongue into her throat.

The girl squirmed and tickled my ribs.

Lowering her head, I kissed her chin and the oyster opening of her neck where her bone structure v'd, until my face
slid farther down, and came to rest in the soft luxury of

her breast. More delicious than fruit, I thought, teasing the wishbone below her breasts.

Still going down, I stopped at her navel.

She said clearly, "Oh," and rose slowly.

Panting, I shoved her back down on the bed, and with my knees, opened her legs. They opened like a pretty, well-constructed fan, and then closed like a fan, engulfing my back.

"Mercy," I sighed, settling in.

She bit my lower lip but didn't say anything. I did not say anything either. But at the climax, I bit *her* lower lip. Her hands were mad on my back.

Now I was breathing deeply; my eyes kept closing. The girl sighed. Then her sharp teeth nipped my cheek with its day-old beard. Pleased, she went on to discover the delight of my nose, the treasure of my ears, my red but large eyeballs. And then, like one looking for truffles, she buried her face against my flat hairless chest.

"Baby," I whispered.

"Love," she said.

I looked tenderly into her smiling face, planted one sounding kiss on her nose. Then I fell against her, and the last thought I had before dozing off to sleep was, "I wonder what The Deb is doing?"

I was awakened by having my neck kissed.

"I've got love to give," the girl said, digging her finger-nails into my backsides.

"Sweetcakes," I sighed, coming to life again.

"I just want to make you happy."

"And I want to make you happy," I said.

"Do you love me a little?"

I was feeling much too good to answer.

The first shadows of evening arrived. There was no moon, I noted through the sheer white curtains. And there were no stars. In the room, there was only the glow of the girl's shining hair and the glow of The Wig.

Silently, she anointed my body with Joy.

Yawning, I said, "I wanna Coke, and put some ice in it."

"Yes, love," she said.

Smiling in the darkness, I put my hands behind my head. I felt good. The frustrations of the day had been spent. The Wig, The Deb, and all those people I had encountered . . .

"Love," the girl called, breaking into my thoughts.

She sat down on the side of the bed and took me in her arms and held the glass of iced Coke as she would for an ill child. With her free hand, she gently stroked my brow.

"I want you to become my lover," she said quietly.

"We've just met," I protested. "We don't even know each other."

"You'll learn to love me. I'm a good woman. I've got money."

I bolted up from the bed. "Where's my jeans? I gotta run, cupcake. Perhaps I'll see you later."

"Please," the girl cried.

"Later," I said softly. I got into my clothes and made it to the door. Just as I shut it behind me, I thought I heard her cry, "I'm going to tell Mr. Fishback on you!"

Midnight found me on the Eighth Avenue A train for Harlem, wearing a pretty flower-printed plastic rainhood I'd luckily snatched up along with my clothes. It was raining out, and otherwise I'd have got The Wig wet. None of the passengers paid me the slightest attention. They had witnessed too many extraordinary happenings on subway trains: such as an old man getting stomped to death by a group of young punks because he didn't have life insurance; or someone getting sick and choking to death. Even statutory rapes had lost their appeal, they'd seen too many of them— so no one was likely to be impressed by a sad-faced, red-eyed young man wearing a plastic rainhood, shivering, biting his fingernails, staring at his reflection in the dirty window of the car.

I began to doze, thinking: when love waxes cold, said Paul in "The Third Coming . . ." then jerked up suddenly as the A train pulled into 125th Street.

I was the only passenger to get off. The platform was deserted. Workmen were spraying the platform with glue. Dazed and a little frightened, I ran up the sticky steps and out into the deserted street and hailed a taxi.

The driver, wearing a gas mask, stuck his head out the window.

"Oh, it's you," said Mr. Fishback, the funeral director. He removed the gas mask, spat false teeth onto the sidewalk. Then he placed a fresh pair of false teeth in his mouth. "It's this goddam country. It's ruining my health. I can't complain, though. They're dying every second. But there won't be anybody around to beautify me when I kick off. Ain't that a bitch?"

I had a sudden urge to rip the taxi door off. "Why are you driving a Yellow Cab?"

"I was waiting for you, Lester Jefferson," Mr. Fishback said innocently. "Why, they brought this big fat mama in and I didn't even have a chance to bang her. Terrible to see them go into the ground before you get what you want. And I didn't wanna upset you by arriving in my hearse."

"Why should that upset me? I've been riding in your hearse all my life."

For reasons known only to him, Mr. Fishback replaced the gas mask. "When love waxes cold . . ."

"What?" I exclaimed. "You been experimenting again?"

"The Deb," Mr. Fishback began. "She got run over by a school bus this afternoon."

Numbed, I could only stare at Mr. Fishback. I took off the rainhood.

"No," Mr. Fishback said solemnly. "You know she had been taken up by café society and was staying high all the time. You had made her see things she had never seen before. Madam X said she called for an appointment but never showed. Under that tough, tart front, she was a sweet kid. An all-American girl. She left her rock 'n' roll record collection to charity. But I might be able to get you a couple of favorites."

"Mr. Fishback," I said, "it's strange, The Deb is dead but my heart's still beating, and I can't cry."

"It happens in all the best families and to the world's greatest lovers."

"Yes, that's true."

"Get in, son," Mr. Fishback said kindly. "Rest assured, The Deb is in the best of hands."

"I know," I said, "but I won't get in, thank you."

"She's a beautiful dead girl."

"Yes. Now please drive slow. I'll walk along beside you. That's the least I can do for her."

"Do you need my gas mask?"

"No."

"It's dangerous."

"I don't care," I said.

Mr. Fishback's mortuary was under the Triboro Bridge, at the edge of the polluted, muddy river. It was a one-story building of solid plate glass, with the roof also of glass, rising up dramatically like the wings of a butterfly. Mr. Fishback parked the taxi (which belonged to his brother-in-law, who was dying, he said), near the bridge and then walked down a lonely garbage-littered slope with me.

Side by side, we walked under a deep gray sky that was just beginning to break with the first light of day. The cool air was refreshing against my feverish face.

Once, for a brief moment, I panicked. "I can't go on."

"Now, son," Mr. Fishback said gently.

"What can I do now?"

"You know what you have to do."

"Yes," I nodded, clutching Mr. Fishback's arm for support. We entered the glass building and walked like mourners to the direct center of the floor. Marble tiles slid back. Mr. Fishback removed his mask. He had a kind, dark, wrinkled face, the face of a genius, though being modest, he had always considered himself just God.

He escorted me down steps into a room the size of a standard bathroom. The room was mirrored and brightly lit, odorless. There was only a red bat-wing chair.

"I'm glad to get rid of these things," Mr. Fishback said, jerking out his false teeth and spitting blood on the floor. "Everything is so unsanitary!"

I flopped into the bat-wing chair: "The poor Deb!"

"Hush, now. You'll feel better after I cut off The Wig. Then one more act and you'll be happy for the rest of your life. While I was abroad, I kept in touch with Madam X. Remarkable woman."

Mr. Fishback pressed an invisble button in the mirrored wall and out popped a brand-new pair of sheep shears.

I closed my eyes. I felt no emotion. It was over. Everything. Loved waxed cold. The Deb—dead.

"Watch out for my ears," I warned. "And hurry up. I'm hungry."

There were tears in Mr. Fishback's eyes as he expertly clipped The Wig in exactly one minute.

"It was so beautiful," he sniffed.

I kicked the magnificent burnished red-golden hair haloed around the wing chair. I smiled at my bald-headed reflection. "It's over. I can always do it again."

"It was so pretty," Mr. Fishback said. "Nobody had hair

like that except Madam X, and that was before she became a saint."

"She's a funny woman. She gave me the creeps. I didn't stay for the first session."

"I know," Mr. Fishback said sharply. "Now stand up and take off your clothes."

"Why?"

"Just do as I say."

"You're always experimenting." I laughed weakly, but I stood up and stripped.

Mr. Fishback sighed. "You've lost weight. You look like a corpse. Think of something nasty and get an erection."

"Like what, for example?"

"Anything. Hell. This country is filled with nasty images."

"The Deb and I will never have children. Why are you torturing me!"

"Not so loud," Mr. Fishback said angrily. "Having children is the greatest sin in this country, according to Madam X. After a series of experiments, Madam X has concluded that having children is a *very* great sin. Hate is an evil disease."

"I've got an erection," I said.

"Fine," Mr. Fishback said happily. He pushed another invisible button in the mirrored wall and out popped a red-hot slender steel rod.

With a deadly-serious expression on his face, Mr. Fishback jabbed the steel rod into the head of my penis.

He counted to ten and jerked it out.

Sighing hard, he asked, "How do you feel?"

"I'm beginning to feel better already," I said, smiling.

JAMES PURDY
from *Cabot Wright Begins* (1964)

> *Editor's note: "Mrs. Bickle," a writer, had been as-*
> *signed by editor Princeton Keith to write an exposé of*
> *the rapist. In time, however, she becomes an ally and*
> *confidant of Wright's.*

✠

Had Cabot Wright understood even the minimum commands given him by Life, you can ask.

He had been born, of course, and toilet-trained, weaned
at an average age. Was sent to the Sunday school of his
peer's choice. Saw portrait of Elijah, Jesus the Christ,
and God in nightgowns talking with other long-haired
gents dressed samely. Entered kindergarten under bad-
breathed spinster name of Sadie F. Harkness. Early
learned to slide down teeter-totter, noticed girls had different behinds than boys, squatted where boys remained
erect. Noticed some people had different skin-textures and
were hiding on the whole behind lilac bushes, was com-
manded to ignore same. Everybody however even then
was riding in big cars. Woodrow F. Harding was dead,
of course, and Theodore F. Truman called to the chair,
China fell to land-hungry boll weevils. C. W. continued his
mass-education learning following subjects: salute to the
community, with pupil community-laity participation program, sliding down escalators, wall-climbing and writing,
doughnut-break, group training with both sexes, Democracy
for little people period, hygiene, physical exercises, leap-

frog, Y.M.C.A. salute night, Field Day with basket-lunch, camp during hot months relieves Mother. College of his choice dictated by friend of the family, Ivy Walls, graduated half *laude*, and entered military service where nothing he did was commented on. His majoring in art at Yale seen to be fiddle-faddle necessary in Eastern gentleman, and after service in khaki shorts entered the Wall Street. America expects every junior-executive general partner to marry & exercise his democratic tool. This Cabot, like all upstanding young blades, did, settling in Brooklyn across the water from his work, bought high-powered telescope to get a lay of the land, wife took ill, mother-father disappeared in pink Caribbean revolution. The rest, reader, you know.

Yet once the Chicago crew and the New York printing Czars dropped him, C. W.'s problem began all over again—learning to feel at last, after having been born anaesthetic from the womb. To recapitulate Cabot's problem: Dr. Bigelow-Martin had taken away all his attention except in his erectile tissue, and the police hoses and nightsticks had removed his attention there. But was this not the problem of the whole USA? Under the different Generals, poker-players, country squires, haberdashers, grandsons of whiskey-barons for President, and while America is fucking the rest of the world or putting a yellow island down the incinerator in the name of freedom, wearing Jehovah's whiskers and the tiara of the Queen of Heaven, the fact remains that the American people at home, *chez eux*, to quote Princeton Keith, outside of the aged and aging who are crying their heads off for free doctors and rectal TV, the rest of the USA citizenry, as a noted magazine calls them, from Maine's retired millionaires to the shores of the gilded Yukon, the American people are all head-wise if not physic-wise anaesthetic. They hear, but they don't get it. They see, but the image is blurry. The rain is falling on their TV screens.

"We have all been here before!" the USA cries as it turns over another page on its TV roller. "Ouch, my bleeding piles."

"We can't tell the difference," the child, the dowager, the millionaire kid from the Chicago department store all say, "we can't tell the difference between General Roosevelt and Captain Truman or Professor Eisenhower from Grover Kennedy Johnson. They all look like boys in charge of a scouting party who don't hear the cry, 'timber!' as the big investors screw away in the jungles, in the sugar islands, the pampas and waters of Lake Titicaca, the dynamite beds under the Prado, Habana, Bolivian tin-mines and Katanga. The boys all look alike to me, the viewers cry, except each succeeding President does promise a little more to the arthritic old and the darker niggers. . . . Hark! Now I hear it! Dong, dong, dong."

"You shall have dong, niggers and outfielders, as long as there is health in my General's body! I will give you dong. I am the President."

"We've all been here before!" the USA is crying in front of the little screen.

But they're so tired. . . .

Suddenly Cabot Wright could laugh. It was the first real laugh he had ever been able to bring off. The early part of his life, real and supposititious, had been devoted to giggles, and though he knew he would never be at attention fully anywhere again in his body, now suddenly he could laugh. First Ha then Ho, then Ha Ha HAR, HAAAAAA!

Laughter!

And Reverend Cross had come to see him. He had held his young ward's hand as the laughter trickled, flowed, cascaded, came in torrents.

Cabot had told Mrs. Bickle nearly everything or had hinted at what he had left out. He had told his whole story, and she would never use it. Maybe she believed it and maybe she did not, which was better. Now he could forget his own story and himself.

Every day Reverend Cross from the Church of His Choice had visited him, though only for a few minutes, but today holding the culprit's hand against his paroxysm of laughter, the preacher said:

"Cabot, my boy, you're better."

A young man in appearance, Reverend Cross suffered from several spiritual diseases of his own, as witness circles under his eyes, rapid pulse, dry mouth, looking at boys' crotches, talking to himself. But he had renounced life for Christ and this was getting him through the world without being beaten and reduced to a pulp.

"Confession, Cabot, is good for the soul," he patted Cabot's knee.

"Told you everything, already, Reverend."

"But you're not sorry, Cab. You're not."

"I'm not tired any more, either, Reverend. Not tired at all. And I told Mrs. Bickle just about everything—after I heard it in that book."

"Pray with me, Cabot," Reverend Cross said. "It won't hurt you even if you don't believe in it. Pray some with me."

"I was a supposititious child," Cabot said dreamily. "God, does that reach your guts when you think about it. But I don't."

"Come pray."

"My scrotum is blue with varicocele, Rev."

"Pray anyhow."

"Hold my pulse then while you mutter, Rev."

He heard in sleep-like underwater thunderings the young preacher's prayer.

"All suffer the deadwood, my boy, having rejected our divine inheritance. Remember those flowers which you so adored as a boy, Cabot? The hunts in the woods for snow-apples, jack-in-the-pulpit, heartsease . . ."

"When I left prison," Cabot confided, "my warden said, 'Cab, maybe this time you better stick to the company of your own sex.'"

"We must all do what is right," Reverend Cross said, and his long black lashes were smashed to his cheek by tears.

"What's right?" Cabot inquired, and when he said that the Reverend Cross looked like his name.

"My mother said that," Cabot reminded the Reverend. "Did she know what was right? All she knew was life-insurance would save her when her mainstay kicked the goosepot. But was she bugged. Both mothers were bugged. They both died. The hand of no-return carried them off without their collecting on their forty years of fleshpot bleeding. Where was my real parents, Rev.? WE SHOULD ALL DO WHAT IS RIGHT. Excuse me while I use my new laugh. Let me tell you something, Reverend Cross. You bug me."

Pacing up and down, the preacher said, "You have set

yourself up against God and man, and especially against yourself. My boy, you are in a state . . ."

"The ugly truth is," Cabot shook his head, looking out the window at the incoming steamer from Cartagena, near Fort Jay, "religion hasn't got anything on the ball. It's all Daddy-rattling and pious alarm."

"I will continue to pray for you, my son."

Now Cabot was alone again with his non-self. Loneliness feels so good after the mythic contact with the social. Dreams become clear, and nightmares are no longer attention-getting. One sucks eight or nine aspirins and allows his calloused thumb to rest on a quilt. The trauma of birth, life and death pass as shadows on the moon. Mother Nature goes right on keeping house even though nobody is to home.

"Hello, Central Information Bureau?" Cabot spoke into a phone. "Weather woman? Are you now or have you ever been in the pay of a Cosmic Bugaboo? I'm not human now and never was, is my fuckworthy answer. Thank you for allowing us to enter your home in the legal frock of spies. We are screwing you, as you know, to protect the innocent. Thank you and good morning. Remove the bandage tomorrow. The stitches are absorbed by the blood stream. You will feel no pain. We repeat. You will feel no pain. Sold, American."

Lying down on his side, Cabot relieved himself in laughter. His laughter was like a paroxysm, neither willing nor unwilling. His regions from the breast-bone down shook in helpless hapless hopeless waves of self-relief, which happily for him was one prolonged orgasm. After all laughter is the greatest boon Nature has bestowed on miserable unjoyous man. The release, the only relief from the pain of being human, mortal, ugly, limited, in agony, watching Death cornhole you beginning with the first emergence from the winking slit above the mother's fundament, pulled into existence from between piss and shit, sorrow and meaninglessness, drudgery and illusion, passion, pain, early loss of youth and vigor, of all that had made it worth while, with the eternity of the tomb, the final word over the hunger for God, the repletion of earth and slime, the shout of the ocean in the ears of death.

Meaning is there is no meaning but the laughter of the moment made it almost worth while. That's all it's about. We was here, finally laughed.

"The roof of my mouth fell in. I laughed!" said Cabot.

He lay in the Brooklyn mud, guffawed weakly. He had laughed until he was in erection again for the first time since the policemen's nightsticks, laughed some more until he was limp as an old man, laughed until he mewed and purled like a new-born babe. Then he lay back on his back silent, weeping a little from the pain of his laughter, a thread of drivel coming down from his mouth onto his pointed dimpled chin.

"I thought I'd die but I lived."

That deadly monotony of the human continuity,
The fog is a sea on earth! . . .

"You act," Curt Bickle addressed his wife some weeks after her return from New York, "and you talk as though you were going to write the story of this youthful rapist yourself."

"But you know perfectly well I won't," Zoe Bickle reassured him, and Curt smiled with relief.

"You're a bright, brainy and even handsome woman today," Curt wiped his spectacles free of blur and stared at her again with complacency.

It was true. Mrs. Bickle had put on weight so that she looked better than she ever had before, her complexion shone, her eyes were bright, and her laugh had lost its edge.

"Believe you me," Mrs. Bickle said, "there was this temptation to write Cabot's story, after Bernie's failure, and with poor dear Princeton dead by his own hand. Well, what has stopped me from finishing the book," she told her husband, "is our culprit himself. He has begun to write *me*. I didn't tell you before because I hoped they would stop—Cabot Wright's letters, I mean. Maybe they are going to stop, now that he's left New York."

She opened a little box Curt had seen but paid no attention to. She drew out a letter, enclosed in a post-office stationery envelope, and read:

After the roof of my mouth fell in, I saw how everything really was, Mrs. Bickle. That was before I could yet laugh—I'm now as you might guess a really professional laugher—yes, my giggling days are over. To think you—thank you—were the first person to listen to me all the way through.

Mrs. Bickle paused, and Curt looked away, embarrassed. He was ashamed, she knew, like all of us, of the human in his human nature.

"Where will a man like that end up?" Curt Bickle said, at last, in a kind of aside.

"A boy like Cabot?" She considered the question. "Perhaps his letter gives us a clue." She continued to read:

Having sold all my property, including a row of brownstones—you will remember how rich I became when I inherited Warby's empire—well, nearly all I inherited is gone. I'm cleaned out. Philanthropy by the mile, unwise investments, and so on. I wanted to get clear of it too. Gave away a lot.

Curt yawned because it was eleven o'clock, but Zoe Bickle went on reading:

My face has broken out in boils and I don't have time to see the doctor. Besides New York is closed for the Jewish holidays, there's a mean southerly wind at 10 knots an hour, and the television set they have in this room is busted so that I don't have any of the big serious faces that make me see America, baseball heroes, disk jockeys, immortal crooners, generals in hats, and living Presidents' wives.

"Oh, how adolescent," Curt said.

As my preacher, Reverend Cross, used to say to me, in every breath we breathe, life and death jockey for position. There have been 77 billion people who have preceded us on this planet, but the big news is that with the increase today population-wise, $\frac{1}{10}$ of all the people who have ever lived are alive today. That's the good thought I want to give you, Mrs. Bickle, before I give you some of the bad news, the necrology, as the better newspapers call it. You really do have to know, if you are going to write the truth about my life as fiction.

NEWS EVENTS & RELEASES:

Goldie Thomas's beauty was nearly completely destroyed when, riding in her bubble car, she ran into a fishing lodge in order to avoid a moose which would not get out of the way in Maine, near a place called Deer Isle, where she was of course vacationing. Gilda Warburton died by her own hand, of gastric upset, in Manhattan, subsequent to drinking liquid cosmetic, which she had mistaken for Campari. This is being hushed up as she had pilfered it from her new colored butler, the boy who replaced Brady, who by the way joined the Merchant Marine. I don't remember whether I told you or not, but my first wife and my only, Cynthia Adams, died of double pneumonia in the loony bin, after never finding out again who she was (some people have luck).

If this letter seems disconnected, it's partly because I can hear from a neighboring apartment, where they are *not* celebrating the holidays, Terry on the vibes playing *"I Love You, Stranger, in Fact I Do."*

Well, before I come to the real drama of necrology, I can say what my Preacher says will always bear repeating, "My own heart was broken before I heard the Coach say 'Go!' " Yes, Princeton Keith is no more. I thought that would smash you, as you were childhood chums. A lot he will need to care about automation. Tell you about a guy like Princeton. He spent 25 years of his life thinking he was permanently landmarked in New York, even though he was from Illinois somewhere, in fact he thought Al Guggelhaupt was only the Moon and he was the Sun. What really killed him wasn't just the quiet of a small town in mid-America, but the shock to his internal system of not having those $50.00 a cloth luncheons, with the seven different beverages. I mean that is a bomb to anybody's insides. Bladder backs up, great colon nonplussed, liver no longer tawny, prostate down in the dumps, great-sphincter utterly collapsed . . .

"Oh, for Pete's sake!" Curt cried. Mrs. Bickle went right on.

If you do ever write anything about me, I would half-like to read it, but am afraid I am more disinterested in my own life, such as it was, than even you were when you showed your disinterest at its height. God, did I admire your noncommitted glance, Mrs. Bickle. (I'll never call you Zoe, 'cause you're the old Ear to me, just drinking in what you didn't even always get. Thank you for that.)

I suppose even Chicago seems a little lilliputian with the jet world all connected up, and the oral contraceptive ads going to the tune of "The Old Rugged Cross." Another friend of mine named Vance Goldanski, who was writing an article on me for a movie magazine, dropped dead on the corner of Fifth Avenue and 57th Street, very young man, had been a French horn player for 10 years, before he got to be a candidate for the World Thought Congress. He felt it was time to give up playing for helping out the world community in trouble, and the day he signed up he fell over.

But what was always on my mind, Mrs. Bickle, as you know from all those hours in the cockroach palace on Joralemon Street, Brooklyn, and that night in Hanover Square, lower Manhattan—and you remember all those clocks that I had when I hid away in the *See River Manor*—the thought always on my mind was *"Do You think there's a Chance for Me if I ever Find out who I is?"* That's why I've come home to my brownstones in Brooklyn Heights (falling fast), have sold same, and am on my way to extended flight, but this time with myself, and in search of same.

The thought occurs to me that this may be the last time we play our little game of hearing and not listening, Mrs. Bickle. Here I am running out on America, if not myself. That's the funny thing to remember—in case I don't send you more news.

No, what I am getting at is that when I had to have all those clocks going, and you remember how many times I took my own pulse, as though I never expected to hear the Coach say "Go" again, well I've got that one problem solved if no other, on account of I don't have to ask those hard questions that nobody now or any of the other 77 billions ever found the answer to, WHAT MAKES ME TICK? I don't care about that now,

Mrs. Bickle, but I do know, *hear* it any way you want, I am ticking as of this letter, anyhow, and I'll write the symbol for the way I feel now, which is HA!

"Well," Mrs. Bickle said, "I guess that will be the last of any letters I ever get from dear Cabot Wright."

"Speaking of paramount issues," Curt Bickle opened his mouth after the briefest of pauses, "you do look around the mouth and eyes as if you might write his story after all."

"Believe you me," Mrs. Bickle intoned, "it's almost a temptation."

Curt waited a little.

"But I won't, pet," she said in a low voice to herself and him. "I won't be a writer in a place and time like the present."

WILLIAM BURROUGHS
from *Nova Express* (1964)

"The Subliminal Kid" moved in and took over bars cafés and juke boxes of the world cities and installed radio transmitters and microphones in each bar so that the music and talk of any car could be heard in all his bars and he had tape recorders in each bar that played and recorded at arbitrary intervals and his agents moved back and forth with portable tape recorders and brought back street sound and talk and music and poured it into his recorder array so he set waves and eddies and tornadoes of sound down all your streets and by the river of all language—Word dust drifted streets of broken music car horns and air hammers—The Word broken pounded twisted exploded in smoke—

Word Falling ///

He set up screens on the walls of his bars opposite mirrors and took and projected at arbitrary intervals shifted from one bar to the other mixing Western Gangsters films of all time and places with word and image of the people in his cafés and on the streets his agents with movie camera and telescope lens poured images of the city back into his projector and camera array and nobody knew whether he was in a Western movie in Hongkong or The Aztec Empire in Ancient Rome or Suburban America whether he was a bandit a commuter or a chariot driver whether he was firing a "real" gun or watching a gangster movie and the city moved in swirls and eddies and tornadoes of image explosive bio-advance out of space to neon—

Photo Falling ///

"The Subliminal Kid" moved in seas of disembodied sound —He then spaced here and there and instaff opposite mirrors and took movies each bar so that the music and talk is at arbitrary intervals and shifted bars—And he also had recorder in tracks and moving film mixing arbitrary intervals and agents moving with the word and image of tape recorders—So he set up waves and his agents with movie swirled through all the streets of image and brought back street in music from the city and poured Aztec Empire and Ancient Rome—Commuter or Chariot Driver could not control their word dust drifted from outer space—Air hammers word and image explosive bio-advance—A million drifting screens on the walls of his city projected mixing sound of any bar could be heard in all Westerns and film of all times played and recorded at the people back and forth with portable cameras and telescope lenses poured eddies and tornadoes of sound and camera array until soon city where he moved everywhere a Western movie in Hongkong or the Aztec sound talk suburban America and all accents and language mixed and fused and people shifted language and accent in mid-sentence Aztec priest and spilled it man woman or beast in all languages—So that People-City moved in swirls and no one knew what he was going out of space to neon streets—

"Nothing Is True—Everything Is Permitted—" Last *Words Hassan I Sabbah*

The Kid stirred in sex films and The People-City pulsed in a vast orgasm and no one knew what was film and what was not and performed all kinda sex acts on every street corner—

He took film of sunsets and cloud and sky water and tree film and projected color in vast reflector screens concentrating blue sky red sun green grass and the city dissolved in light and people walked through each other—There was only color and music and silence where the words of Hassan i Sabbah had passed—

"Boards Syndicates Governments of the earth Pay—Pay back the *Color* you stole—

"Pay Red—Pay back the red you stole for your lying flags and your Coca-Cola signs—Pay that red back to penis and blood and sun—

"Pay Blue—Pay back the blue you stole and bottled and doled out in eye droppers of junk—Pay back the blue you stole for your police uniforms—Pay that blue back to sea and sky and eyes of the earth—

"Pay Green—Pay back the green you stole for your money

—And you, Dead Hand Stretching The Vegetable People, pay back the green you stole for your Green Deal to sell out peoples of the earth and board the first life boat in drag— Pay that green back to flowers and jungle river and sky—

"Boards Syndicates Governments of the earth pay back your stolen colors—*Pay Color* back to Hassan i Sabbah—"

PAY OFF THE MARKS?

Amusement park to the sky—The concessioners gathered in a low pressure camouflage pocket—

"I tell you Doc the marks are out there pawing the ground,

" 'What's this Green Deal?'

" 'What's this Sky Switch?'

" 'What's this Reality Con?'

" 'Man, we been short-timed?'

" 'Are you a Good Cook?'

" 'A good Nigger?'

" 'A Good Human Animal?'

"They'll take the place apart—I've seen it before—like a silver flash—And The Law is moving in—Not locals—This is Nova Heat—I tell we got to give and fast—Flicker, The Movies, Biologic Merging Tanks, The lot—Well, Doc?"

"It goes against my deepest instincts to pay off the marks— But under the uh circumstances—caught as we are between an aroused and not in all respects reasonable citizenry and the antibiotic handcuffs—"

The Amusement Gardens cover a continent—There are areas of canals and lagoons where giant gold fish and sala-manders with purple fungoid gills stir in clear black water and gondolas piloted by translucent green fish boys—Under vast revolving flicker lamps along the canals spill The Bio-logic Merging Tanks sense withdrawal capsules light and soundproof water at blood temperature pulsing in and out where two life forms slip in and merge to a composite being often with deplorable results slated for Biologic Skid Row on the outskirts: (Sewage delta and rubbish heaps—terminal addicts of SOS muttering down to water worms and float-ing vegetables—Paralyzed Orgasm Addicts eaten alive by

crab men with white hot eyes or languidly tortured in cha-
rades by The Green Boys of young crystal cruelty)

Vast communal immersion tanks melt whole peoples into
one concentrate—It's more democratic that way you see?—
Biologic Representation—Cast your vote into the tanks—
Here where flesh circulates in a neon haze and identity tags
are guarded by electric dogs sniffing quivering excuse for
being—The assassins wait broken into scanning patterns of
legs smile and drink—Unaware of The Vagrant Ball Player
pant smell running in liquid typewriter—

Streets of mirror and glass and metal under flickering
cylinders of colored neon—Projector towers sweep the city
with color writing of The Painter—Cool blue streets between walls of iron polka-dotted with lenses projecting The
Blue Tattoo open into a sea of Blue Concentrate lit by pulsing flickering blue globes—Mountain villages under the blue
twilight—Drifting cool blue music of all time and place
to the brass drums—

Street of The Light Dancers who dance with color writing
projected on their bodies in spotlight layers peel off red yellow blue in dazzling strip acts, translucent tentative beings
flashing through neon hula hoops—stand naked and explode in
white fade out in grey—vaporize in blue twilight— . . .

ARE THESE EXPERIMENTS
NECESSARY?

Saturday, March 17, 1962, Present Time Of Knowledge—
Scio is knowing and open food in The Homicide Act—Logos
you got it?—Dia through noose—England spent the weekend with a bargain before release certificate is issued—Dogs
must be carried reluctant to the center—It's a grand feeling—There's a lot ended—This condition is best expressed
queen walks serenely down dollar process known as overwhelming—What we want is Watney's Woodbines and the
Garden Of Delights—And what could you have?—What
would you? State of news?—Inquire on hospital? what?—
Would you permit that person revived peat victory hopes of
Fortria? Pre-clear to look around and discover Sheila's Cot-

tage?—Death reduces the cycle of action—Venus Vigar choked to death in the direction of "havingness"—His diary thoughts they went back other identities—The whole world had valence is false identity—Further talks today with "barriers" and "purposes"—Vital clue that links the murders is: game one special way just want to die—Spreading the New Zealand after film was in the hospital—Yards of entrails hung about the toilet—The observer left his scio and vanished with confessed folk singer logos—Dia through noose found dead on the old evacuation—Release certificate of Vigar's birth is issued naked—This condition is best expressed uncontrolled flash bulbs popped process known as "overwhelming"—

"Sir I am quite prepared—other identities—Woman is at the clear out if is fundamentally agreement"—

"Look around here and tell me are these experiments really necessary?"—All this to "overwhelm"—? Apparency bustle through the red hair—I have said Scio Officers at any given time dictate place of years—Dead absolute need condition expressed process known as "overwhelming"—Silence—Don't answer—What could that person "overwhelm?"—Air?—The great wind revolving what you could have—What would you?—Sound and image flakes fall—It will be seen that "havingness" no more—

Paralyzed on this green land the "cycle of action"—The cycle of last door—Shut off "Mr. Bradly Mr. Apparent Because We Believe It"—Into air—You are yourself "Mr. Bradly Mr. Other Identities"—Action is an apparency creating and aggravating conflict—Total war of the past—I have said the "basic pre-clear identities" are now ended—Wind spirits melted "reality need" dictates use of throat bones—"Real is real" do get your heavy summons and are melted—Through all the streets time for him be able to not know his past walls and windows people and sky—Complete intentions falling—Look around here—No more flesh scripts dispense Mr.—Heard your summons—Melted "Mr. Bradly Mr. Martin"

MELTED INTO AIR

Fade out muttering: "There's a lover on every corner cross the wounded galaxies"—

Distant fingers get hung up on one—"Oh, what'll we do?"

Slowly fading—I told him you on tracks—All over for sure—I'm absolutely prophesized in a dream grabbing Yuri by the shirt and throwing last words answer his Yugoslavian knife—I pick up Shannon Yves Martin may not refuse vision —Everybody's watching—But I continue the diary—"Mr. Bradly Mr. Martin?"—You are his eyes—I see suddenly Mr. Beiles Mr. Corso Mr. Burroughs presence on earth is all a joke—And I think: "Funny—melted into air"—Lost flakes fall that were his shadow: This book—No good junky identity fading out—

"Smoke is all, boy—Dont intersect—I think now I go home and it's five times—Had enough slow metal fires—Form has been inconstant—Last electrician to tap on the bloody dream"—

"I see dark information from him on the floor—He pull out—Keep all Board Room Reports—Waiting chair to bash everybody—Couldn't reach tumescent daydream in Madrid— Flash a jester angel who stood there in 1910 straw words— Realize that this too is bad move—No good—No bueno— Young angel elevated among the subterraneans—Yes, he heard your summons—Nodded absently—"

"And I go home having lost—Yes, blind may not refuse vision to this book—"

CLOM FLIDAY

I have said the basic techniques of nova are very simple consist in creating and aggravating conflicts—"No riots like injustice directed between enemies"—At any given time recorders fix nature of absolute need and dictate the use of total weapons—Like this: Collect and record violent Anti-Semitic statements—Now play back to Jews who are after Belsen—Record what they say and play it back to the Anti-Semites—Clip clap—You got it?—Want more?—Record white supremacy statements—Play to Negroes—Play back answer—Now The Women and The Men—No riots like injustice directed between "enemies"—At any given time position of recorders fixes nature of absolute need—And dictates the use of total weapons—So leave the recorders running and get your heavy metal ass in a space ship—Did it—Nothing here now but the recordings—Shut the whole thing right off—*Silence*—When you answer the machine you provide it with more recordings to be played back to your "enemies" keep the whole nova machine running—The Chinese character for "enemy" means to be similar to or to answer—Don't answer the machine—Shut it off—

"The Subliminal Kid" took over the streets of the world—Cruise cars with revolving turrets telescope movie lenses and recorders sweeping up sound and image of the city around and around faster and faster cars racing through all the streets of image record, take, play back, project on walls and windows people and sky—And slow moving turrets on slow cars and wagons slower and slower record take, play back, project slow motion street scene—Now fast—Now slow—slower—*Stop*—Shut off—No More—My writing arm is paralyzed—No more junk scripts, no more word scripts, no more flesh scripts—He all went away—No good—No bueno—Couldn't reach flesh—No glot—Clom Fliday—Through invisible door—Adios Meester William, Mr. Bradly, Mr. Martin—

I have said the basic techniques creating and aggravating conflict officers—At any given time dictate total war of the past—Changed place of years in the end is just the same—I have said the basic techniques of Nova reports are now ended—Wind spirits melted between "enemies"—Dead absolute need dictates use of throat bones—On this green land recorders get your heavy summons and are melted—Nothing here now but the recordings may not refuse vision in setting forth—*Silence*—Don't answer—That hospital melted into air—The great wind revolving turrets towers palaces—Insubstantial sound and image flakes fall—Through all the streets time for him to forbear—Blest be he on walls and windows people and sky—On every part of your dust falling softly—

falling in the dark mutinous "No more"—My writing arm is paralyzed on this green land—Dead Hand, no more flesh scripts—Last door—Shut off Mr. Bradly Mr.—He heard your summons—Melted into air—You are yourself "Mr. Bradly, Mr. Martin—" all the living and the dead—You are yourself—There be—

Well that's about the closest way I know to tell you and papers rustling across city desks . . . fresh southerly winds a long time ago.

September 17, 1899 over New York

July 21, 1964
Tangier, Morocco
William Burroughs

JOHN BARTH
from *The Floating Opera* (1956)

> Editor's note: It needs to be pointed out that this is the
> night Todd Andrews has chosen for his suicide—the night
> of the great "showboat" extravaganza during which he
> plans quietly to take his own life. "Capt. Osborn" is his
> companion, "Jeannine" the ailing daughter of his friends
> Harrison and Jane Mack. Andrews has no reason not to
> suppose that Jeannine is his own flesh and blood.

XXVII. *The Floating Opera*

Plain enough by day, the *Original & Unparalleled Floating
Opera* was somewhat more ornamented as Capt. Osborn and
I approached it across Long Wharf in the hot twilight. Power
lines had been run from a utility pole near the dock, and
the showboat was outlined in vari-colored electric lights,
which, however, needed greater darkness for their best effect.
On the roof of the theater Prof. Eisen and the thirteen members of his $7,500 Challenge Atlantic & Chesapeake
Maritime Band were installed in their bandstand, rendering, as
I recall, "I'm a Yankee Doodle Dandy" to the crowd of several
hundred onlookers gathered around—many of whom, particularly among the Negroes, came only to hear the free concert
and regard the "Op'ry Barge" with amazement, not having

money to spare for admission to the show. The box office was open (it was nearly showtime), and a line was queued up from the ticket window down the gangplank to the bulkheads. Capt. Osborn grew excited and used his cane to nudge small running urchins out of his path, which led unswervingly to the ticket line.

The band wound up George M. Cohan and began a Stephen Foster medley. When we reached the top of the gangplank I looked around at the crowd and saw Harrison, Jane, and Jeannine just taking a place in line. They were occupied with opening Jeannine's popcorn bag, and didn't notice me.

The auditorium was already nearly half filled with the citizens of Cambridge. Capt. Osborn and I took seats about seven rows from the rear, on the extreme starboard side of the theater—he complaining that we hadn't arrived earlier to get really good seats. The hall was illuminated with electric lights, each built into a double fixture along with a gas mantle for use at less progressive landings. Scanning the audience, I saw almost no unfamiliar faces. Col. Morton and his wife sat in the front row on the aisle. Marvin Rose, a showboat *aficionado*, sat a few rows behind. Bill Butler waved cheerily to me from across the theater. My partner Mr. Bishop was there with his wife, whom one seldom saw in public. Harrison, Jane, and Jeannine came in—if they saw me, they made no sign, although I waved to them—and sat on the other side of the theater. Jimmy Andrews, as I'd anticipated, was absent—doubtless out sailing with his fiancée, for a mild but usable breeze had sprung up earlier in the evening.

Above our heads the $7,500 Challenge Band concluded its free concert with "The Star-Spangled Banner." There was some uncertainty in the house as to whether it was necessary to stand, since the band was outside. Some men made a half-hearted motion to rise, hesitated, and sat down embarrassed, laughing explanations at their wives with much pointing of fingers toward the roof. Finally Col. Morton stood unfalteringly, without a backward look, and the rest of us followed suit, relieved to have a ruling on the matter. When the anthem ended there was applause from the freeloaders outside, and much discussion inside about whether it had really been necessary for us to stand. Soon, however, everyone's attention was focused on the small door under the stage, from which the members of the orchestra, resplendent in gold-braided red uniforms, began filing into the pit. When all were in their places, and instruments had been tootled cacophoniously, Prof. Eisen himself—lean, hollow-cheeked, vanDyked, intense—stepped to the podium amid generous applause from orchestra and balcony, rapped for attention, and raised his baton, on the tip of which the whole house hung. The lights dimmed slightly, the baton fell, and the band crashed into "The Star-Spangled Banner." An instant's murmur and then we sprang to our feet again, none more quickly than the Colonel—although Evelyn was a trifle flustered.

No sooner had the final cymbal clashed than the house lights went out completely and the electric footlights rose, playing on the mauve velvet stage curtain. Prof. Eisen's baton fell again, and the sprightly overture was commenced: a potpourri of martial airs, ragtime, a touch of some sentimental love ballad, a flourish of buck-and-wing, and a military finale. We applauded eagerly.

Captain Jacob Adam himself stepped from behind the curtain, bowed to our ovation, and smilingly bade us listen.

"Good evenin', good evenin', friends!" he cried. "I can't say how happy I am to see ye all here tonight. It does my heart good when the *Floatin' Op'ry* comes round Hambrook Light, I'll tell ye, 'cause I know that means it's Cambridge ahead, and I tell John Strudge, my calliope man, I say to him, 'John,' I say, 'get up a good head o' steam, boy, and let's have "Dem Golden Slippers," 'cause that there's Cambridge yonder,' I says, 'and ye'll sail a lot o' water 'fore ye meet finer folks than ye'll see a-plenty in Cambridge!' Now, then!"

We cheered.

"Well, sir, folks, I'm glad so many of ye got out tonight, 'cause we got such a fine new show this year I was anxious for all my friends and even my enemies in Cambridge to see it." He squinted over the footlights. "Guess my friends'll be in later," he mumbled loudly, and grinned at once lest we miss the jest—but we were alert, and laughed especially loud.

"Yes, sir, a brand-new line-up this year, folks, from a crackerjack start to a whiz-bang finish! But before we haul back the curtain and get on with the fun, I'm afraid I'll have to disappoint ye just a wee bit."

We murmured sympathy for ourselves.

"Now I know ye was pinin' to see Miss Clara Mulloy, the Mary Pickford of the Chesapeake, do her stuff in *The Parachute Girl*. So was I, I got to admit, 'cause no matter how many times in a row I watch Miss Clara jump down in that there par'chute, them legs o' hers is so durn pretty I can't see my fill!"

We laughed more raucously, Capt. Osborn jabbing me in the ribs and exploding with mirthful phlegm.

"But I'm sorry to say Miss Clara Mulloy has caught a germ from someplace—must have been Crisfield, couldn't of been Cambridge—and I swear if she ain't got the laryngitis so bad she can't say a durn word!"

We voiced our disappointment, some of us resentfully.

"I know, I know," Capt. Adam sympathized. "I feel like walkin' out myself. Hey, Miss Clara," he shouted into the wings, "come on out here and show the people yer—ah— yer *laryngitis!*" He winked at us, we roared, and then Miss Clara Mulloy—brown-haired, brown-eyed, trimly corseted— curtsied onto the stage, the sequins flashing on her black gown, a red flannel scarf tied incongruously around her white neck. She curtsied again to our ovation, pointed to her throat, and moved her lips in silent explanation, while Captain Adam looked on adoringly.

"What do ye say?" he cried to us. "Shall we call the whole thing off? I'm willin'!"

"NO!" we shouted, almost as one man—two or three rowdies cried "*Yes!*" but we glared them down.

"Do I hear *yes?*" the Captain asked.

"NO!" we roared again, our stares defying contradiction from the one or two hoodlums who are forever spoiling honest folks' fun. "No!" we pleaded, hoping Capt. Adam wouldn't judge us citizens of Cambridge by our most unfortunate element.

"*Yes!*" one of the incorrigibles snickered.

"That man should be thrown out!" I heard the Colonel declare in exasperation.

"Well, I say let's be fair and square," Capt. Adam said. "Any man, woman, or child that wants to leave can get up right now and go, and John Strudge'll give ye yer full admission money back at the box office, despite ye already heard the overture!"

We laughed at this last and applauded his generosity. The house lights came up for a moment, but no one dared move.

"All right, then, let's get on with the show!"

The house lights were extinguished, Miss Clara Mulloy

rewarded our applause with a blown kiss (her eyes dewy), Prof. Eisen struck up a lively tune, and we relaxed again.

"Now, then," the Captain announced. "Instead o' *The Parachute Girl* I'm proud to present the great T. Wallace Whittaker, one o' the finest singers and actors that ever trod the boards. Ye all know T. Wallace Whittaker as the great Southern tenor—got a voice like a honeycomb in a sweet-gum stump, I swear! But what ye probably don't know is that T. Wallace Whittaker is one o' the best Shakespearian actors in the U.S.A.! Ladies and gentlemen, I have the *great* honor to present T. Wallace Whittaker, the eminent tragedian, in Scenes from the Bard!"

Uncertain applause. The band played heavy chords in a minor key, the curtain opened, and we looked in a Victorian parlor (first set for *The Parachute Girl*), in the center of which bowed T. Wallace Whittaker. He was a broad-beamed, Sunday-schooly young man, and he wore a tight black Hamlet-looking outfit. From the tone of his very first words—a lofty "I shall begin by reciting the famous speech of the duke Jacques, from Act Two of *As You Like It*"—He lost the sympathy of us men, although some wives nodded knowingly.

T. Wallace walked to the footlights, struck a declamatory pose, and closed his eyes for a moment. He did not clear his throat, but some of us cleared ours.

"*All the world's a stage*," he declared, "*and all the men and women merely players: They have their exits and their entrances; and one man in his time plays many parts. . . .*"

Already Capt. Osborn had the fidgets, and began ticking his cane against his high-top shoe. The rest of us sat uncomfortably as T. Wallace ran through the seven ages of man.

"*. . . Last scene of all . . . mere oblivion, sans teeth, sans eyes, sans taste, sans every thing!*"

Polite applause, especially from the ladies. I thought I heard Jeannine ask shrilly for more popcorn, but it could have been some other child. One of the rowdies made a sneering remark that I couldn't catch, but that set his neighbors chuckling, no longer so hostile to him as before, and rewarded him with a flash of T. Wallace Whittaker's eyes.

"Mark Antony's funeral oration, from Act Three of *Julius Caesar*," he announced. "*Friends, Romans, countrymen, lend me your ears. . . .*"

"Ye can have mine, boy," the hoodlum said loudly. "I've

took enough!" He stalked out of the theater, and the rest of us were shamefully amused. Even some wives stifled smiles, but T. Wallace Whittaker went on, blushing, to inflame an imaginary mob against Brutus and company. The oration was long, for T. Wallace went through the whole routine of Caesar's will. By the time he insinuated his desire to move the stones of Rome to rise and mutiny, his audience was on the verge of doing likewise; we were tapping our feet, sneezing, and whispering among ourselves. When he cried at the end, *"Mischief, thou art afoot, take thou what course thou wilt!"* someone whistled and flung a handful of pennies onto the stage.

T. Wallace ignored the insult; rather, he acknowledged it with a defiant glare, but refused to be bowed.

"What I shall recite now," he said grimly, "is the most magnificent thing in the whole English language. I shan't expect a noisy rabble to appreciate its beauty, but perhaps a respectful silence will be granted, if not to me, at least to Shakespeare!"

"Where's the minstrels?" someone shouted. "Bring on the minstrels!" More pennies sailed over the footlights.

"The soliloquy from *Hamlet*," T. Wallace Whittaker whispered.

"Go home!"

"Take 'im away!"

"Come on, minstrels!"

"To be, or not to be: that is the question. . . ."

"Ya—a—a—ah!"

The audience was out of hand now. Several young men stood on their chairs to take better aim with their pennies, which no longer merely fell at T. Wallace's feet, but struck his face, chest, and gesticulating arms until he was forced to turn half around. But he would not be vanquished.

"To die, to sleep; to sleep: perchance to dream: ay, there's the rub. . . ."

One pimply-faced lad, standing in a front-row seat, began aping T. Wallace's gestures, to our delight, until Col. Morton struck at him with his gold-headed cane.

"For who would bear the whips and scorns of time, the oppressor's wrong . . ." T. Wallace Whittaker was determined that we should have our culture. I greatly admired him.

"*. . . the proud man's contumely, the pangs of despised love, the law's delay . . .*"

"Yahoo! Boo! Hsssss!"

It was open warfare now; T. Wallace could no longer be heard, but nevertheless he continued undaunted. Capt. Adam appeared from the wings, disturbed lest we begin taking the vessel apart, but we greeted his conciliatory wavings with more boos. He went to T. Wallace, doubtless to ask him to call it a day, but T. Wallace declaimed in his face. Capt. Adam grew panicky, then angry, and tried to drag him off; T. Wallace shoved him away, still gesticulating with the other hand. Capt. Adam shook his finger at the young man, shouted, "Yer fired!" and signaled to Prof. Eisen to strike up the band. The $7,500 Challenge Maritime Band waltzed into "Over the Waves." T. Wallace Whittaker stepped through the closing curtains, and shaking both fists at us through a copper shower (to which I, too, contributed, standing up and flinging all my change at him), in blind defiance he screamed: "*Thus conscience does make cowards of us all, and thus the native hue of resolution is sicklied o'er with the pale cast of thought!*" Finished at last, he scooped a handful of pennies from the stage, flung them back at us, and disappeared behind the curtain.

A few more late-thrown pennies sailed after him, hit the curtain, and clicked onto the stage. We were all laughing and comparing notes, a little sheepish, but exhilarated for all that—none more so than I, for it is sometimes pleasant to stone a martyr, no matter how much we may admire him. For my part, as I believe I've mentioned elsewhere in this book, I'm seldom reluctant to assist in my small way in the persecution of people who defy the crowd with their principles, especially when I'm in favor of the principles. After all, the test of one's principles is his willingness to suffer for them, and the test of this willingness—the only test—is actual suffering. What was I doing, then, but assisting T. Wallace Whittaker in the realization of his principles? For now, surely, having been hooted from the stage and fired from his job in the cause of Shakespeare, he would either abandon his principles, in which case they weren't integrated very strongly into his personality, or else cling to them more strongly than ever, in which case he had us to thank for giving him the means to strength.

Capt. Adam appeared next from the wings, smiling thinly,

and raised his hands. We were willing enough now to be silent, having made our point.

"Oh, well, who likes Shakespeare anyhow?" He shrugged cravenly, kicking a few pennies around the footlights. "If ye think yer gittin' any o' these pennies back, though, yer crazy!"

We laughed, relieved as wayward children who learn that they won't be punished after all.

"Now, then, see if ye can't be a little nicer to the next folks," Capt. Adam grinned. "At least pitch quarters at 'em. Ladies and gents: those knights of the burnt cork, the U.S.A.'s greatest sable humorists, the chaste and inimitable Ethiopian Tidewater Minstrels!"

We applauded complacently, for this was what we'd come to see. . . .

There were banjo exhibitions, comic dances, novelty songs, more jokes.

"And now, ladies and gents," Capt. Adam announced, "for the last feature on our program: the world-renowned imitator Burley Joe Wells, all the way from New Orleans, Louisiana! . . ."

"Steamboat race," growled Burley Joe, who wasted none of his art on introductions. "De *Natchez* soun' like dis [*A high-pitched chugging, pumping, swishing sound. A shrill whistle*], an' de *Robert E. Lee* soun' like dis [*A low, throaty throb. A resonant bass whistle*]. Hyar dey goes, now."

It was amazing. Ship's bells clanged. Orders were shouted, soundings called. The great pumps thundered. The stern wheel spun. A deep blast of the whistle announced the *Lee*'s departure. Some moments later a deck hand cried "Steamboat 'round de bend!" and a faint shrill whistle identified the *Natchez* ahead. Prof. Eisen insinuated soft, excited music under the throb of the engines. *Toot toot!* The *Lee* flung down the gantlet. *Peep peep!* The *Natchez* accepted the challenge. A race was on! More orders, excited cries, signal bells. The engines accelerated, the music likewise.

I glanced at Capt. Osborn: he was entranced. At the house in general: enthralled. At my wrist watch: ten o'clock. A spotlight directed at Burley Joe was the only illumination in the house at the moment. Quietly, but with no particular attempt at secrecy, I left my seat, slipped down the aisle next to the starboard wall, and stepped out through a side exit, attracting little attention. Inside, the *Lee* gained slowly on the *Natchez.*

It was, of course, entirely dark outside except for the *Opera*'s lights. I found myself, as I'd planned, on the outboard side of the theater. No watchman was in sight. I walked swiftly down the starboard rail to that small companionway in the stern which I'd fixed in my mind during the afternoon's tour, and let myself into the dining room, under the stage, closing the door behind me. Over my head the *Lee* and the *Natchez* were side by side. The music was louder and faster; the minstrels called encouragement to one or the other of the ships; an occasional excited cry broke from the audience. I struck a match and lit three kerosene lanterns mounted along the dining-room walls, then went to the valve labeled DO NOT OPEN UNTIL READY TO LIGHT FOOTLIGHTS and turned it full on, feeling under my hand the rush of acetylene to the stage. Finally I entered the galley, a few feet away, put a match to one burner, and turned the others (and the oven and the boiler) full on, unlighted. A strong odor of bottled illuminating gas filled the little room at once.

Upstairs the *Robert E. Lee* forged slightly ahead of its rival, and the audience cheered. Gas hissed from the burners.

Re-entering the dining room, I glanced around carefully, checking my work. As a last touch I removed the chimneys from all three lanterns and turned up the wicks. Then I slipped out as I'd entered and took my place again in the audience, now wonderfully agitated as the *Natchez* threatened to overtake the valiant *Lee.* My heart, to be sure, pounded violently, but my mind was calm. Calmly I regarded my companion Capt. Osborn, shouting hoarse encouragement to the *Robert E. Lee.* Calmly I thought of Harrison and Jane: of perfect breasts and thighs scorched and charred; of certain soft, sun-smelling hair crisped to ash. Calmly too I heard somewhere the squeal of an over-excited child, too young to be up so late: not impossibly Jeannine. I considered a small body, formed perhaps from my own and flawless Jane's, black, cracked, smoking. Col. Morton, Bill Butler, old Mr. and Mrs. Bishop—it made no difference, absolutely.

My heart thumped on like the *Robert E. Lee*, and I smiled at the thought that I might expire of natural causes before the great steamboat explosion. The audience was wild.

"Ladies and gentlemen!" shouted Capt. Adam, standing in the interlocutor's chair. *"Please make ready for the great explosion of the sidewheeler* James B. Taylor! *Do not leave your seats!"*

Some women cried out, for no transition had been made at all from the one act to the other, nor did the $7500 Challenge Maritime Band pause for a quaver: indeed, they redoubled their efforts. But the race, apparently, was forgotten. From the pit, under the frenzied music, came a slow rumbling as of tympani, its volume gradually increasing. From Burley Joe—now rising slowly from his knees, arms outstretched, eyeballs bulging—came a hackle-raising hiss like escaping steam. The drums thundered; trumpets whinnied like horses; children grew hysterical; Tambo and Bones hid behind their neighbors. From high on his chair Capt. Adam regarded his brood with an olympian smile—and calmly, more godlike than he, I too smiled.

Like some monstrous black serpent, Burley Joe poised now on tiptoe, arms overhead. The hissing and the music peaked; there was a double flash from the wings, a choked scream, a stunning explosion; the stage filled at once with thick white smoke.

After an instant of complete silence, Evelyn Morton, on the front row, quietly fainted; the Colonel caught her as she keeled. Then Prof. Eisen tore into "Lucy Long," the smoke began drifting away, and the minstrels appeared in a laughing, dancing row on the stage: Tambo, Bones, J. Strudge, Burley Joe Wells (bowing), the two guitarists, Capt. Adam himself (bowing)—and with them Sweet Sally Starbuck and Miss Clara Mulloy, dewy-eyed and blowing kisses. The audience laughed and exclaimed sharply to one another. Husbands looked at wives, wives at children, with an instant's new eyes.

"Lucy Long!" "Lucy Long!" The wonderful panithiopliconica, it turned out, was not more nor less than a grand old-fashioned minstrel walk-around—bones, tambourines, banjos, guitars. The minstrels danced, sang, leaped, cartwheeled. "Lucy Long" became "The Essence of Old Virginny"; faster and faster the minstrels cavorted, to a final, almost savage breakdown. The cymbals crashed, the performers bowed low, Tambo and Bones tumbled into the orchestra pit, and our wild applause saluted the curtains of the Original & Unparalleled Floating Opera.

XXVIII. *A Parenthesis*

If you do not understand at once that the end of my *Floating Opera* story must be undramatic, then again I'm cursed with imperfect communication. Say what you wish about the formal requirements of storytelling; this is my opera, and I'll lead you out of it as gently as I led you in. I've little use, as a principle, for slam-bang finishes like Burley Joe's.

I helped Capt. Osborn to his feet (he was still shaken with the excitement of the steamboat race) and ushered him out with the crowd. There was still a possibility, of course, that the theater might explode—gas accumulated in the bilges of a vessel is particularly volatile—but I rather suspected that either some hidden source of ventilation (Capt. Adam had claimed the *Opera* was safe) or wandering member of the crew had foiled my plan. Need I tell you that I felt no sense either of relief or of disappointment? As when the engine of the law falls sprawling against my obstacles, I merely took note of the fact that despite my intentions six hundred ninety-nine of my townspeople and myself were still alive.

Why did I not, failing my initial attempt, simply step off the gangplank into the Choptank, where no fluke could spoil my plan? Because, I began to realize, a subtle corner had been turned. I asked myself, knowing there was no ultimate answer, "Why not step into the river?" as I had asked myself in the afternoon, "Why not blow up the Floating Opera?" But now, at once, a new voice replied casually, "On the other hand, why bother?" There was a corner for you! Negotiated unawares, but like that dark alleyway in Baltimore which once turned me dazzled onto the bright flood of Monument Street, this corner confronted me with a new and unsuspected prospect—at which, for the moment, I could only blink.

We met Harrison, Jane, and Jeannine at the foot of the crowded gangplank.

"How'd you like the show?" Harrison laughed. "The folks really eat that stuff up, don't they?"

"And so do I," I said.

"Oh, well, I enjoy it too, in a sense," Harrison chuckled briskly. "Hear those horrible old jokes again. Jeannine liked it, anyhow." He indicated his daughter, lying like a sleeping angel in his arms.

"We'd better get her home, I guess," Jane said pleasantly. I believe she and Harrison both were somewhat uncomfortable in Capt. Osborn's presence—though certainly no more so than was that gentleman in hers. "Good night, Toddy," she smiled, still pleasantly, but without warmth. "I guess we'll be seeing you around."

"Of course," Harrison agreed at once, moving off.

"Certainly," I said at the same time, pleasantly but without warmth, and we parted. I've spoken to my friend Harrison on three separate occasions since then; to Jane only once, during a party in 1938 celebrating the final decision of the Maryland Court of Appeals in Harrison's favor (his presence hadn't been necessary when I argued the case, and he sent the firm a $50,000 check via a vice-president of the pickle company); to my beautiful Jeannine, now a twenty-one-year-old debutante of Ruxton and Gibson Island, not at all, though I note her activities occasionally on the society page of the Baltimore *Sun*. Upon their return from eighteen months in Amalfi, Cannes, and Biarritz, the Macks settled just outside Baltimore to live, and so there is nothing remarkable in the fact that I don't see them any more.

Capt. Osborn and I walked back up High Street to the hotel then, and I bade him good night in the hallway.

"Hold on, Toddy," he grinned. "C'mon in my room here; I got a s'prise for ye."

I followed him in, and smiling broadly he presented me with a pint of Southern Comfort.

"There, now!"

"What's this for?" I broke the seal and sniffed appreciatively.

The old man blushed. "I owed it to ye. That little business we was talkin' about this mornin', for one thing."

"Come on, then, let's drink it up," I said. "You'll need

it as badly as I will, because that particular show's all over with."

"Shucks, it would've been all over with anyhow, far's I'm concerned," Capt. Osborn declared.

"How about Young Haecker?" I suggested. "Suppose we cut him in on it, too?"

I went up to the top floor to Mister Haecker's little dormer room and knocked, but though a flickering light shone under the door, he didn't reply.

"Mister Haecker?" I turned the knob, for it was doubtful that a man of his age and circumstances would be either out or asleep at ten-thirty.

The door opened onto a strange scene: a single tall white candle burned in a brass holder on the writing desk beside the bed, and flickered in the small breeze from the window. Also on the writing desk, as I saw on approaching it, were an alarm clock stopped at ten-fifteen; a volume of Shakespeare opened to Act Three, Scene One, of *Hamlet* (with, believe it or not, the words *not all* noted in the margin opposite the line *Thus conscience does make cowards of us all*); a stack of thirteen fat notebooks each labeled *Diary, 19—*(I never had nerve enough to examine those); and a glass bottle with two sleeping pills left in it. On the bed Mister Haecker lay dressed in black pajamas, his eyes closed, his arms crossed in the manner of Miss Holiday Hopkinson, next door, his features calm (*composed* is a more accurate adjective), his pulse and respiration—as I discovered upon snatching up his wrist and putting my ear to his chest—almost imperceptible.

As far as I could see there was nothing to be done in the way of first aid; I hurried downstairs and notified Hurley Binder, the night clerk, who in turn telephoned the hospital for an ambulance. Then the two of us returned to Mister Haecker's room with Capt. Osborn, who pleaded with us to help him up the stairs so that he wouldn't miss the excitement, and had our drinks there while waiting for the ambulance to arrive. Hurley Binder and Capt. Osborn clucked their tongues and shook their heads and drank their Southern Comfort, mightily impressed by Mister Haecker's elaborate preparations for departure.

"What d'ye think of that?" Capt. Osborn said several times. "And him such a educated feller!"

From time to time I relt Mister Haecker's pulse: he seemed to be losing no ground—but then there was little to lose, for pulses do not beat much more slowly. Presently the ambulance cried up past Spring Valley, and Mister Haecker was carted off to the hospital, black pajamas and all.

"Makes a man stop and think now, don't it?" Capt. Osborn said.

"It does indeed," I agreed mildly, and said good night. What I thought, personally, was that should he live through this foolishness, Mister Haecker might find the remaining years of his life less burdensome than the ones recently past, because both his former enthusiasm for old age and his apparent present despair of it were (judging from appearances) more calculated than felt, more elaborate than sincere. I should enjoy saying that history proved me correct; in fact, however, upon recovering from his generous dose of barbiturates Mister Haecker went from the hospital to a sanitorium in Western Maryland, it having been discovered that he was incipiently tubercular; there, in 1940, he attempted once again to take his life, by the same means and with as much flourish as before, and succeeded.

Alone in my room then, I sat on the window sill and smoked a cigar for several minutes, regarding the cooling night, the traffic light below, the dark graveyard of Christ Episcopal Church across the corner, and the black expanse of the sky, the blacker as the stars were blotted out by storm clouds. Sheet lightning flickered over the Post Office and behind the church steeple, and an occasional rumbling signaled the approach of the squall out over the Chesapeake. How like ponderous nature, so dramatically to change the weather when I had so delicately changed my mind! I remembered my evening's notes, and going to them presently, added a parenthesis to the fifth proposition:

V. There's no final reason for living (or for suicide).

XXIX. *The Floating Opera*

That's about what it amounted to, this change of mind in 1937: a simple matter of carrying out my premises completely to their conclusions. For the sake of convention I'd like to end the show with an emotional flourish, but though the progress of my reasoning from 1919 to 1937 was in many ways turbulent, it was of the essence of my conclusion that no emotion was necessarily involved in it. To realize that nothing makes any final difference is overwhelming; but if one goes no farther and becomes a saint, a cynic, or a suicide on principle, one hasn't reasoned completely. The truth is that nothing makes any difference, including that truth. Hamlet's question is, absolutely, meaningless.

While finishing my cigar I made a few more idle notes for my *Inquiry*, which was, you understand, open again. They are of small interest here—which is to say, they are of some interest. It occurred to me, for example, that faced with an infinitude of possible directions and having no ultimate reason to choose one over another, I would *in all probability*, though not at all necessarily, go on behaving much as I had thitherto, as a rabbit shot on the run keeps running in the same direction until death overtakes him. Possibly I would on some future occasion endeavor once again to blow up the Floating Opera, my good neighbors and associates, and/or my mere self; most probably I would not. I and my townsmen would play that percentage in my case as, for that matter, we did in each of theirs. I considered too whether, in the real absence of absolutes, values less than absolute mightn't be regarded as in no way inferior and even be lived by. But that's another inquiry, and another story.

Also reopened were the *Letter to My Father* and that third peach basket, the investigation of myself, for if I was ever to explain to myself why Dad committed suicide, I must explain to him why I did not. The project would take time. I reflected that Marvin Rose's report on my heart would reach me in next day's mail after all, and smiled: never before had the uncertainty of that organ seemed of less moment. It was beside the point now whether endocarditis was still among my infirmities: the problem was the same either way, the "solution" also. At least for the time being; at least for me.

I would take a good long careful time, then, to tell Dad the story of *The Floating Opera*. Perhaps I would expire before ending it; perhaps the task was endless, like its fellows. No matter. Even if I died before ending my cigar, I had all the time there was.

This clear, I made a note to intercept my note to Jimmy Andrews, stubbed out (after all) my cigar, undressed, went to bed in enormous soothing solitude, and slept fairly well despite the absurd thunderstorm that soon afterwards broke all around.

Part IV

Criticism and Comment

The academicians have yet to concentrate fully on Black Humor as a whole, though a few have analyzed individual writers. When scholarly attention comes, we will probably see the death of the term itself. "Black Humor" is far more emotive than descriptive; Richard Poirier, toward the end of his fine book, *A World Elsewhere*, uses the term "Comic-Apocalyptic writers," and its accomplishes the task of literary definition a shade better than Knickerbocker's term. It tells us, in brief, more about the specific formal qualities associated with these writers. For myself, however, I shall be sorry to see the phrase "Black Humor" go, for its nonliterary connotations—to my mind—are both valuable and instructive.

To date, then, the best criticism and commentary, for and against the subject, has appeared in the popular reviews, newspapers, and magazines. I do not apologize for drawing from these sources; it is only there at this time that we will find critics both writing well and without the provincial blandness that characterizes most scholarly/critical journals. The Fall, 1963, issue of *Critique: Studies in Modern Fiction*, I hasten to say, is in several ways an exception to this rule. The issue is devoted entirely to Hawkes and Barth; among several outstanding articles is one by Richard Schickel, called "The Floating Opera," which marks one of the first attempts to define a common bond between writers like Barth, Hawkes, Thomas Berger, Heller, Percy, and Donleavy. Its predominant focus (on Barth's *Floating Opera*) is so narrow, however, that it was unsuitable for inclusion here.

The material that I have included in this section offers a representative mix of critical opinion and reportage on Black Humor *in general*—Knickerbocker bringing the first news, Kostelanetz refining him; Elliott and McLuhan differing widely on the issues raised by the work of Burroughs, largely because of the opposition of their approaches, with Elliott writing as an agent of the old humanism, and McLuhan of the new technology, Poirier and Bellow differing on related issues, also, Poirier in the course of reviewing Pynchon, Bellow in assessing the whole state of American writing now. I have placed at the end a selection from Wylie Sypher's *Loss of the Self in Modern Literature and Art*, although it dates before all the other commentaries, even before some of the main selections in this anthology were written. I have reprinted the material by Sypher partly because it picks up so cleanly the theme of the Self raised by Bellow, partly because it beautifully summarizes so many of the thoughts stirred in this anthology by editor, writers, and critics, and partly because it strikes me as a first-rate job of literary prophecy, knowing or unknowing.

CONRAD KNICKERBOCKER
"Humor With a Mortal Sting" (1964)

Something terrible (to many people) and marvelous (to others) has happened to the national sense of humor since World War II. Not only is more serious American fiction funnier, but our comic writers, like medieval magicians, have divided into two camps, white and black. "White" humorists such as Max Shulman and William Brinkley are as harmless as Lucille Ball or the Flintstones. They chuckle at our foibles, but when the chips are down, they support the familiar comforts of the status quo. Their adherents are many, for everyone agrees that a good laugh—moderate of course—is a wonderful tonic in this careworn world of ours.

Everyone, that is, except an immoderate new breed of American writers, who have wrenched the status quo until it begins to emit tormented laughter. Bitter, perverse, sadistic and *sick*—as the righteous defenders of a sick society aver—the new humor is black in its pessimism, its refusal of compromise and its mortal sting. Its adherents are few as yet but increasing. Bored beyond tears by solemnity and pap, an increasing audience finds in black humor no tonic, but the gall of truth. There are no more happy endings. A cheery wave and a fast shuffle no longer leave them laughing. New for us, black humor has been part of the response of wiser peoples in other times. Its appearance in American fiction may signal the end of certain innocences.

The list of American talents who have opted for a Bronx cheer instead of a handshake has been growing for 10 years. Terry Southern unmasks fraud in its slickest guises. J. P. Donleavy demolishes matrimony. William Burroughs hoots at our ideas of criminal behavior. Warren Miller conjures new saviors and the free state of Harlem. Bruce Jay Friedman aborts motherhood. Charles

Simmons unsmuts smut. Thomas Pynchon, Hughes Rudd, William Gaddis, John Barth, Joseph Heller, Donald Barthelme, Elliott Baker, Ivan Gold and Richard G. Stern, all in their various ways are stampeding the vast herd of American sacred cows.

These writers belong to no round table. The mass book audience has not heard of most of them. They work independently in Mexico City, Chicago or Connecticut. Their views, which have in common the savagery of their conclusions, signal a major new, and perhaps the only new, development in American fiction since the war.

Incapable of a *détente*, the black humorists torment the American mind by taking nothing at face value. They hate preconceptions, stereotypes and spiritual fat. They laugh in tune with the man on the gallows who asked, "Are you sure this thing is safe?" because their social realities seem just as precarious. They are afraid not so much of the cliché of the Bomb as the more awful prospect that we will survive after all only to win the space race and eliminate washday blues.

We have always had satirists, but "A Connecticut Yankee" and "Main Street" are gentle nudges in the ribs compared to the neo-Swiftian assaults of Mr. Southern's "The Magic Christian" or Mr. Burroughs's "Naked Lunch." Petronius Arbiter, his barbs incurring the wrath of Nero, opened his veins and recited frivolous verses to his friends as he died. Certain modern humorists may instead shoot heroin into their veins, but the message is the same. As societies convulse, art turns emetic. Whether the new humor ominously resembles the Latin satire that flourished while the totalitarian power of the Empire grew, or the glittering harpoons of Dr. Johnson's age that drew their aim on stupendous social arrogance, indifference and misery, depends on who has the last laugh. One thing is certain: the new humorists bear witness to convulsions.

"I am in the position of liking the roots, somehow, of America and loathing everything it stands for today," James Purdy, one of the grimmest of the grim humorists, wrote a friend recently. "We live in the stupidest cultural era of American history. It is so stupid it inspires me."

Only disappointment—an irremediable sense of expectations betrayed—can account for the violent and amusing shapes that fill his novel "Malcolm" and stories like "Daddy Wolf." "The theme of my work is the estrangement of the human being in America," he has said, an America "based on money and competition, inhuman, terrified of love, sexual and other, obsessed with homosexuality (Hemingway, O'Hara, etc.) and brutality . . . opposing anything that opposes money."

With a kind of glossolalia of imagery, the new humorists testify to a world filled with discontinuities too huge for normal expression. Benny Profane, the "human yo-yo" who is the hero of Mr. Pynchon's novel "V," finds solace in New York sewers shooting the gift alligators children have flushed down toilets. The First Church of Christ, Astronaut, calls its followers to the desert to await the arrival of saviors from outer space in Mr. Miller's "Waiting for the General." But then, after attempting suicide, Lee Harvey Oswald complained about the chow in the Russian hospital where he was recovering: black humor is well acquainted with the incredible facts of the day. Starting from scratch and with an evangelical momentum, these shaggy anchorites in a desert avoid the amenities, the little courtesies to reader and reviewer that have enervated many of our more "normal" writers. Their freedom gives them the elbow room for onslaught, the vigor to deal directly, as the traditional novel seems less and less able to do.

"Normal" novelists prefer to seduce the reader with clever mixtures of the probable and the derived; this kind of fiction waits coyly to be consumed and explained in the normal fashion. The black humorists prefer rape. They ambush the reader and savage his convictions that war, success, big cars, families and fancy restaurants are worth living for.

It was more than 15 years after V-J Day before any American author raised the point that a war of noble purpose could also be a boondoggle not dissimilar to some gigantic used-car auction. Mr. Heller did it in "Catch-22." Thousands of ex-G.I.'s winced but also winked. Stanley Elkin's "Boswell" concerns a wrestler who worships the ideal of strength, but muscles grown too large bind into immobility. Mr. Gaddis's "The Recognitions," one of the most serious, most memorable novels of the 1950's, has long stretches of black humor that amplify its themes of spiritual and artistic forgery. In "The Revelations of Dr. Modesto," Alan Harrington's young man receives a mail-order course on the art of living that actually brings results. Then he discovers that his mentor has been a long-term patient in a psychiatric hospital. These novels bear one message, forceful, repetitive, almost repetitious: in the midst of progress, as we photograph moon craters, as wars continue, and as power structures proliferate, we regress.

Of course this kind of conceptualization is self-defeating, and particularly in relation to the new humorists, with their antagonism toward abstract analysis. The minute one says, "I'm cool," one has lost one's cool. The minute one says, "I laughed. Here's why," one has lost some humor. In a review of Mr. Southern's "Candy" in *The New Republic,* Albert Goldman smacked his lips and attempted the last word on the "liberal, intellectual audience of readers and critics who are forever trying to understand and explain everything, and who seem constitutionally incapable of enjoying fantasy or humor without indulging in the cant of 'redeeming social value.' "

But his statement itself demonstrates the paradox deplored by black humor. Liberal, intellectual readers look to agencies of articulation for their vocabulary. The trouble is that these agencies, with their conflicting presentations, only add to the confusion.

The press, the movies, television, advertising, the universities, business, the government, the military, medicine—every vested social interest that claims the right to articulate the national identity contributes to the national psychosis. Our failure is that we tell ourselves too well who we are. The experts and exegetes each provide specially tailored, ready-to-wear identities. Black humor explodes these articulations as contradictory and irrational. The American psyche, like putty, awaits any imprint, even *The New Republic*'s.

Guy Grand, the eccentric billionaire who spends millions "making it hot for them" in "The Magic Christian," torments the blank American with infinite jests, exaggerations, switcheroos, and put-ons. Richard G. Stern's Golk, a television producer, manipulates the cameras to convince his audience that they are witnessing humorous real-life vignettes. Everybody roars; the program wins national acclaim. Actually all that he has shown is people wounding each other. Grand's and Golk's hoaxes confirm hoggishness. We have not only lost dignity, but like all fat men, we are funny.

It began to show in the 1930's, even as various new orders seemed to promise solutions. Nathanael West in America and Louis-Ferdinand Céline in France used black humor to warn against dream merchants. The French bought Céline's "Death on the Installment Plan" by the thousands. Later the panzers of the greatest dream merchant of them all rolled into Paris. Nobody here paid a great deal of attention to West. We were busy with a new order of our own, rebuilding prosperity, bolstering our souls with De Mille.

The enemy, according to the black humorists, is made up of men of gesture, manipulators of acceptable ideas, wise in the incantation of popular brainstorms. The new humor is anti-intellectual in the conventional sense. The idea, the concept logically advanced by critics, professors, senators and psychiatrists, has been tried and found wanting. John Barth's "The Sot-Weed Factor," a novel of great learning, has as its target the edifice of the intellect, particularly as guarded by its chief articulator, the university. Purportedly a ribald account of colonial American life, the book squares off at the Ph. D. candidate, with his view that history is somehow redemptive and that progress is the natural order of things. Our early national aspirations were just as squalid as those of the next nation's. The only difference is that we prefer delusions to illusions. Mr. Barth tells us, and he uses the techniques of a doctoral dissertation to give the coup-de-grace.

Most national styles of humor contain elements of social criticism, but the target usually lies without, unless there are worms within. Englishmen used to prefer jokes about the French and Irish; now the English physic themselves continually. In earlier days on the American stage, Uncle Sam and the Yankee trader told jokes about the English; now Mort Sahl tells jokes about the liberal intellectual; the liberal intellectual explains why, and Mr. Barth calls a plague on both houses. The new humor is self-directed. Underneath lie spasms of self-loathing. More, we have begun to lose our accustomed responses to the event. The excesses of civilization have stupefied us. Brutalized, we scream "Jump!" to the man on the ledge.

A number of writers no longer use ideas to explain events, for events have become too mysterious. The black humorists recount events in their natural—which is to say nonlogical—sequence. Events can, after all, be found in similar sequence on the front page of any newspaper, equally incomprehensible. "Naked Lunch" consists of a series of dispatches from America and abroad interlaced with a treatise on narcotics addiction. Never mind that the geography is hallucinated. Our laughter is the sad delight of recognition, not to be found in pamphlets on the national purpose.

A collection of short stories by Donald Barthelme, "Come Back, Dr. Caligari," is a testament to the non-sequiturs of the contemporary event. The stories become prose pop art, spilling past the hitherto agreed-on limits of fiction into realms as mysterious as daily life. Ideally, one should read them while drinking beer, reading *Time*, watching television, and listening to Dizzy Gillespie. More than stories, they are literary "happenings." In "A Shower of Gold," the hero is selected as a contestant on a television program called "Who Am I?" The master of ceremonies asks the hero if he loves his mother. "Yes," he replies, but a bell rings, the tote board flashes, and the announcer screams, "He's lying!" Shortly before this, he has been visited by the player of a cat-piano, a sinister device encasing eight live cats. His mother, furthermore, had always paid for his karate lessons. He is confused.

"Turn off your television sets," he finally rages in the pandemonium of the studio. "Cash in your life insurance, indulge in a mindless optimism. Visit girls at dusk. Play the guitar . . . Think back and remember how it was." The audience shrieks and howls.

More literal, less given to flights, but just as antidotal is Hughes Rudd's short story, "Miss Euayla is the Sweetest *Thang!*" winner of The Paris Review prize for humor in 1961. Rudd demonstrates how ordinary aspirations have transcended the absurd to reach, at last, the purely stupid. Lafond T. Cunningham, the hero, is a would-be Texas radio personality who describes himself as no taller than a shotgun, just as Truman Capote once did. In a few pages, Lafond stumbles through the entire range of Southern irrelevancies, capped by the explosion of a mail-order diamond ring. In ways beyond the scope of traditional fiction, Rudd's distortion of regional posturing reveals the emptiness behind the false fronts of our social landscape.

Certain critics may tell us the spirit of alienation—a vitalizing force in much of our best literature—is dying, and that American fiction is moving into a period of accommodation with things-as-they-are. This idea may have been suggested by the present self-satisfaction of our traditional novelists. As always, trying to hear what has already sounded, critics tend to ignore new thunder on the horizon.

Traditional art forms, in which, the surfaces of life fit neatly together, cope less and less. Black humor more and more expertly points out the inconstancies of modern experience, the fragmented zaniness of a day at any office. Laughter itself may be a form of accommodation, as the critic Webster Schott has suggested, but if so, it is the only point of juncture between the black humorists and the times in which they live. They are irreconcilable.

So, indeed, are more of us than the image-packagers would care to admit. Black humor has infiltrated middle culture in movies such as "Dr. Strangelove" and the upcoming "Goldstein," in theater with "Who's Afraid of Virginia Woolf?" and "Oh What a Lovely War," in the nightclub dementia of Lenny Bruce and Jonathan Winters, in the pop-art put-ons of Roy Lichtenstein and Andy Warhol. The Ginger Man might not speak for all of us, but his mockery prophesies a time when life will be lived exactly as blueprinted in the beer commercials, unless we hoot loud enough.

By default, the black humorists have become keepers of conscience. Strident, apt, they challenge the hypnotists and the hysterics. They urge choices on us. Amid the banality, the emptiness and excess, they offer the terrors and possibilities of self-knowledge. "There ought to be no barriers," Terry Southern recently told a Life magazine interviewer in an enigmatic put-on. Stop kidding yourself and recover joy, he may have meant. Has the age of hollow laughter dawned? Soon, perhaps, we will move forward to the sound of exploding windbags all around.

RICHARD KOSTELANETZ
"The American Absurd Novel" (1965)

We have come to think of absurd literature as a peculiarly contemporary, post-second world war phenomenon; and by absurd literature I mean works that embody a very specific literary convention: a series of absurd—that is, nonsensical and ridiculous—events that suggest the ultimate absurdity, the ultimate meaninglessness, of human existence. In Ionesco's *The Chairs*, perhaps the neatest model of the convention, a hired lecturer addresses a non-existent audience in an indecipherable tongue. This is the absurd surface. Since the lecturer's message is supposed to represent the final wisdom of a ninety-five-year-old couple, the meaningless message becomes a symbol for a metaphysical void.

As a descriptive term "absurd literature" must, I think, be used as precisely as possible; it does not apply to all literary works that deal with human absurdity. In the plays and fiction of Sartre and Camus, for contrary examples, the surface is too realistic, the sense of human causality too conventional; and the characters, along with the writer and reader, deduce absurdity from the course of credible events. Truly absurd literature does not discover meaninglessness; from its opening moments it accepts the condition and presents it as a theme. Absurd literature has an antirealistic, preposterous surface; it embodies a stylized vision of human reality, rather than an accurate representation of it. In addition, it must treat questions of ultimate significance, such as the quality of contemporary life, belief in final truths, or the underlying pattern of human history. It embodies absurdity in both the small events and the entire vision, in both the subject matter and the form.

The most familiar body of absurd literature is post-war

French theatre, particularly Samuel Beckett and Eugène Ionesco. In fiction, the absurd masterpieces are Beckett's later novels; but only in America in the nineteen-sixties do we find a large body of absurd fiction—the novels and stories of James Purdy, Donald Barthelme, Kenneth Koch, and particularly three novels I want to discuss in closer detail: *Catch-22*, by Joseph Heller, Thomas Pynchon's *V.*, and *The Sot-Weed Factor*, by John Barth.

A writer who deals with metaphysical issues must create a microcosm of experience that has enough symbolic resonance to stand for larger human issues. The European and English absurd writers attempt to create a single pregnant image: in Ionesco's play, the hired lecturer addressing the non-existent audience; in Beckett's last novel, *Comment c'est*, Pim dragging his bag of possessions through the mud of existence; in *Waiting for Godot*, two men waiting for a Godot who obviously is not coming. The American absurdist, in contrast, resorts to strategies of overstatement, rather than a single suggestive scene; and although these American novelists treat large areas of human experience, they are still exploiting these areas as symbolic microcosms for even larger issues.

Heller's *Catch-22*, which has the narrowest focus of the three novels, depicts the activities of some American soldiers in the second world war; Pynchon's novel has two faintly interconnecting plots, one portraying a group of American layabouts, the other a search for a woman whose name starts with the letter V., a search conducted against a background of European history in the twentieth century; and Barth's *The Sot-Weed Factor*, set in the late seventeenth and early eighteenth centuries, tells of the adventures of Ebenezer Cooke, in England and Colonial America, with flash-backs to John Smith's experiences with Pocahontas in the early seventeenth century. And to suit the breadth of their interests, all these novels are huge: both Heller's and Pynchon's run to 500 pages, and *The Sot-Weed Factor* to over 800, at 500 words to a page.

On the surface of life, each of these novelists finds more disorder than continuity, more incongruity than meaning. Heller, for one, portrays a world in which there is no relation between intention and result. This discrepancy he defines as the law of *Catch-22*, the book's central symbol, introduced in the following dialogue between Yossarian, Heller's main character, and Doctor Daneeka:

> "Is Orr crazy?"
>
> "He sure is."
>
> "Can you ground him?"
>
> "I sure can but first he has to ask me to. That's part of the rule."
>
> "Then why doesn't he ask you to?"
>
> "Because he's crazy . . . He has to be crazy to keep flying combat missions after all the close calls he's had. But first he has to ask me."
>
> "And then you can ground him?"
>
> "No then I can't ground him."
>
> "You mean there's a catch?"
>
> "Sure there's a catch. Catch-22. Anybody who wants to get out of combat duty isn't really crazy."

In a world ruled by Catch-22, a character with the preposterous name of Major Major Major Major should impress people, as Heller writes, 'by how unimpressive he was'; and another character named Colonel Cathcart 'was so awful a marketing executive that his services were much sought after by firms eager to establish losses for tax purposes.' In *Catch-22*, Yossarian should be told he is jeopardizing his political freedoms by daring to exercise them; and the book as a whole attempts to demonstrate that since the world's standards of value and behavior are so various, syllogistic logic can preach only contradictions.

Like Heller, Pynchon is obsessed with the discontinuity of human experience. Two-thirds of the way through his novel, one of Pynchon's internal narrators, Fausto Maijstral, introduces his own narrative with these suggestive words: 'No apologia is any more than a romance—half a fiction—in which all the successive identities taken on and rejected by the writer as a function of linear time are treated as separate characters.' A few lines later, Maijstral adds: 'It isn't so much to pay for eyes clear enough to see past the fiction of continuity, the fiction of cause and effect, the fiction of humanized history, endowed with "reason."' Maijstral, then, is one of Pynchon's identities, creating an incoherent story within an already confused narrative; and Maijstral's story, like Pynchon's, is a calculated denial of continuity as a principle in fiction and its usefulness as a tool in understanding human history. Pynchon's method has affinities with the Quantum Theory which says that experience that is discontinuous defies precise definition—its direction is indeterminate; and phenomena that have a semblance of meaning turn out, on closer inspection, to suggest a multiplicity of answers.

The letter V, Pynchon's most imaginative projection, is the central symbol of the book and one of the prime indicators of its meaning. The letter V is first introduced as the object of search of a character named Stencil—indicatively, as Stencil was born in 1900, he is 'a child of the century'; and, like much else in the novel, the letter V is capable of meaning many things: such as a large number of similar, perhaps successor characters, ranging from Victoria, an English girl seduced in Cairo in the late nineteenth century, to the grotesque Veronica Manganese with a jewel in her navel, as well as, to quote the summary of the American critic Stanley Edgar Hyman, 'Some great female principle . . . She is the goddess Venus and the planet Venus, the Virgin, the town of Valletta in Malta, the imaginary land of Vheissu with its iridescent spider monkeys and volcanoes. She is Vesuvius, Venezuela, the Violet of the vulgar mnemonic; ultimately she is the V of the spread thighs and the *mons veneris*.' Pynchon's special achievement, then, is devising a symbol for metaphysical reality that suggests not ambiguity as, say, Moby Dick does, but unbounded multiplicity.

Unlike Pynchon, who accepts basic historical facts as true, John Barth doubts our standard versions of the past; and in *The Sot-Weed Factor* he systematically distorts, mostly debunks, traditional accounts of history to create versions that are just as probable as those in the textbooks. In Barth's narrative Sir Isaac Newton and Henry More, the Cambridge neo-Platonist, emerge as lubricous pederasts who provide refuge for orphaned boys. And whereas Addison described late seventeenth-century coffee-house conversation as being intellectual, in Barth's novel the chatterers sooner turn to sex. The third Lord Baltimore, known to history as an undistinguished Catholic ruler, in Barth's book runs a network of spies and saboteurs in his war against the Protestants. The book's principal character, Ebenezer Cooke, gives himself the dubious title of 'Poet and Laureate' of Maryland, and goes off to the New World to write his *Marylandiad*. In the course of his travels he discovers some supposedly authentic documents, *The Privie Journall of Sir Henry Burlingame*, and *The Secret Historie* of John Smith, both written in magnificently faked seventeenth-century English prose.

These documents provide Barth with his most extensive opportunity for historical debunking, for they reveal the hidden story behind the Pocahontas myth. In the legend, we remember, the English explorer, John Smith, about to be executed by the Indian chief Powhatan, was saved by the intervention of the chief's daughter, Pocahontas. The version recounted in the novel's 'documents' is, of course, quite different. They reveal that John Smith was a lecher who first obtained Powhatan's friendship by giving him pornographic pictures and later won his confidence by satisfying the chief's otherwise insatiable wife. Later, thanks to a secret 'egg-plant' potion, Smith manages to deflower the much-tried, but previously impenetrable, virgin Pocahontas. The Indians, likewise untrue to historical form, confiscate Smith's immense collection of erotic literature.

Although one character in the novel rejects sentimental interpretations of history, saying 'More history's made in the bed-chamber than the throne room.' Barth is sophisticated enough to suggest that not much history is made in bed either. To Barth, history is thoroughly disordered and the search for first causes or definitive interpretations uncovers only contradictions; and more persistent search, only multiple confusions. A chapter heading near the book's end expresses Ebenezer's befuddlement as well as Barth's and the reader's:

> The Poet Wonders Whether the Source of Human History is a Progress, a Drama, a Retrogression, a Cycle, an Undulation, a Vortex, a Right- or Left Handed Spiral, a Mere Continuum, or What Have You Certain Evidence is Brought Forward, but of an Ambiguous and Inconclusive Nature.

In addition to burlesquing written history, *The Sot Weed Factor* thoroughly ridicules fictional conventions.

and in this way undercuts literature's pretensions to com-
prehending life. The satirical blade is aimed obliquely at
all fat popular historical novels (this one being too fat;
too difficult, and largely faked as history) and particularly at the eighteenth-century novel whose penchant for
digressive chapter headings is exaggerated as absurdly
as its favourite plot devices are repeated. The search for
the father, the reversal of roles, the accidental recognition scene, transformation through disguises, moments of
near incest, and especially preposterous coincidences all
occur again and again in Barth's novel.

In the end Barth successfully transforms two serious
quests—that of Cooke for his muse and that of his companion, Burlingame, for the identity of his parents—into
a long series of incidents so incredible that their serious
purposes are twisted into high comedy. And then, before
the novel is over, the book's spine is twisted back again
into Barth's essentially serious concern with human history. In mocking the conventions of the eighteenth-century novel by overusing them to absurd lengths, in suggesting that the history we know is as unlikely as his
rewriting of it, in doing both these things with such
imaginative wit and breadth of reference, Barth ultimately
says that not only are the single events of life preposterous—that is, absurd—but also that life as a whole,
which resists any ordering interpretation, is similarly, at
base, absurd. Amid all these facts Barth has only one
truth, that there is no truth. This conclusion, I think,
strikes appropriate undertones in our time; for the world
yields to our efforts no ordering scheme, only nonsense
with each twist of complexity multiplying itself to infinite
degrees.

Although these novels are all new in their fusion of
absurd base with absurd surface, they descend from several distinct literary traditions. First, they belong with
those prose works that reveal the influence of François
Rabelais and Laurence Sterne; and, like their predeces-
ors, these new American novelists are, at once, both
prodigiously erudite and endlessly imaginative. Neither
the form nor the action of their novels bows to accepted
conventions of literary reality or propriety; and while
they deal with the facts of existence these authors reserve
the right to transform the facts—indeed, to transform

all experience—through their rich imaginations. Secondly, these novels belong to the American tradition of anti-realistic romance, particularly those novels concerned with individual man and oppressive civilization, a line that includes *Huckleberry Finn*, *Billy Budd*, the novels of Saul Bellow and Ralph Ellison. And like their predecessors, these new American novels all tell us, again and again, that human society is so cruel that individual man, no matter how strong his will, can find no salvation within it.

All these novels seem more extensively preplanned than most fiction. Their authors appear to start writing with a theme in the very front of their minds, rather than a situation, a conflict, a single character or a specific technical device; and then they devise ways to illustrate their theme. Yet it is not their themes which are easily identified and summarized but the methods by which these themes are realized that makes these books interesting and artistically important. Surely it would be fairly easy to outline an absurd novel, but to take the absurd formula and give it the embellishment that these novels have is extremely difficult.

The artistic problems in creating an absurd novel are, then, twofold. First, the situation described must be an effective enough symbol to suggest metaphysical absurdity. A contrasting failure in this respect is Bernard Malamud's first novel, *The Natural,* which has a marvellously comic absurd surface. For example, when the manager of the baseball team instructs his batter in baseball slang, 'to knock the cover off the ball,' the batter pulls the impossible trick of batting the baseball so hard its leather cover falls off. But Malamud's baseball team fails, I think, to become a metaphysical symbol, and his novel never achieves the serious resonance which it constantly suggests. The other hazard of an absurd novel is over-embellishment, particularly as the strategy of surface discontinuity pushes the novel over the line of effectiveness into outright, thorough incoherence. Perhaps the most notorious example of this is William Gaddis's 956-page novel, *The Recognitions*; more recent incoherent, possible absurd novels include Lawrence Ferlinghetti's *Her* and Harry Mathews's *The Conversions*.

To my mind, the novels by Pynchon, Heller, and Barth

achieve metaphysical pertinence and avoid the perils of excessive incoherence; and all three are realized primarily as novels—they contain a structure and effects that only fiction can achieve; and, except for *Catch-22*, I cannot imagine any of them being adapted into another artistic medium, such as the cinema, without having its essence distorted or destroyed.

These American absurd novels show us that, even in these post-Joycean, post-Gidean, post-Faulknerian times, the novel as an art form is far from dead. Indeed, in an age in which everything artistically appears to have been done, these writers reaffirm the possibility of creating novels that are, in the contemporary sense, crucially new, and, in the traditional sense, realized achievements.

GEORGE P. ELLIOTT
"Nihilism" (1964)

With the novel, *Nova Express*, Grove Press binds together another 187 pages of the writing of William Burroughs. This segment of his output differs from the author's earlier novel, *Naked Lunch*, in two respects. It is less revolting because there is less joyless pornography in it, and it is more frustrating because it seems to have elements of a cohesive story, some sort of galactic cops-and-criminals game, whereas *Naked Lunch* did not arouse even muddled expectations which it then frustrated. But the difference between these two non-books is slight beside their similarity. Neither has a form of its own. The disgusting anti-eroticism of the one and the failed science fiction of the other function not as unifying components of contained wholes but as two manifestations of the same dislocated imagination.

Scattered through the pages are evidences that this imagination was once capable, or might have become capable, of poetry, intelligence, humor and observation. "Mendicant the crooked crosses and barren the dark streets"—that is a handsome line, whether Burroughs made it up himself or is quoting it from someone else. However, for it to realize its full potential it must have a context to give it strength, and this context Burroughs does not provide. By giving it a worthy context, he would have made it his own even if he borrowed it from another writer. By setting it in an anti-context, he throws it away even if he invented it himself. "He knew what it meant to kick an SOS habit": in isolation that is wry and witty enough to satisfy anybody, and, as part of a context worthy of it, it would have had a genuine satiric edge. But Burroughs has made it the beginning of a short paragraph whose cliché violence drains that sentence of its contained power: "White hot agony of thawing metal— And the suffocating panic of carbon dioxide withdrawal. . . ."

There is no point in going down the list of the ways Burroughs's writing fails literarily and intellectually. Reading it is like reading a batch of very bad little magazines at one sitting: doom croaking, dianetics, sparks of verbal brilliance, Wilhelm Reich, yelps of outsider envy, glee at shocking, echoes of *The Waste Land*, a loathing of social and literary conventions, elegant insights, all present and more where they came from. Reading very bad, slick-magazine writing is intellectually more soporific but less maddening because what is wasted there is vulgar and sentimental cunning rather than talented intelligence. But both these kinds of depressing writing deserve only the censure of silence, unless they are taken seriously—and Burroughs is acquiring a certain intellectual vogue, in this country as well as abroad.

Naked Lunch received staggering praise from writers whose opinions matter—Mary McCarthy, Norman Mailer and Robert Lowell among many—and the Grove Press edition, issued in 1962, has sold 34,000 copies as of Oct. 1, 1964. (How widely copies of the earlier Olympia Press edition were circulated among Americans, I do not know.) *Nova Express* may do less well, because the big puff for Burroughs's reputation has already been made and also because pornography, even the revolting species, can probably find a larger market now than other kinds of equally bad writing, though whether it will continue to do so after the novelty of being able to buy it legally has worn off is another matter.

It is a toss-up whether *Nova Express* is even more boring than *Naked Lunch*: I had thought on the evidence of the earlier book that the pornography of disgust could generate more intense boredom than any other literary vice, but now I am uncertain, for the new book demonstrates that inept and pseudo-science fiction can stupefy mightily. But this is a quibble, like trying to choose between a bad cold in the head and a severe attack of hay fever.

Looked at symptomatically as the charting of a diseased mind, Burroughs's writing has a certain interest. By inspecting it you can learn a good deal about the fantasies and hatreds of perverse sexuality and drug addiction, and can appreciate vicariously the unresting nastiness of emotion and thought which vitiates such a mind. Sure of nothing but its own zigzags, it has been figuratively lobotomized from the sexual, social, intellectual, literary experience it nevertheless cannot leave alone but must, in its vengeful impotence, try to spoil for others. But his writing has not been recommended to us for clinical reasons. It is commonly spoken of as literature with value of its own. Burroughs is treated as an important novelist and is referred to as a satirist worthy of comparison to the greatest, Swift. Because this claim is so wild it is worth at least a glance. Of what is *it* a symptom?

Revolt of all sorts—from mere dissent to utter nihilism, both the revolt of rebellion and the revolt of revulsion—has long been fashionable in some advanced intellectual circles. There, it is a dogma of the age that "the artist" is a rebel. (Bach? The painters of Lascaux? Chaucer? Balanchine? Rouault?) So vigorous has this fashion become that a writer nowadays must be wary. When he feels the urge to affirm, to celebrate, coming over him he had better stick to birds. The moment he veers toward contemporary experience, his writing had better rebel against or express revulsion with the way our things are, unless he wants to risk having it cast into outer darkness along with *The Reader's Digest*.

Yet fashion is insatiable as a vampire. Revolt alone has ceased to be enough to titillate the jaded appetite; total nihilism is better. Normal revolt is not only against a bad order but for a good one, whereas the energies of genuine nihilism are unpolluted—demolition is *all* it wants. A nihilist like Burroughs goes the whole way, even beyond a Henry Miller, who is comparatively old-fashioned and square: he likes to walk around in the world; he is actually capable of looking at other people; he even rejoices that two or three of them are there.

Fortunately the thoroughness of Burroughs's nihilism should prevent his books from remaining fashionable for very long. For one thing, his rage against order is total: his books themselves are a jumble. He probably intends their disorder both to figure forth the disorder of the world he is accusing and also to shake his readers out of any sense of order they may be deluding themselves with. But the actual result, once the shock wears off, is the monotonous repetitiveness which jumble always produces. The other reason why Burroughs will probably not stay in fashion long is that he is right at the limit of the region where communication begins to break down altogether. Beyond this dead end of a blind alley, no words, just urks.

We are all soul-sick, as the wise teachers have always

said men are, but must we compete for sickest? Do we have to become connoisseurs of vomit? Is the world doing so badly at tearing itself apart that it needs the aid of gifted writers to finish the job?

MARSHALL McLUHAN
"Notes on Burroughs" (1964)

1. Today men's nerves surround us; they have gone outside as electrical environment. The human nervous system itself can be reprogramed biologically as readily as any radio network can alter its fare. Burroughs has dedicated *Naked Lunch* to the first proposition, and *Nova Express* (both Grove Press) to the second. *Naked Lunch* records private strategies of culture in the electric age. *Nova Express* indicates some of the "corporate" responses and adventures of the Subliminal Kid who is living in a universe which seems to be someone else's insides. Both books are a kind of engineer's report of the terrain hazards and mandatory processes which exist in the new electric environment.

2. Burroughs uses what he calls "Brion Gysin's cut-up method which I call the fold-in method." To read the daily newspaper in its entirety is to encounter the method in all its purity. Similarly, an evening watching television programs is an experience in a corporate form—an endless succession of impressions and snatches of narrative. Burroughs is unique only in that he is attempting to reproduce in prose what we accommodate every day as a commonplace aspect of life in the electric age. If the corporate life is to be rendered on paper, the method of discontinuous non-story must be employed.

3. That man provides the sexual organs of the technological world seems obvious enough to Burroughs, and such is the stage (or "biological theatre" as he calls it in *Nova Express*) for the series of social orgasms brought about by the evolutionary mutations of man and society. The logic, physical and emotional, of a world in which we have made our environment out of our own nervous systems, Burroughs follows everywhere to the peripheral orgasm of the cosmos.

4. Each technological extension involves an act of collec-

tive cannibalism. The previous environment with all its private and social values, is swallowed by the new environment and reprocessed for whatever values are digestible. Thus, Nature was succeeded by the mechanical environment and became what we call the "content" of the new industrial environment. That is, Nature became a vessel of aesthetic and spiritual values. Again and again the old environment is upgraded into an art form while the new conditions are regarded as corrupt and degrading. Artists, being experts in sensory awareness, tend to concentrate on the environmental as the challenging and dangerous situation. That is why they may seem to be "ahead of their time." Actually, they alone have the resources and temerity to live in immediate contact with the environment of their age. More timid people prefer to accept the content, the previous environment's values, as the continuing reality of their time. Our natural bias is to accept the new gimmick (automation, say) as a thing that can be accommodated in the old ethical order.

5. During the process of digestion of the old environment, man finds it expedient to anesthetize himself as much as possible. He pays as little attention to the action of the environment as the patient heeds the surgeon's scalpel. The gulping or swallowing of Nature by the machine was attended by a complete change of the ground rules of both the sensory ratios of the individual nervous system and the patterns of the social order as well. Today, when the environment has become the extension of the entire mesh of the nervous system, anesthesia numbs our bodies into hydraulic jacks.

6. Burroughs disdains the hallucinatory drugs as providing mere "content," the fantasies, dreams that money can buy. Junk (heroin) is needed to turn the human body itself into an environment that includes the universe. The central theme of *Naked Lunch* is the strategy of by-passing the new electric environment by becoming an environment oneself. The moment one achieves this environmental state all things and people are submitted to you to be processed. Whether a man takes the road of junk or the road of art, the entire world must submit to his processing. The world becomes his "content." He programs the sensory order.

7. For artists and philosophers, when a technology is new it yields Utopias. Such is Plato's *Republic* in the 5th century B.C., when phonetic writing was being established. Similarly,

More's *Utopia* is written in the 16th century when the printed book had just become established. When electric technology was new and speculative, *Alice in Wonderland* came as a kind of non-Euclidean space-time Utopia, a grown-up version of which is the *Illuminations* of Rimbaud. Like Lewis Carroll, Rimbaud accepts each object as a world and the world as an object. He makes a complete break with the established procedure of putting things into time or space:

> That's she, the little girl behind the rose bushes, and she's dead. The young mother, also dead, is coming down the steps. The cousin's carriage crunches the sand. The small brother (he's in India!) over there in the field of pinks, in front of the sunset. The old men they've buried upright in the wall covered with gilly-flowers.

But when the full consequences of each new technology have been manifested in new psychic and social forms, then the anti-Utopias appear. *Naked Lunch* can be viewed as the anti-Utopia of *Illuminations*:

> During withdrawal the addict is acutely aware of his surroundings. Sense impressions are sharpened to the point of hallucination. Familiar objects seem to stir with a writhing furtive life. The addict is subject to a barrage of sensations external and visceral.

Or, to give a concrete example from the symbolist landscape of *Nova Express*:

> A guard in a uniform of human skin, black buck jacket with carious yellow teeth buttons, an elastic pull-over skirt in burnished Indian copper . . . sandals from calloused foot soles of young Malayan farmer . . .

The key to symbolist perception is in yielding the permission to objects to resonate with their *own* time and space. Conventional pictorial and literary perception seeks to put diverse objects into the *same* time and space. Time and space themselves are subjected to the uniform and continuous visual processing that provides us with the "connected and rational" world that is in fact only an isolated fragment of reality— the visual. There is no uniform and continuous character in the non-visual modalities of space and time. The symbolists freed themselves from visual conditions into the visionary world of the iconic and the auditory. Their art, to the visually oriented and literary man, seems haunted, magical and often incomprehensible. It is, in John Ruskin's words

> . . . *the expression, in a moment, by a series of symbols thrown together in bold and fearless connections, of truths which it would have taken a long time to express in any verbal way, and of which the connection is left for the beholder to work out for himself; the gaps, left or overleaped by the haste of the imagination, forming the grotesque character* (Modern Painters).

The art of the interval, rather than the art of the connection, is not only medieval but Oriental; above all, it is the art mode of instant electric culture.

8. There are considerable antecedents for the Burroughs attempt to read the language of the biological theatre and the motives of the Subliminal Kid. *Fleurs du Mal* is a vision of the city as the technological extension of man. Baudelaire had once intended to title the book *Les Limbes*. The vision of the city as a physiological and psychic extension of the body he experienced as a nightmare of illness and self-alienation. Wyndham Lewis, in his trilogy *The Human Age,* began with *The Childermass*. Its theme is the massacre of innocents and the rape of entire populations by the popular media of press and film. Later in *The Human Age* Lewis explores the psychic mutations of man living in "the magnetic city," the instant, electric and angelic (or diabolic) culture. Lewis views the action in a much more inclusive way than Burroughs whose world is a paradigm of a future in which there can be no spectators but only participants. All men are totally involved in the insides of all men. There is no privacy and no private parts. In a world in which we are all ingesting and digesting one another there can be no obscenity or pornography or decency. Such is the law of electric media which stretch the nerves to form a global membrane of enclosure.

9. The Burroughs diagnosis is that we can avoid the inevitable "closure" that accompanies each new technology by regarding our entire gadgetry as *junk*. Man has hopped himself up by a long series of technological fixes:

> *You are dogs on all tape. The entire planet is being developed into terminal identity and complete surrender.*

We can forego the entire legacy of Cain (the inventor of

gadgets) by applying the same formula that works for *junk* —"apomorphine" extended to all technology:

> *Apomorphine is no word and no image. . . . It is simply a question of putting through an inoculation program in the very limited time that remains—Word begets image and image is virus. . . .*

Burroughs is arguing that the power of the image to beget image, and of technology to reproduce itself via human intervention, is utterly in excess of our power to control the psychic and social consequences:

> *Shut the whole thing right off.* Silence—*when you answer the machine you provide it with more recordings to be played back to your "enemies." Keep the whole nova machine running—the Chinese character for "enemy" means to be similar to or to answer—Don't answer the machine—Shut it off—*

Merely to be in the presence of any machine, or replica of our body or faculties, is to close with it. Our sensory ratios shift at once with each encounter with any fragmented extension of our being. This is a non-stop express of innovation that cannot be endured indefinitely:

> *We are just dust falls from demagnetized patterns—Show business.*

It is the medium that is the message because the medium creates an environment that is as indelible as it is lethal. To end the proliferation of lethal new environmental expression, Burroughs urges a huge collective act of restraint as well as a non-closure of sensory modes—"The biological theater of the body can bear a good deal of new program notes."

10. *Finnegans Wake* provides the closest literary precedent to Burroughs's work. From beginning to end it is occupied with the theme of "the extensions" of man—weaponry, clothing, languages, number, money and media *in toto.* Joyce works out in detail the sensory shifts involved in each extension of man, and concludes with the resounding boast:

> *The keys to. Given!*

Like Burroughs, Joyce was sure he had worked out the formula for total cultural understanding and control. The idea of art as total programming for the environment is tribal, mental, Egyptian. It is, also, an idea of art to which electric technology leads quite strongly. We live science fiction. The bomb is our environment. The bomb is of higher learning all compact, the extension division of the university. The university has become a global environment. The university now contains the commercial world, as well as the military and government establishments. To reprogram the cultures of the globe becomes as natural an undertaking as curriculum revision in a university. Since new media are new environments that reprocess psyche and society in successive ways, why not bypass instruction in fragmented subjects meant for fragmented sections of the society and reprogram the environment itself? Such is Burroughs's vision.

11. It is amusing to read reviews of Burroughs that try to classify his books as non-books or as failed science fiction. It is a little like trying to criticize the sartorial and verbal manifestations of a man who is knocking on the door to explain that flames are leaping from the roof of our home. Burroughs is not asking merit marks as a writer; he is trying to point to the shut-on button of an active and lethal environmental process.

RICHARD POIRIER
from "Wescac and the Messiah" (1966)

With this fourth novel [*Giles Goat-Boy*], John Barth at
36 increases the likelihood that the years since World War II
are among the most rewarding in the history of American
fiction. There have been greater American novelists, conspicu-
ously Melville, James, and Faulkner, than any now at work
is likely to become, but never before have we had so many
distinguished writers at one time, each as markedly different
in style as Nabokov, Mailer, Bellow, Ellison, Barth, and perhaps Pynchon. Nor has there ever been what is always the sup-
porting evidence of any period of major accomplishment: such
a large number of highly accomplished but relatively minor
writers of fiction.

One explanation is that these American novelists, like their
French contemporaries but with more lively results, have
discovered a new mass of fictional material. They have discovered this material in the novel itself—its history, its conventions, its structures and styles, all weighted with pre-
sumptions about the nature of reality—and in the various
philosophical and psychological theories by which contemporary experience has been analyzed. Novelists have of
course always parodied one another; but the novel of self-
parody, which takes pleasure in exposing the limits of its
own procedures, has had up to now very few exponents
except Sterne and Joyce. And, rather than Faulkner or Hemingway, Joyce is now the important influence, along with
Lawrence, Sartre, Beckett, and, in Barth's case, probably the
Argentinian Juan Borges. These are writers for whom the
question of how to organize or tell a story is at the center
of dramatic interest formerly occupied by the psychological
career of a character.

Not surprisingly, the heroes in the works of many of
these American novelists are literary or academic people who

find in metaphysical or literary plotting an enterprise as passionate as sexual pursuit. Mailer's Rojack in *An American Dream* and Bellow's Herzog are recent examples. Before them was Todd Andrews, the hero of Barth's first novel, *The Floating Opera* (1956). Like Rojack and Herzog, he, too, is ostensibly the author-narrator of the book which features him, and he self-consciously tells us at the outset that being a "writer" is new to him, that he will try to give shape to his life by dividing it into its "five" intense moments prior to his decision to commit suicide, and that his first name is itself symbolic of his obsession with death. He is an academic close-reader of himself, much as is Jacob Horner, the English teacher who begins Barth's second and still better novel, *The End of the Road* (1958), with the existentialist remark that "In a sense, I am Jacob Horner." Horner's ideal of "articulation" is kind of *raison d'être* for the Protean brilliance of Barth's novels. "Articulation! There, by Joe, was *my* absolute, if I could be said to have one. At any rate, it is the only thing I can think of about which I ever had, with any frequency at all, the feelings one usually has for one's absolutes. To turn experience into speech—that is, to classify, to categorize, to conceptualize, to grammarize, to syntactify it—is always a betrayal of experience, a falsi-fication of it; but only so betrayed can it be dealt with at all, and only in so dealing with it did I ever feel a man, alive and kicking. . . . When my mythoplastic razors were sharply honed, it was unparalleled sport to lay about with them, to have at reality. In other senses, of course, I don't believe this at all."

One can reverse T. S. Eliot's famous remark about James to say of Barth that he has a mind so fine that it violates any idea that comes into it. The intellecutal sportiveness of this passage is of course only on loan to Horner. It belongs to Barth, to a mind that invents ideas in order to flout them, a mind considerably more interesting than the one Bellow is able to lend Moses Herzog. The personality vigor-ously alive in these sentences would obviously cast aside any absolute that tried to impose itself, and there is an implicit denial of schematizations even in the manner by which they are proposed: in parodies of genteel thinking, like the allu-sion to the "feelings one usually has about one's absolutes," and in the contrivance of infinitives so zestful as to make "articulation" sound like a physical, even sexual, exertion

that offers, predictably, no permanent satisfaction. Barth is
the kind of man who does not always have cause even to
think about "articulation"; even if it were a satisfactory
absolute, and there are none in Barth more satisfactory,
much of daily life would erupt independently of it. Life
would consist, so to speak, in digressions.

As measured by systems, structures, or theories, most of
the life in Barth's novels is digressive. In this, as in other
ways, his works are apt to remind readers of the 18th century: of Sterne, in *The Floating Opera*, of Fielding, in *The
Sot-Weed Factor*. His parodies extend, however, even to these
digressive tendencies. Digression in Barth is often an expression of existential liberty on the part of such hero-narrators
as Horner, and existentialism in *Giles Goat-Boy*, as in the
earlier novels, is treated as no more than an absolute about
the absurdity of absolutes.

What Barth is doing in this passage and in all his novels
usually works best in small units, in a paragraph, a scene,
or, at most, in novels as short as his first two. Making
structures in order to blow them up is an activity that can
become tediously repetitive in what it communicates unless,
as in *The End of the Road*, it is made inextricable from
the destiny not merely of all human contrivances but of the
human lives that can be ruined or exalted by them. Too
often in *The Sot-Weed Factor* and in *Giles Goat-Boy* there
is, as in some sections of Joyce's *Ulysses*, a process of
structural elaboration and disposal that dramatizes altogether less about the characters than about the author's role
as a novelist. The trouble with making literary and philosophical structures in themselves the object of parody is
that once the intention becomes clear, the exercise of it becomes, over any length, unnourishing and repetitious. And
it can be said of *The Sot-Weed Factor* and of *Giles Goat-Boy*
what Johnson said of *Paradise Lost*: "none ever wished it
longer than it is."

Barth must entertain such impertinence from his readers
simply because, like Fielding's "dear readers," we are invited
to join the author at a worldly remove from the work he is
offering to us. Especially in *Giles Goat-Boy*, he writes much
as Horner "articulates": in order to question the authenticity
of what he is doing. The novel is preceded by a "Publisher's
Disclaimer" and a "Cover-Letter to the Editors and Publishers" in which it is pretended that the entire manuscript

was written by someone or something else. The typed copy was left on Barth's desk, we are told, by the son of Giles, a "new mutant" as described by Leslie Fiedler, who has himself only read and corrected the text as it was fed to him by a computer named WESCAC. The book is divided into "reels" and "tapes." In a "Postscript to the Posttape" Barth even suggests that the final "tape" is a fraudulent interpolation.

These "disclaimers" are more than a good joke elegantly contrived. They are, more importantly, a bid for freedom of invention in the body of the work unrestricted by standards of verisimilitude or morality. Despite *longueurs* scarcely avoidable in a book so long, despite also the many merely formal and ingenious exemplifications of this freedom, Barth exploits his opportunities in order to construct a dazzlingly intricate allegory of the philosophical-academic-literary-sexual life of these times. Being a rarity among American novelists in having a brilliant philosophical mind, Barth is of course aware of the curious ways by which "these times" are a compendium of all times. In addition, therefore, to being characteristic of his rejection even of what he himself invents, the "disclaimers" have the virtue of letting him pretend that *Giles Goat-Boy* is not in the details of its allegory about Barth's own time and place but only about some strange world extraordinarily like it that embraces the whole of human history since the Greeks. For example, Giles and his friends attend a contemporary verse play entitled *Taliped Decanus* which is a parody, carried on much too long, of *Oedipus Tyrannus* and involves a Dean and his faculty in place of the king and his court. In addition to being an allegory of a literary and historical myth, the play is made into a satire of university life which is in turn an allegorization of contemporary political crises and of the problems of parentage, identity, and incest that are an obsession which his characters derive from psychoanalysis. . . .

Barth's treatment of sexual matters is a key and a warning, I think, about how we should confront the joking, despairing complexity of this book. Though it exists in a limbo world, the allegory is yet so exactly equivalent to current people and events as to suggest that the allegory isn't so much an invention about us as a record of what we essentially really are: our existence *is* allegorical. The ultimate joke of this book, though it is hardly a pleasant one to face, is that it requires no analysis, no translation at all. Indeed, we can read Barth's earlier novels retrospectively as a warning that really to use the instruments of analysis created by man so that we can make sense of the allegorical dream world in which we live is to arrive at a sense of life at once dreary and pointless. If all categories and structures are equally inconclusive, then all are equally good and are apparently necessary to the conduct of life.

From such a view it is only a step to the conclusion that psychoanalysis is not wrong but unnecessary. In this particular novel, the refusal to deal with human actions as if they existed for psychological rather than for philosophical inquiry is licensed by the fact that the hero is possibly part goat, probably fathered by a machine, and in either case nurtured in a way that has absolved him the human burden of guilt and suffering. He only begins to suffer at the end when, married, a father, and founder of a sect, he develops a human consciousness of time and therefore of love and death. He decides that perhaps truth is found only in the loving eye—again an allusion to Oedipus—not in any of the various efforts he has made to fulfill the roles assigned him as goat, human, Grand Tutor, or even husband. It is always surprising to discover that the most complicated examples of modern and of contemporary literature, like *Ulysses* and *The Waste Land*, (the ending of which is parodied, it would seem, by the end of this novel), are very often contemptuous of their own formal and stylistic difficulties. The absolutes to which in despair they seem finally to appeal are what we mistakenly take for simple: peace, the pleasures of the body, love. Barth writes not so much in praise of these things but in search of them through the labyrinths that have been made of life, including the labyrinth of novels like *Giles Goat-Boy*.

SAUL BELLOW
from "Some Notes on Recent American Fiction"
(1963)

Gertrude Stein is supposed to have explained to Hemingway that "remarks are not literature." Here I am offering some remarks, and I make no claim for them whatever. A writer's views on other writers may have a certain interest, but it should be clear that he reads what they write almost always with a special attitude. If he should be a novelist, his own books are also a comment on his contemporaries and reveal that he supports certain tendencies and rejects others. In his own books he upholds what he deems necessary, and usually by the method of omission he criticizes what he understands as the errors and excesses of others.

I intend to examine the view taken by recent American novelists, and short-story writers of the individual and his society, and I should like to begin with the title of the new book by Wylie Sypher: *Loss of the Self in Modern Literature and Art*. I do not propose to discuss it; I simply want to cite the title, for in itself it tells us much about the common acceptance of what the Spanish critic Ortega y Gasset described some years ago as "the dehumanization of the arts." One chapter is devoted to the Beats, but, for the most part, Sypher finds, as we might have expected, that the theme of annihilation of Self, and the description of an "inauthentic" life which can never make sense, is predominantly European and particularly French. The names he most often mentions are those of André Gide, Sartre, Beckett, Sarraute, and Robbe-Grillet: writers whose novels and plays are derived from definite theories which make a historical reckoning of the human condition and are peculiarly responsive to new physical, psychological, and philosophical theories. American writers, when they are moved by a similar spirit to reject and despise the Self, are seldom encumbered by such intellectual baggage, and this fact pleases their European contemporaries, who find in them a natural, that is, a brutal or violent acceptance of the new universal truth by minds free from intellectual preconceptions.

In the early 'twenties D. H. Lawrence was delighted to discover a blunt, primitive virtue in the first stories of Ernest Hemingway, and twenty years later André Gide praised Dashiell Hammett as a good barbarian.

European writers take strength from German phenomenology and from the conception of entropy in modern physics in order to attack a romantic idea of the Self, triumphant in the 19th century but intolerable in the 20th. The feeling against this idea is well-nigh universal. The First World War with its millions of corpses gave an aspect of the horrible to romantic over-valuation of the Self. The leaders of the Russian Revolution were icy in their hatred of bourgeois individualism. In the Communist countries millions were sacrificed in the building of socialism, and almost certainly the Lenins and the Stalins, the leaders who made these decisions, serving the majority and the future, believed they were rejecting a soft, nerveless humanism which attempted in the face of natural and historical evidence to oppose progress.

A second great assault on the separate Self sprang from Germany in 1939. Just what the reduction of millions of human beings into heaps of bone and mounds of rag and hair or clouds of smoke betokened, there is no one who can plainly tell us, but it is at least plain that something was being done to put in question the meaning of survival, the meaning of pity, the meaning of justice and of the importance of being oneself, the individual's consciousness of his own existence.

It would be odd, indeed, if these historical events had made no impression on American writers, even if they are not on the whole given to taking the historical or theoretical view. They characteristically depend on their own observations and appear at times obstinately empirical.

But the latest work of writers like James Jones, James Baldwin, Philip Roth, John O'Hara, J. F. Powers, Joseph Bennett, Wright Morris, and others shows the individual under a great strain. Laboring to maintain himself, or perhaps an idea of himself (not always a clear idea), he feels the pressure of a vast public life, which may dwarf him as an individual while permitting him to be a giant in hatred or fantasy. In these circumstances he grieves, he complains, rages, or laughs. All the while he is aware of his lack of power, his inadequacy as a moralist, the nauseous pressure of the mass media and the weight of money and organization, of cold war and racial brutalities.

Adapting Gresham's theorem to the literary situation one might say that public life drives private life into hiding. People begin to hoard their spiritual valuables. Public turbulence is largely coercive, not positive. It puts us into a passive position. There is not much we can do about the crises of international politics, the revolutions in Asia and Africa, the rise and transformation of masses. Technical and political decisions, invisible powers, secrets which can be shared only by a small élite, render the private will helpless and lead the individual into curious forms of behavior in the private sphere.

Public life, vivid and formless turbulence, news, slogans, mysterious crises, and unreal configurations dissolve coherence in all but the most resistant minds, and even to such minds it is not always a confident certainty that resistance can ever have a positive outcome. To take narcotics has become in some circles a mark of rebellious independence, and to scorch one's personal earth is sometimes felt to be the only honorable course. Rebels have no bourgeois certainties to return to when rebellions are done. The fixed points seem to be disappearing. Even the Self is losing its firm outline. . . .

We are dealing with modern attitudes towards the ancient idea of the individual and the many, the single Self in the midst of the mass or species. In modern times the idea of the unique Self has become associated with the name of Rousseau. Nietzsche identified the Self with the God Apollo, the god of light, harmony, music, reason and proportion, and the many, the tribe, the species, the instincts and passions, with Dionysus. Between these two principles, the individual and the generic, men and civilizations supposedly work out their destinies. It is to Nietzsche, too, that we owe the concept of the "last man." His "last man" is an obituary on the unitary and sufficient Self produced by a proud bourgeois and industrial civilization. Dostoevsky's Underground Man is an analogous figure. Atheism, rationalism, utilitarianism, and revolution are signs of a deadly sickness in the human soul, in his scheme of things. The lost Selves whose souls are destroyed he sees as legion. The living soul clearly discerns them. It owes this illumination to Christ the Redeemer. More optimistically, an American poet like Walt Whitman imagined that the single Self and the democratic mass might complement each other. But on this side of the Atlantic, also, Thoreau described men as leading lives of quiet desperation, accepting a deadly common life: the individual retires from the community to define or re-define his real needs in isolation beside Walden Pond.

Still later a French poet tells us *"Je est un autre."* Rimbaud and Jarry launch their bombs and grenades against the tight little bourgeois kingdom of the Self, that sensitive sovereign. Darwin and the early anthropologists unwittingly damage his sovereignty badly. Then come the psychologists, who explain that his Ego is a paltry shelter against the unendurable storms that rage in outer reality. After them come the logicians and physical scientists who tell us that "I" is a grammatical expression. Poets like Valéry describe this Self as a poor figment, a thing of change, and tell us that consciousness is interested only in what is eternal. Novelists like Joyce turn away from the individualism of the romantics and the humanists to contemplate instead qualities found in dreams and belonging to the entire species—Earwicker is everybody. Writers like Sartre, Ionesco, and Beckett or like our own William Burroughs and Allen Ginsberg are only a few of the active campaigners on this shrinking front against the Self. One would like to ask these contemporaries, "After nakedness, what?" "After absurdity, what?"

But, on the whole, American novels are filled with complaints over the misfortunes of the sovereign Self. Writers have inherited a tone of bitterness from the great poems and novels of this century, many of which lament the passing of a more stable and beautiful age demolished by the barbarous intrusion of an industrial and metropolitan society of masses or proles who will, after many upheavals, be tamed by bureaucracies and oligarchies in brave new worlds, human anthills.

These works of the first half of our century nourish the imagination of contemporary writers and supply a tonal background of disillusion or elegy.

There are modern novelists who take all of this for granted as fully proven and implicit in the human condition and who complain as steadily as they write, viewing modern life with a bitterness to which they themselves have not established clear title, and it is this unearned bitterness that I speak of. What is truly curious about it is that often the writer automatically scorns contemporary life. He bottles its stinks artistically. But, seemingly, he does not need to study it. It is enough for him that it does not allow his sensibilities to thrive, that it starves his instincts for nobility or for spiritual qualities.

But what the young American writer most often appears to feel is his *own* misfortune. The injustice is done to *his* talent if life is brutish and ignorant, if the world seems overcome by Spam and beer, or covered with detergent lathers and poisonous monoxides. This apparently is the only injustice he feels. Neither for himself nor for his fellows does he attack power and injustice directly and hotly. He simply defends his sensibility.

Perhaps the reason for this is the prosperity and relative security of the middle class from which most writers come. In educating its writers it makes available to them the radical doctrines of all the ages, but these in their superabundance only cancel one another out. The middle class community trains its writers also in passivity and resignation and in the double enjoyment of selfishness and good will. They are taught that they can have it both ways. In fact they are taught to expect to enjoy everything that life can offer. They can live dangerously while managing somehow to remain safe. They can be both bureaucrats and bohemians, they can be executives but use pot, they can raise families but enjoy bohemian sexuality, they can observe the laws while in their hearts and in their social attitudes they may be as subversive as they please. They are both conservative and radical. They are everything that is conceivable. They are not taught to care genuinely for any man or any cause. . . .

The absolute individualism of the Enlightenment has fallen. Contemporary writers like Brecht, or Beckett, or the Beats, and recently and most atrociously William Burroughs in his *Naked Lunch*, have repudiated it in a spirit of violence. Some have been violently comic at its expense, others ruthlessly nihilistic and vengeful. Among them there are some who gather unto themselves more and more and more power only to release it destructively on this already discredited and fallen individualism. In this they seem at times to imitate the great modern consolidations of power, to follow the example of parties and states and their scientific or military instruments. They act, in short, like those who hold the real power in society, the masters of the Leviathan. But this is only an imitation of the real power. Through this imitation they hope perhaps to show that they are not inferior to those who lead the modern world. Joint Chiefs or Pentagons have power to do as they will to huge populations. But there are writers who will not reckon themsleves among these subordinate masses and who aim to demonstrate an independent power equal to the greatest. They therefore strike one sometimes as being extraordinarily eager to release their strength and violence against an enemy, and that enemy is the false conception of Self created by Christianity and by Christianity's successors in the Enlightenment. Modern literature is not satisfied simply to dismiss a romantic, outmoded conception of the Self. In a spirit of deepest vengefulness it curses it. It hates it. It rends it, annihilates it. It would rather have the maddest chaos it can invoke than a conception of life it has found false. But after this destruction, what?

I have spoken of complaint, stoicism, sensibility, and nihilistic rage, and I would like to touch now on recent American writers who have turned to comedy. It is obvious that modern comedy has to do with the disintegrating outline of the worthy and humane Self, the bourgeois hero of an earlier age. That sober, prudent person, the bourgeois, although he did much for the development of modern civilization, built factories and railroads, dug canals, created sewage systems, and went colonizing, was indicted for his shallowness and his ignoble and hypocritical ways. The Christian writer (see Dostoevsky's portrait of Luzhin in *Crime and Punishment*) and the revolutionary (see Mangan in Shaw's *Heartbreak House*) repudiated him and all his works. The First World War dealt a blow to his prestige from which it never recovered. Dada and surrealism raised a storm of laughter against him. In the movies René Clair and Charlie Chaplin found him out. He became the respectable little person, the gentlemanly tramp. Poets of the deepest subversive tendencies came on like bank clerks in ironic masquerade.

The trick is still good as J. P. Donleavy has lately shown

in his novel *The Ginger Man*. His hero, Sebastian Dangerfield, a free-wheeling rascal and chaser, presents himself with wickedly comic effect, as an ultra-respectable citizen with an excellent credit rating, one who doesn't know what it is to hock other people's property for the price of a drink, the gentlemanly sack-artist.

The private and inner life which was the subject of serious books until very recently now begins to have an antique and funny look. The earnestness of a Proust towards himself would seem old-fashioned to-day. Indeed, Italo Svevo, a contemporary of Proust, in *The Confessions of Zeno*, made introspection, hypochondria, and self-knowledge the subjects of his comedy. *My* welfare, *my* development, *my* advancement, *my* earnestness, *my* adjustment, *my* marriage, *my* family—all that will make the modern reader laugh heartily. Writers may not wholly agree with Bertrand Russell that "I" is no more than a grammatical expression, but they do consider certain claims of the "I" to be definitely funny. Already in the 19th century Stendhal became bored with the persistent "I-I-I" and denounced it in characteristic terms.

Perhaps the change that has occurred can be clearly illustrated by a comparison of Thomas Mann's *Death in Venice* with Nabokov's *Lolita*. In both stories an older man is overcome by sexual desire for a younger person. With Mann, however, this sad occurrence involves Apollo and Dionysus. Gustave von Aschenbach, an overly civilized man, an individual estranged from his instincts which unexpectedly claim their revenge, has gone too far, has entered the realm of sickness and perversity and is carried away by the plague. This is a typically Nietzschean theme. But in *Lolita* the internal life of Humbert Humbert has become a joke. Far from being an Aschenbach, a great figure of European literature, he is a fourth- or fifth-rate man of the world and is unable to be entirely serious about his passion. As for Lolita's mother, the poor thing only makes him laugh when she falls in love with him—a banal woman. To a very considerable extent Humbert's judgment of her is based on the low level of her culture. Her banality makes her a proper victim. If her words about love and desire had not come out of a bin in which the great American public finds suitable expressions to describe its psychological and personal needs, she might have been taken more seriously. The earnestness of Mann about love and death might be centuries old. The same subject is sadly and maliciously comical in *Lolita*. Clare Quilty cannot be made to take even his own death seriously and while he is being murdered by Humbert, ridicules his own situation and Humbert's as well, losing at last a life that was not worth having anyway. The contemporary Aschenbach does not deny his desires, but then he is without the dignity of the old fellow and is always on the verge of absurdity. Wright Morris in his new novel *What a Way to Go* explicitly makes comedy of the *Death in Venice* theme. His American professors in Venice, discussing *Death in Venice* all the while, seem to feel that there is small hope for them. They decline to view themselves with full seriousness. They believe their day is over. They are unfit, and dismiss themselves with a joke.

We must carefully remind ourselves that, if so many people today exist to enjoy or deplore an individual life, it is because prodigious public organizations, scientific, industrial, and political, support huge populations of new individuals. These organizations both elicit and curtail private development. I myself am not convinced that there is less "selfhood" in the modern world. I am not sure anyone knows how to put the matter properly. I am simply recording the attitudes of modern writers, including contemporary Americans, who are convinced that the jig of the Self is up.

What is the modern Self in T. S. Eliot's *The Waste Land*? It is the many, crossing the bridge in the great modern city, who do not know that death has already undone them; it is the "clerk carbuncular" taking sexual liberties of brief duration with the "lovely lady" who, after she has stooped to folly, puts a record on the gramophone. What is the Self for French novelists of the first post-war era like Louis Ferdinand Céline, or for writers like Curzio Malaparte or Albert Camus in the second post-war era? Man, in a book like *The Stranger* is a creature neither fully primitive nor fully civilized, a Self devoid of depths. We have come a long way from Montaigne and his belief in a self-perfecting, self-knowing character.

Recent American comic novels like *Lolita*, or *The Ginger Man*, or Burt Blechman's *How Much?*, or Bruce Jay Friedman's first novel *Stern* examine the private life. It is as if they were testing the saying of Socrates, that the unexamined life was not worth living. Apparently they find the examined life funny too. Some cannot find the life they are going to examine. The power of public life has become so vast and threatening that private life cannot maintain a pretense of its importance. Our condition of destructibility is ever-present in everyone's mind. Our submission seems required by public ugliness in our cities, but the public nonsense of television which threatens to turn our brains to farina within our heads, by even such trifling things as Muzak broadcasts in the elevators of public buildings. The Self is asked to prepare itself for sacrifice, and this is the situation reflected in contemporary American fiction.

As for the future, it cannot possibly shock us since we have already done everything possible to scandalize ourselves. We have so completely debunked the old idea of the Self that we can hardly continue in the same way. Perhaps some power within us will tell us what we are, now that old misconceptions have been laid low. Undeniably the human being is not what he commonly thought a century ago. The question nevertheless remains. He is something. What is he?

And this question, it seems to me, modern writers have answered poorly. They have told us, indignantly or nihilistically or comically, how great our error is, but for the rest they have offered us thin fare. The fact is that modern writers sin when they suppose that they *know*, as they conceive that physics *knows* or that history *knows*. The subject of the novelist is not knowable in any such way. The mystery increases, it does not grow less as types of literature wear out. It is, however, Symbolism or Realism or Sensibility wearing out, and not the mystery of mankind.

WYLIE SYPHER
from "Existentialism and Entropy" in *Loss of the Self in Modern Literature and Art* (1962)

Existentialism has been complicated and qualified by a post-existentialist literature and painting where another question is implicit: How if the self has only an uncertain existence? How if the self that chooses is one more figment? Suppose its existence is entirely contingent? This phase of post-existential thought appears when Jean Grenier remarks apropos of "brutal" painting that we now walk in a universe where there is no longer an echo of the "I." In so saying Grenier presses to an extreme the dilemma of men without qualities: their experiences are no longer their own, in a more radical sense than Musil guessed. Our *situation*—the field in which our experiences happen to us, if they be our experiences at all—seems to be more actual than the self on which these experiences are imposed.

How, then, can we describe experience without a self on which to pivot this experience? This question gives existentialism another cast. What does experience mean after the self has been diminished or, perhaps, has vanished? It is a question that occurs to Eddie in Elizabeth Bowen's *Death of the Heart*: Eddie says he was sure he was himself simply because he was nobody else. Eddie's self is what is left after the others have been subtracted. But suppose we cannot even subtract the others, who also have no selves? We are subtracting a missing value from a missing value. According to the old logic, multiplying a minus by a minus gave a plus. No longer. Such logic has broken down not only in mathematics but also in post-existentialist speculations upon the human condition. The difficulty is the more bewildering because after all the identities, or possible identities, of the self are subtracted, there seems to remain some existence, however minimal—some residue of a self that still causes us trouble, malaise, unhappiness. This minimal self, a nearly spectral identity that refuses to vanish, or that cannot vanish, is the cornerstone on which a new humanism must be based—a humanism so strange it seems not to be humanistic.

In any case this is a problem facing writers of a-literature, with characters who are anti-heroes appearing in fictions known as the anti-novel, dramas known as anti-theater, and, I presume, if we include Allen Ginsberg, poems that are anti-poetry. This kind of writing is aptly called a scuttling of literature. It is also the scuttling of a humanism that persisted in existential self-centeredness.

As everyone recognizes, the scuttling of literature started a century ago. Verlaine wanted to take eloquence and wring its neck; after the poem became music, all the rest was literature. The nonsense written by Lewis Carroll is anti-poetry; and in our day Eliot once wrote that the "poetry does not matter" since words slip, crack, and perish, always in different kinds of failure. The anti-drama was full blown in Alfred Jarry's *Ubu Roi*; and Strindberg's *Dream Play* proved by a logic of discontinuity that "anything can happen" to characters with a "slight groundwork of reality," for they can "split, double, and multiply. They evaporate, crystallize, scatter and converge" in a plot "without law." This improvising went further in Pirandello, who analyzed and often demolished the conventions of the well-made play. The anti-novel appeared as far back as Sterne's *Tristram Shandy* (1760-67)—if it had not already appeared in Cervantes—and the so-called realists sometimes wrote a kind of anti-literature. Flaubert's *Bouvard and Pécuchet* is an instance; and *Sentimental Education* is an early anti-novel with an anti-hero. The demolition of conventional fiction was hastened by stream-of-consciousness, used in Edouard Dujardin's *Les Lauriers Sont Coupés* (1887). One can trace a whole tradition of anti-literature.

Meanwhile Nietzsche was creating a sort of anti-philosophy, putting reason in the service of the will and leaping beyond the confines of logic to free the spirit of man. Nietzsche shook to its foundation the systematic thought of the century when he stated that "a culture based on the principles of science must be destroyed when it begins to grow illogical—that is, to retreat before its own conclusions." Both literature and science were forced to retreat before their own conclusions until a rout was imminent: Rimbaud intended his work to be one way of assassinating poetry, and Whitehead saw how the mechanistic science of the age could not dislodge the conviction that man is a self-determining organism. The radical inconsistency between ideas of freedom and ideas of determinism gives a destructive tone to Hardy's *Jude the Obscure*, which in temper, if not in technique, is an anti-novel savage in its hostility to man and also to the laws of nature.

In France the impressionists invented their own sort of anti-painting, promptly condemned as the ruination of art. The academic palette broke up, and brushwork at last turned barbaric among the Fauves, who successfully demonstrated that painting can precede thinking. Much of this revolt from "art" and literature took the guise of immoralism, decadence, or primitivism. The sabotage of reason, painting, and poetry continued after the First World War in the antics of Dada and surrealism. Anti-painting and anti-literature are not new.

Yet the subversion of art now in progress is not like these half-romantic subversions, which were almost an act of insolence against convention and society. Many of the writers, especially, were rebels in the nineteenth-century manner, holding to a principle announced by Nechaev when he addressed a generation of Russian assassins: "Our task is universal, total, and final destruction." The nihilist, even in literature, was a variety of terrorist. But terrorism is a form of irritated individuality—one man against the world, embarked headlong on a course Marx sneeringly called a Robinsonade, man playing a Promethean role he could not bring himself to discard until the war to make a world safe for democracy caused many to say goodbye to all that.

It took Hiroshima and the concentration camps to ruin once for all this Promethean image of man. The destruction was so total during and after the Second World War that art went down with everything else; and as Czeslaw Milosz remarks, we have almost no literature of modern frightfulness because the artist was overborne by the scale of the calamity. We have lived through gigantic disasters, but they do not seem to be ours. To write about them would be a romantic luxury; we are struck dumb before such catastrophe. Our need is not to seek a self—much less to assert a self—but to get out from under a self, to escape from a heavy burden of freedom. It is perhaps more than this: we want to get beyond the self, beyond personality. T. S. Eliot must have felt a need for some such disburdening when he noted that the poet must escape from his personality in his verse, not exploit his personality.

The urge to be rid of the last heroisms of the romantic self is partly due to the terror we have seen; but it is also due to an absorption of the self into the culture-media of our world. Again the character of Ulrich in Musil's novel speaks for the moderns as he speculates on his own negative form of existence, and accounts for his lack of responsibility by saying, "There has arisen a world of qualities without a man to them, of experiences without anyone to experience them, and it almost looks as though . . . the comforting weight of personal responsibility would dissolve into a system for formulae for potential meanings." For his part the "dissolution of the anthropocentric attitude has finally begun to affect the personality itself; for the belief that the most important thing about experience is the experiencing of it, and about deeds the doing of them, is beginning to strike most people as naïve." Ulrich has a sense that the value of his actions depends not upon himself but upon "the whole complex to which they belonged." In his own eyes Ulrich does not *live*; instead he belongs to a system of relationships where everything that happens is a symbol for other happenings to be felt only as they bear upon still more remote happenings. Because of its unfocused meanings Ulrich's life seems "tiresome"; it is merely a function dependent on other functions whose significance levels off into distances and circumstances quite beyond his comprehension or concern. Ulrich sees himself as a trivial item in some vast equation of forces—the forces that tend, as he says, to run down into an average condition, a compromise, and inertia. "The events of people's lives have, after all, only to the least degree originated in them." By feeling so negligible, he is deprived of the assurances and safeguards Western man has had since the Greeks.

When man is alienated from his own experiences, psychology does not help. In a remark that has become a cliché Nathalie Sarraute has requested the novelist who hears the word psychology to lower his eyes and blush. In asking this Mme. Sarraute is once again proving that the artist feels what is happening before the rest of us feel it. We have turned to psychology as a means of dealing with our selves and with others. Much of this psychology is based upon the very poetic theory of Freud, who has mythologized our experience for us. Is it blasphemous to say that Mme. Sarraute is right and that Freud is wrong, that she has a better reading of today's self? The Freudian creed has taken nearly scholastic form precisely at an hour when the self has been canceled by the laws of large numbers.

Nobody has given us a nobler ethic than Freud, whose effort was to make the civilized self master of the barbaric self, whose aim as a scientist was to cleanse the Id, to let the Ego rule in its own house. But how if Freud was a belated romantic with a concept of the self that is no longer valid? How if the Ego be a romantic notion like Shelley's vision of Prometheus? Erich Fromm has suspected there is something wrong with Freudian theory, and tries to account for the new selflessness of modern man by saying that we are alienated from ourselves by our marketing orientation. The self, he says, becomes impersonal whenever it is looked upon as something to be exploited like a product on the market, like a sum to be invested. Then the person is identical only with his economic role, the role he plays in the open market along with other alienated selves, who are also saleable commodities. Or worse, our selves are identical with our roles as consumers whose desires must be immediately satisfied by products we buy to give us the status we wish. Since we do not need what we consume, even our satisfactions are alienated from the self. Thus we have projected the self into things, and have lost ourselves in worshiping idols of the market place.

Beyond doubt Fromm has cited one of the reasons for Ulrich's feeling that his life is a negligible part of a great social complex that does not matter to him. Ulrich says that his life is tiresome. Fromm says that man is dead. There is another aspect of his exhaustion, for the forces of the market, too, may tend toward a state of inertia. Physicists have had a good deal to say about entropy, a notion that is as anti-romantic as the marketing orientation. In effect entropy is the tendency of an ordered universe to go over into a state of disorder. This is another way of saying that the behavior of things tends to become increasingly random; and in any system tending toward the random there is a loss of direction. The universe as we have thought of it from Aristotle to Einstein was a system controlled by laws that produced a cosmos intead of a chaos—that is, the universe was highly structured; but entropy is a drift toward an unstructured state of equilibrium that is total.

The meaning of entropy is illustrated in Boltzmann's theory that with the passage of time there is a gradual transition in nature from the systematic to the random because the universe suffers a leveling of energy until all distinctions are obliterated. The natural order runs down, we say, like an unwound clock, losing its capacity to work. In classical physics it was presumed that the future is like the past, since there are uniform, continuing laws of energy by which things act and react. It is now argued, however, that this continuing operation of uniform laws would rob the future of its very meaning; for the future is not like the past or the present. The future is that in which time becomes effective; and the mark of time is the increasing disorder toward which our system tends.

The future is more random than the present or the past. Jacob Bronowski compares the future to a stream of gas shot from a nozzle: the farther the gas is propelled from the nozzle, the more random the motion of the molecules. The gas diffuses; it loses direction. Thus during the course of time entropy increases. Time can be measured by the loss of structure in our system, its tendency to sink back into that original chaos from which it may have emerged. Technically entropy is spoken of as a drift toward thermodynamical equilibrium—a squandering of energy into a permanent state where no observable events occur. Every isolated system increases in entropy until it reaches a condition of rest. One meaning of time is the drift toward inertia.

It is not hard to see what the theory of entropy does to the nineteenth-century ideal of progress, the far future as Tennyson hopefully called it, the wonder that is to be, and all other utopian visions on which the romantics and Victorians depended. Tennyson's Ulysses was a hero who believed that beyond the twilight there were always gleaming worlds. We seem to be moving toward no enchanted future, but toward a darkness from which comes no morning. Entropy is evolution in reverse.

More dismal still: the erasure of personality which exhausts Ulrich is a form of entropy in the social order. Age itself is entropy, and life is a form of negative entropy: a living organism wins its individuality by resisting a tendency to fade back into the stuff of dreams from which we are made and into which we seem, together with our great globe, destined to vanish. In the closing passages of Camus' *Stranger* Meursault has his own sort of bleak Prospero-vision when he feels cleansed of rebellion and emptied of all hope as he looks up at a dark sky still spangled with stars but signifying to him a benign indifference in a universe that has ceased to concern him. Meursault has done with the anger and contempt he felt for a while, and even with the automatism of his life among the others; he is willing to surrender to a cosmic neutrality. Before he goes to the guillotine Meursault has a Hamlet-like sense that the earth with its overhanging firmament is sterile, flat, weary, and unprofitable; but he can make his quietus because there will be no bad dreams after he has ceased to be. The destiny of man is obliteration, and our life is only a brief rebellion against the randomness into which things are ebbing. Unlike Hamlet, Meursault speaks prosaically; there is no poetry left in him or his universe. But in his barren and constrained prose he is able to hint at the force of the dark winds blowing against him from his future, and asks what difference it makes to him or to anybody. Meursault refuses any longer to swim upstream; he is willing to accept a fate that cancels out all heroism and overtakes him like a great fatigue. He succumbs to entropy.

Schopenhauer and the romantics told us that not to will is not to live. But to will is to expend the energy that enables us to resist drifting toward darkness. While we live, we succeed for a little while in freeing ourselves from the disorder we create by the very process of our living. Our life is a way of dissipating the forces that organize our system. There is a parallel to the theory of entropy in Schopenhauer himself, for his pessimism arose from his knowledge of the agony of willing, a striving that is incapable of any satisfaction. If, for a moment, the will attains its aim, then boredom sets in; and for the nineteenth century boredom was not, as Schopenhauer says, an evil to be lightly thought of, but "real despair." The only redemption from the torment of the will was to quench it, to silence it finally and utterly by a total resignation of the impulse to live. By such resignation we reduce the world to nothingness, for if our world is but a mirror of the self that wills it into being, then "to those in whom the will has turned and denied itself, this very real world of ours with all its suns and galaxies, is—nothing."

Under the guise of the death-wish Freud gave psycho-analysis its own version of the theory of entropy. If, he says, the tendency of instinct is toward repeating or restating an earlier condition, then the desire to return to the in-organic is irresistible, and our instinct is to obliterate the disturbance we call consciousness. "The organism is resolved to die in its own way," and the path of our life is simply our own way of choosing our progress toward death. The ultimate pleasure is an untroubled security of not-being; therefore the drag toward inertia (Thanatos) is constantly behind that self-assertion which we call living. "The inani-mate was there before the animate"—a wisdom graven ineffaceably, though illegibly, within the unconscious self. Like Schopenhauer or Nietzsche, Freud assumes that the root of all our troubles is our individuality, which we would extinguish.

As Sartre and the existentialists phrase it, the ground of our being is nothingness; and if nothingness is the support of our being, our true being is a heightened consciousness of the nothingness of our being. Our death is the crisis in our life. If we translate the theory of entropy into meta-physical language, we have something resembling the thought of Heidegger, for whom existence is a mode of standing-out, an EX-stasis. The standing-out of the self over a brief span of time is miraculous because the ultimate horizon of our being is nothingness; and if this is so, our authentic exist-ence arises from seeing the self existing against the boun-dary of the future—the future that is really different from the present or the past, the future that gives time its desperate meaning. For the ultimate horizon of our future is our death. Heidegger assigns us an existence that is nega-tive—negative in that it is *not* entropic. Our lives have meaning only in the perspective of our death, of our ceasing to be, of our extinction by entropy. In a more symbolic phrase Thomas Mann speaks of entropy by saying that death—nothingness—is not strange; life—our rebellion against nothingness—is strange, for life is merely a fever in matter.

Only against the horizon of one's death can one attain one's fate, which is unique for each because only our death is inalienably our own. Heidegger defines the self as the silence of a being before its own situation, into which it is "thrown" by no will of its own; and without having any choice whether to exist, we appear, then choose, then disappear. What freedom we have is reduced to a recognition that we are finite and doomed. There is an axiom in classical philosophy that from nothing, nothing is made: *ex nihilo nihil fit*. Heidegger revises this axiom to read: from Nothing all that is, is. In tragic guise Heidegger and Sartre give their sanction to the scientific notion of entropy: existence affirms itself in the face of nothingness, in the consciousness of its ultimate nothingness. On such terms it is hard to be romantic about the self.

Our recent literature—or a-literature—proves that romanticism is unnecessary. Further, it may prove that most preceding literature and art, like most preceding ethic, has been romantic in one way or another. A-literature implies that the humanism we inherited from the Greeks was too romantic. Perhaps we have lived through an era in thought and history more revolutionary than we have guessed. To the truly modern mind man appears in a perspective different from the perspective any former Western philosophy has given, different from any former perspective in Western art. This revolution troubles us, and justly, because it may be a final deromanticizing of man's view of himself; it suggests that any surviving humanism must be based upon a negative view of the self, if not a cancellation of the self. By this I mean a humanism that is not, to use Musil's term, anthropocentric. This displacement of man from the center is quite unlike the displacement of man by renaissance science; for that displacement was itself only a feat of man's own reason by which he explained the universe through new laws of his own devising, an exploit about which scientists now have grave doubts. And any such neutralizing of the self in the modern sense will require us to alter our notions of tragedy.

Is it thinkable that even our so-called classical views of man were also romantic? That in making men heroic in a classic way, they only disguised the romanticism by calling it tragic? When I say our perspective is unlike any perspective Western man has had, I hint that Eastern man has had another perspective, a perspective in many ways like the perspective-toward-nothingness in our notion of entropy and our existentialism. One of the reasons Zen has its hold on us is, obviously, that Eastern man has been able to surrender to nothingness more easily than Western man. The horizon of Eastern thought has always been more distant and indistinct than the horizon of Western thought, as the art of Sung and Tang periods shows; and Eastern man has been able to give himself to the drift of things, to nature, more selflessly than man in the West, tormented as he has been by an active will, the fever at the core of his being. The romantics called this fever *Weltschmerz*.

To be sure the Greeks did not run this romantic fever, for they had no clear notion of the will; yet they did believe that man determines his fate to the extent that he is answerable for the choices he makes. The Greeks were inclined to suppose with Aristotle that however passional the nature of man may be, he has the ability to decide (*Proairesis*), and that however his life may be subject to chance, misdirection, or misfortune, his tragic blunder is due to some error for which he is accountable. Only the gods are exempt from making this sort of blunder; or if they blunder, they are not liable to any moral law of retribution. The Greek tragic world was constructed by extending into the cosmos the moral laws of the *polis*, and according to these laws the tragic hero, as well as the political man, must try to make the right decision for the right reasons and with the right disposition or "character." Greek tragedy was humanistic in the sense that man had to assume responsibility for his choices, his blindness, his offenses against laws written in the heavens, laws that gave a moral structure to nature. Even Greek science was humanistic, or anthropomorphic, for the Greeks were able, happily, to exist in a limited, closed, provincial world that conformed to *Logos*. Just as the Greek tragic sense persisted in the background of drama until the present, so also the Greek *Logos* persisted through the whole era of renaissance science. But now the scientist and the artist have recognized, at almost the same instant, that we are walking in a universe where there is no echo of the "I." If our science is unlike past science, our literature— or anti-literature—is unlike past literature; and I suspect that our new perspective in literature comes to us along with a new perspective in science. Jacob Bronowski has remarked that crucial periods in literature have often coincided with crucial periods in science. . . .

FOR FURTHER READING

Barth, John. "—————— ——————.: An Interview," *Wisconsin Studies in Contemporary Literature* (Winter-Spring, 1965).

Benstock, Bernard. "On William Gaddis: In Recognition of James Joyce," *Wisconsin Studies in Contemporary Literature* (Summer, 1965).

Hassan, Ihab. "The Subtracting Machine: The Work of William Burroughs," *Critique: Studies in Modern Fiction* (Spring, 1963).

Hawkes, John. "—————— ——————: An Interview," *Wisconsin Studies in Contemporary Literature* (Summer, 1965).

Jacobs, Paul and Landau, Saul. *The New Radicals: A Report with Documents* (New York, 1966).

Jacobson, Dan. "Liberalism and Literature," *New Statesman* (March, 1963).

Leech, Clifford. "When Writing Becomes Absurd," *Colorado Quarterly* (Summer, 1964).

Lippard, Lucy. *Pop Art* (New York, 1966).

Phillips, William. "The New Immoralists," *Commentary* (April, 1965).

Pryce-Jones, Alan. "The Fabulists' Worlds: Vladimir Nabokov," *The Creative Present*, eds. Balakian and Simmons (New York, 1963).

Richter, Hans. *Dada: Art and Anti-Art* (New York, 1966).

Ricks, Christopher. "Congress Achieved," (rev.-art.), *New Statesman* (April 17, 1964).

Schickel, Richard. "The Floating Opera," *Critique: Studies in Modern Fiction* (Fall, 1963).

Smith, Herbert F. "Barth's Endless Road," *Critique: Studies in Modern Fiction* (Fall, 1963).

Trachtenberg, Alan. "Barth and Hawkes: Two Fabulists," *Critique: Studies in Modern Fiction* (Fall, 1963).
Waldberg, Patrick. *Surrealism* (New York, 1966).